SARAH COLKER
231 1937 HALL

An Introduction to Linear Algebra

Robert C. Fisher
The Ohio State University

An Introduction to Linear Algebra

Dickenson Publishing Company, Inc.
Encino, California and Belmont, California

Library of Congress Catalog Card Number: 72-131139

Printed in the United States of America

2 3 4 5 6 7 8 9 10—73 72 71

Contents

Preface

This book is an introduction to some of the basic concepts of linear algebra. It can be profitably studied by anyone who has had an introductory calculus course and some elementary experience with geometric vectors. The treatment of the topics in linear algebra in this book is very geometric, and the ideas of length and angle are introduced in terms of an inner product at an early stage so as to emphasize this aspect of our study.

The book does not assume a great deal of experience with abstract mathematics. In fact, one of the goals of this book is to help the student become familiar with the process of "abstracting" a mathematical idea from a concrete situation. Throughout the book, but particularly in the early chapters, an attempt was made to intersperse some concrete and computational material with the more abstract statements and theorems. Thus, the student has a chance to become familiar with a language and a way of thinking that may be new to him, while making some progress with the less abstract parts of the material. Nevertheless, the student is confronted with a lot of new language and terminology in the first couple of chapters. He should not become too discouraged if it appears somewhat overwhelming at first. As a matter of fact, nearly everything he learns in the first couple of chapters is used later on in the book, so he will have a chance to reinforce his understanding of these concepts by using them.

The notational problem in linear algebra is rather complicated, no matter how you look at it. The notation used in this book was not selected capriciously, but only after a number of trials and errors in the classroom. Undoubtedly notation is partly a matter of taste, but experience has shown that it pays to be explicit at times. Thus, when the notation $[F]^E_{\hat{E}}$ for the matrix of a linear map $F: V \to \hat{V}$ with bases E and $\hat{E}$ is encountered for the first time, it may appear to be burdensome. But there is no way to avoid the fact that it is sometimes necessary to display the map, the matrix, and the bases explicitly to explain precisely what is going on. The Einstein convention of omitting the summation sign is used sparingly. It is easy to spot, because a summation is indicated only if Greek letter indices are used "up and down." Most students who have difficulty dealing with sums in linear algebra do not seem to be either helped or hindered by the lack of a summation sign, and certain formulas and expressions look a little less forbidding with the summation sign (or perhaps two summation signs) omitted. The convention of using upper indices for the components of a vector seems also to be acceptable to students, and since it is the correct notation from the tensor point of view it is used here.

In Chapter One the basic properties of arrows and geometric vectors are gathered together and the notion of a vector space (over the real numbers) is simply a formal specification of certain properties as axioms. The remainder of the chapter is devoted to developing the usual basic properties of a vector space. Although the main thrust of the book in later chapters is in the direction of finite-dimensional spaces, the space of functions with n continuous derivatives is explicitly discussed, and many of the early definitions, results, and proofs are valid in spaces that are not finite-dimensional.

Chapter Two deals with the fundamental ideas related to linear maps and linear operators. The discussion deals primarily with the finite-dimensional case. The notion of a matrix as determined by a linear map and a pair of bases is the central idea introduced in this chapter. Matrix algebra is studied, and the isomorphism between maps and matrices is established.

In Chapter Three the theme of "abstracting from the concrete" is played again. This time the variation has to do with obtaining the idea of an inner product space from the properties of a geometric "dot product" defined in terms of lengths and angles. Once again the finite-dimensional space is emphasized, but enough work with the integral inner product in function spaces is given to suggest that non-finite–dimensional inner product spaces are important. The idea of a projection, so basic in later work, is first encountered here in a simple form so that when a projection operator appears later the student is somewhat prepared for it.

In Chapter Four systems of equations are treated. Here some of the earlier abstract results are used in a very concrete way to discuss the dimension of a solution space and to answer questions about the existence of solutions. The first two sections of this chapter (Sections 14 and 15) are basic to later work in the book, but Sections 16 and 17 may be omitted with no loss of continuity if it is desired to reach the spectral theory in the last chapter more quickly.

The "abstraction" theme is played again in Chapter Five. This time the idea of a signed volume in an n-dimensional space is abstracted from a concrete discussion of signed area in a two-dimensional space. The idea of the determinant of a matrix is encountered in a natural way in the discussion of signed volume. The determinant of an operator as a volume magnification factor is introduced, and the basic properties of determinants are developed in this chapter.

The final chapter is the geometric climax of the book. In it is a characterization of all linear operators in terms of magnifications and reflections. This task is accomplished by first sketching a proof that every isometry in an n-dimensional space is a product of reflections, then proving the Spectral Theorem for symmetric operators in finite-dimensional spaces, and finally proving a decomposition theorem in which every linear operator is decomposed into an isometry and a positive symmetric operator. The existence of eigenvalues for a symmetric operator is established, using a maximum-minimum argument that is understandable to students who have had elementary calculus.

As was mentioned earlier, Sections 16 and 17 may be omitted in order to complete the book more quickly. Another modification to produce a course with more numerical emphasis is to stop with Section 20 and discuss Appendix A. Thus, in addition to a course in which the book is studied cover to cover, the following options make well-rounded courses:

Sections 1–15 { Sections 16–20, Appendix A (Numerical emphasis)
Sections 1–15 { Sections 18–25 (Geometric-operator emphasis)

In any case, this book was written to provide an elementary introduction to the important subject of linear algebra that did more than merely provide tools that a student would use in later courses. This attempt could not have been made without the help of a number of my colleagues. In particular, N. Levine and H. D. Brown made some very useful suggestions. I am most grateful to the many students at the Ohio State University who cheerfully put up with the usual imperfect preliminary edition, and who provided me with some valuable insights into the stumbling blocks that students encounter in studying linear algebra. Thanks also go to my editors, W. E. Mangas and Jack Reid, and to my wife, Genie, all of whom put up with a lot of nonsense during the writing of this book.

Columbus, Ohio R.C.F.

One

Vector Spaces

A vector space is defined in this chapter and some of the basic properties of vector spaces are developed here. A vector space is an "abstract" mathematical concept in the sense that it is defined by "abstracting" some basic algebraic properties that occur in many different mathematical settings. The vector space idea is important precisely because there are so many mathematical systems with vector space properties. We will begin by considering directed line segments, or arrows in the plane. After discussing the idea of direction, which suggests that the situation is not so simple as it first seems to be, some informal geometric reasoning is used to gather together some basic properties of geometric vectors. These properties then become the basic building blocks, or axioms, of a vector space. We then proceed to give some other important examples of vector spaces, and to develop some of the basic properties of vector spaces. Many times you will want to sketch a picture to help guide your thinking as you read. But you should also try to follow the reasoning we use because pictures alone are not sufficient in most cases.

Part of the difficulty in studying any new subject stems from the fact that you must learn some new language and notation. Linear algebra is no exception, and, in fact, the notational problem may be somewhat more difficult. Hence, the first two chapters may seem to be somewhat more difficult than they really are. Since we will refer to some of the topics in this chapter many times in later chapters, you may find yourself re-reading portions of this chapter as you proceed through the rest of the book. Each time you read it the language, notation, and ideas in this chapter will seem a little more friendly.

1 GEOMETRIC VECTORS AND VECTOR SPACES

A geometric vector in either two or three dimensional space can be represented by an arrow, but technically speaking we will distinguish between vectors and arrows. An ***arrow*** is a directed line segment determined by an ordered pair of points. If the initial point of an arrow is P and the terminal point is Q, the arrow will be denoted by $\boldsymbol{PQ}$. The length of the arrow is denoted by $|\boldsymbol{PQ}|$. We call the ordered pair $\boldsymbol{PP}$ an arrow even though $|\boldsymbol{PP}| = 0$. If P and Q are distinct points (we write $P \neq Q$), the arrows $\boldsymbol{PQ}$ and $\boldsymbol{QP}$ are different arrows even though the segment PQ and the segment QP contain the same points. We write $\boldsymbol{QP} = -\boldsymbol{PQ}$.

The set of points consisting of the segment PQ and all points R such that Q is between P and R is called a ***ray*** (or half-line), and we denote it by ray PQ. Notice that ray QP is not the same set of points as ray PQ. In fact (see Fig. 1-1),

$$\text{ray } PQ \cap \text{ray } QP = \text{segment } PQ,$$

whereas

$$\text{ray } PQ \cup \text{ray } QP = \text{line } PQ.$$

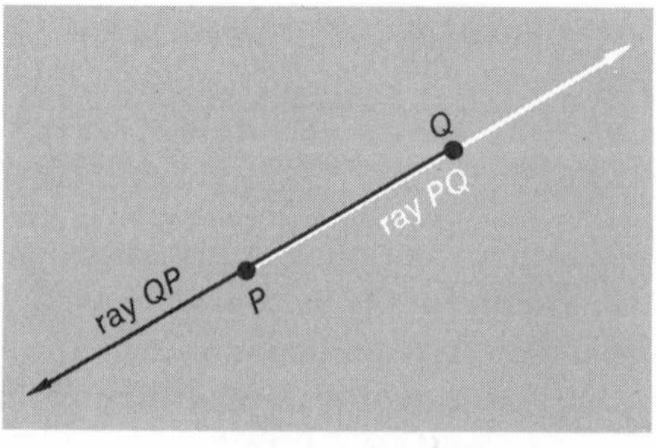

Figure 1-1

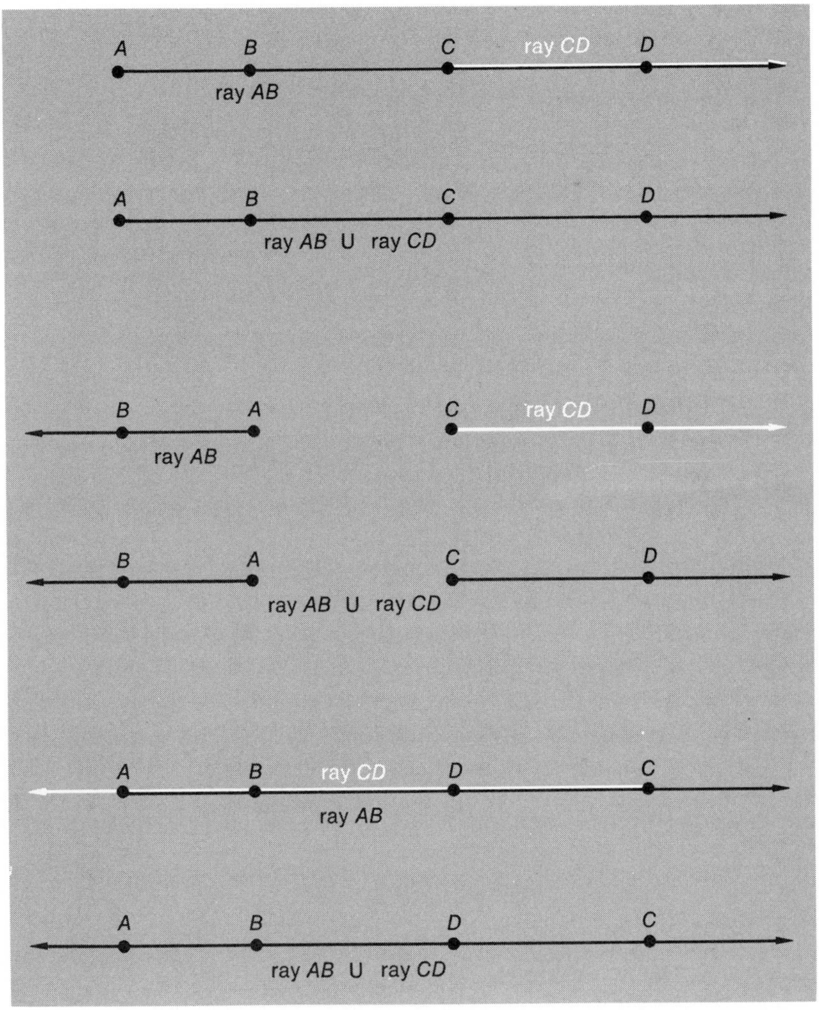

Figure 1-2

Our next task is to make clear what we mean when we say that two arrows ***AB*** and ***CD*** have the same direction. First, let us assume that $A \neq B$ and $C \neq D$. If A, B, C, and D are collinear points (see Fig. 1-2), then ray $AB \cup$ ray CD may, or may not, be a ray. We say that arrows ***AB*** and ***CD*** have the same direction if ray $AB \cup$ ray CD is a ray (half-line). If A, B, C, and D are not collinear, we say ***AB*** and ***CD*** have the same direction if line AB is parallel to line CD and segment AD intersects segment BC (see Fig. 1-3). If $A = B$ or $C = D$ we have a degenerate situation, and we do not assign a direction to the arrow ***AA***. If ***AB***

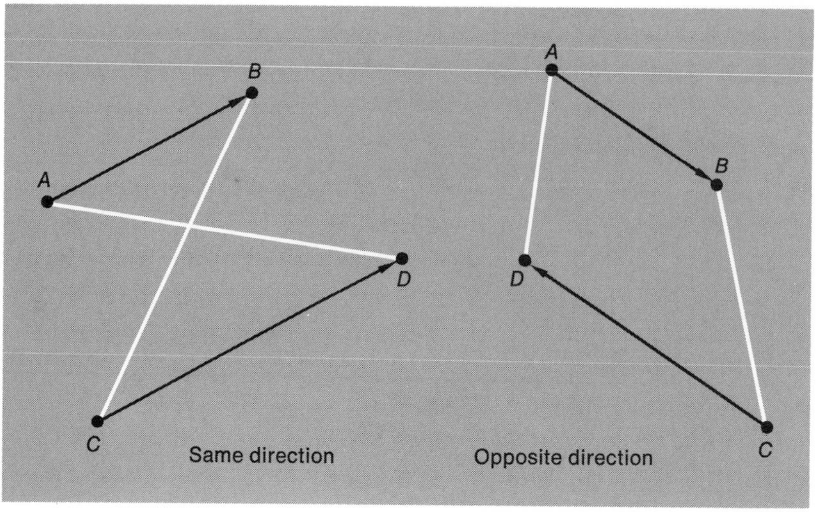

Figure 1-3

and $\boldsymbol{CD}$ have the same direction, we say that $\boldsymbol{BA}$ and $\boldsymbol{CD}$ have the opposite direction.

If c is a real number and $P \neq Q$, we define $c\boldsymbol{PQ}$ to be the arrow $\boldsymbol{PR}$ such that R is a point on line PQ satisfying two conditions: (i) $|\boldsymbol{PR}| = |c||\boldsymbol{PQ}|$; (ii) $\boldsymbol{PR}$ and $\boldsymbol{PQ}$ have the same direction if $c > 0$ and the opposite direction if $c < 0$. The existence of such a unique point R is a fundamental fact of geometry. We note that

$$1\boldsymbol{PQ} = \boldsymbol{PQ} \text{ and } -1\boldsymbol{PQ} = \boldsymbol{QP} = -\boldsymbol{PQ}.$$

In the degenerate case we define $c\boldsymbol{PP} = \boldsymbol{PP}$.

The sum of arrows $\boldsymbol{PQ}$ and $\boldsymbol{QR}$ is defined by the equation

$$\boldsymbol{PQ} + \boldsymbol{QR} = \boldsymbol{PR}.$$

We note that

$$(\boldsymbol{PQ} + \boldsymbol{QR}) + \boldsymbol{RS} = \boldsymbol{PQ} + (\boldsymbol{QR} + \boldsymbol{RS}) = \boldsymbol{PS}.$$

In particular,

$$\boldsymbol{PQ} + (-\boldsymbol{PQ}) = \boldsymbol{PQ} + \boldsymbol{QP} = \boldsymbol{PP}.$$

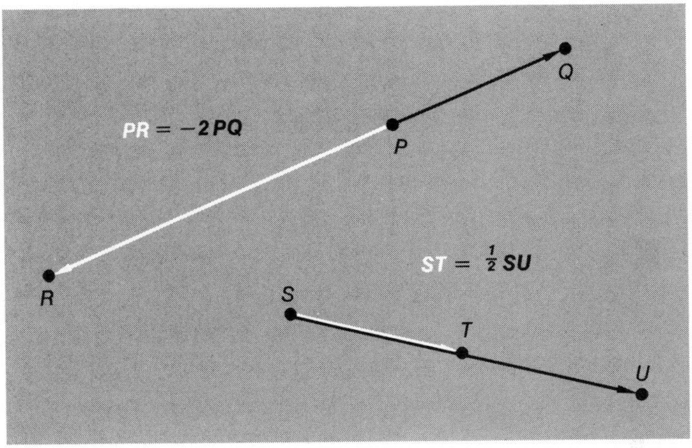

Figure 1-4

In elementary physics we study things such as force, velocity, and acceleration, which have both magnitude and direction. Those entities are called vector quantities and are represented by arrows. Velocities represented by two arrows are considered equal if the arrows have the same length and direction. Thus, we are led to consider the set of all arrows with the same length and direction as an entity itself. That entity we will call a ***geometric vector***. Thus, technically speaking, a geometric vector is a set of arrows such that every arrow in the set has the same length and direction. A geometric vector can be "represented" by any arrow in that set. We denote a vector by a single bold-faced letter. When we write $\boldsymbol{v} = \boldsymbol{PQ}$, it means that $\boldsymbol{v}$ is the collection of all arrows that have the same length and direction as $\boldsymbol{PQ}$. Thus, if $\boldsymbol{RS}$ and $\boldsymbol{PQ}$ have the same length and direction, we write $\boldsymbol{v} = \boldsymbol{PQ}$ or $\boldsymbol{v} = \boldsymbol{RS}$. We say that $\boldsymbol{PQ}$ is equal to $\boldsymbol{RS}$, and write $\boldsymbol{PQ} = \boldsymbol{RS}$, which means that $\boldsymbol{PQ}$ and $\boldsymbol{RS}$ have the same length and direction even though they are not identical sets of points in the geometric space. When we draw pictures, we may also label several different (but equal) arrows

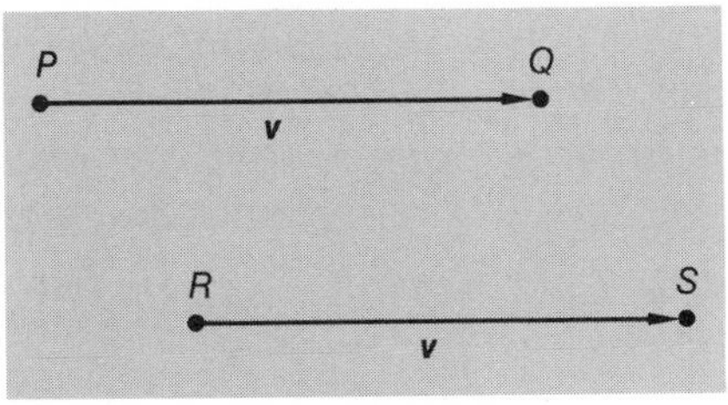

Figure 1-5

with the same vector symbol. In the degenerate case $\boldsymbol{PP} = \boldsymbol{QQ}$ for any two points P and Q. We write $\mathbf{0} = \boldsymbol{PP}$ and call $\mathbf{0}$ the zero vector.

We have defined addition of arrows in certain cases and multiplication of arrows by numbers. Now we define these operations for vectors in terms of our operations with arrows. Suppose that $\boldsymbol{v}$ and $\boldsymbol{w}$ are vectors. Choose an arrow $\boldsymbol{PQ} = \boldsymbol{v}$ and an arrow $\boldsymbol{QR} = \boldsymbol{w}$. We define $c\boldsymbol{v} = c\boldsymbol{PQ}$ and $\boldsymbol{v} + \boldsymbol{w} = \boldsymbol{PQ} + \boldsymbol{QR} = \boldsymbol{PR}$. Now we are faced with an important question. Suppose we had chosen different arrows to represent $\boldsymbol{v}$ and $\boldsymbol{w}$, say $\boldsymbol{v} = \boldsymbol{AB}$ and $\boldsymbol{w} = \boldsymbol{BC}$. Then we would have $c\boldsymbol{v} = c\boldsymbol{AB}$ and $\boldsymbol{v} + \boldsymbol{w} = \boldsymbol{AC}$. Is $c\boldsymbol{AB} = c\boldsymbol{PQ}$? Is $\boldsymbol{AC} = \boldsymbol{PR}$? The answer to both of these questions is *yes*. The proof of the answer is a matter of geometry (Fig. 1-6), and we will not go into the details here. Mathematicians describe the situation by saying that $\boldsymbol{v} + \boldsymbol{w}$ and $c\boldsymbol{v}$ are well-defined vectors.

Using some geometric knowledge the following properties of our vector operations can be established. We will not give proofs here, but you should draw pictures and see if you can give geometric proofs for some of the properties in the two-dimensional case.

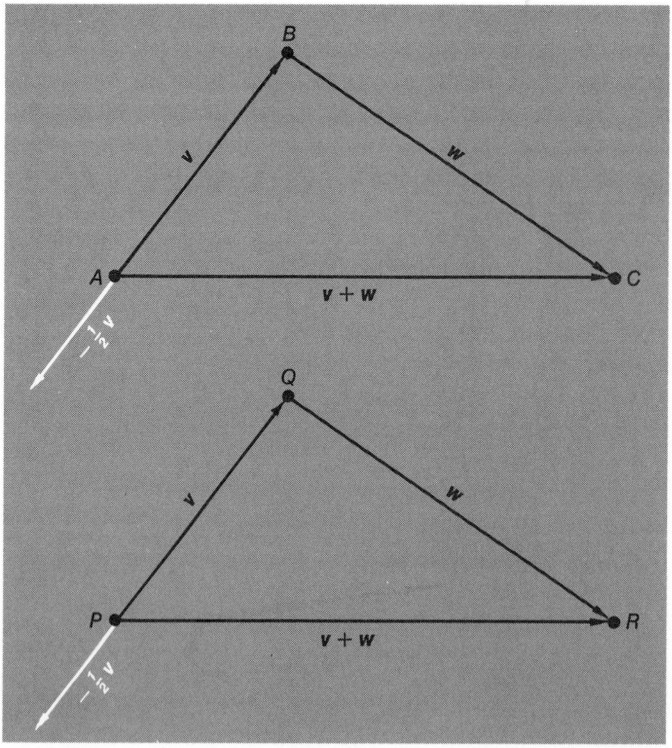

Figure 1-6

(1-1)

1. $\boldsymbol{v} + \boldsymbol{w} = \boldsymbol{w} + \boldsymbol{v}$.
2. $(\boldsymbol{u} + \boldsymbol{v}) + \boldsymbol{w} = \boldsymbol{u} + (\boldsymbol{v} + \boldsymbol{w})$.
3. There is a zero vector $\mathbf{0}$ such that $\boldsymbol{v} + \mathbf{0} = \mathbf{0} + \boldsymbol{v} = \boldsymbol{v}$.
4. To each vector $\boldsymbol{v}$ there corresponds a vector $-\boldsymbol{v}$ such that $\boldsymbol{v} + (-\boldsymbol{v}) = (-\boldsymbol{v}) + \boldsymbol{v} = \mathbf{0}$.
5. $(a + b)\boldsymbol{v} = a\boldsymbol{v} + b\boldsymbol{v}$.
6. $a(\boldsymbol{v} + \boldsymbol{w}) = a\boldsymbol{v} + a\boldsymbol{w}$.
7. $(ab)\boldsymbol{v} = a(b\boldsymbol{v})$.
8. $1\boldsymbol{v} = \boldsymbol{v}$.

Let us summarize our discussion. We have defined vectors as sets of arrows. Based on some geometry (about which we were not too specific) we have given meaning to the addition of geometric vectors and the multiplication of geometric vectors by numbers. At this point we are going to put our development on a firmer logical basis, not by going back to a deeper study of geometry, but rather by choosing a new starting point. We will take the eight rules listed in Equations 1-1 as our fundamental starting point and see how much mathematics we can develop. This procedure would be somewhat pointless except for the following two facts. First, it turns out that a great deal of mathematics can be developed by taking these eight rules as axioms, and second, the mathematics developed is extremely useful because many important mathematical entities behave "like" vectors. We will see some examples of this fact in the next section. First, let us state our formal definition of a vector space.

DEFINITION 1-1

A vector space V is a set of objects that we call vectors which can be added together and multiplied by a number (scalar) such that:

(I) The sum of two vectors is a vector in V, and the product of a number times a vector is a vector in V. We say that V is closed with respect to addition and multiplication by scalars.

(II) For all numbers a and b and all vectors $\boldsymbol{u}$, $\boldsymbol{v}$, and $\boldsymbol{w}$ the eight rules listed in Equations 1-1 hold.

Because of Rule 2, we can write $\boldsymbol{u} + \boldsymbol{v} + \boldsymbol{w}$ without any parenthesis, and no confusion will occur. Rules 2, 5, 6, and 7 can be extended to apply to any number of terms in the sum or product, and we will use these extensions without further proof. Finally, we can define subtraction just as it is defined for numbers.

DEFINITION 1-2

$\boldsymbol{u} - \boldsymbol{v} = \boldsymbol{w}$ if, and only if, $\boldsymbol{u} = \boldsymbol{v} + \boldsymbol{w}$.

We close this section with a theorem that sets forth many algebraic results. It shows us that the algebra in vector spaces has a familiar look to it. We will prove some of the results from our basic axioms and leave the proofs of the rest of the results for you to do in Problems 1.

THEOREM 1-1

Suppose that $\boldsymbol{u}$, $\boldsymbol{v}$, and $\boldsymbol{w}$ are vectors in a vector space.

(i) If $\boldsymbol{v} + \boldsymbol{w} = \boldsymbol{v}$, then $\boldsymbol{w} = \mathbf{0}$. (There is only one zero vector.)

(ii) If $\boldsymbol{v} + \boldsymbol{w} = \mathbf{0}$, then $\boldsymbol{w} = -\boldsymbol{v}$. (The inverse of $\boldsymbol{v}$ is unique.)

(iii) $0\boldsymbol{v} = \mathbf{0}$.

(iv) $(-a)\boldsymbol{v} = -(a\boldsymbol{v})$ and, in particular, $(-1)\boldsymbol{v} = -\boldsymbol{v}$.

(v) $\boldsymbol{v} - \boldsymbol{w} = \boldsymbol{v} + (-\boldsymbol{w})$.

(vi) $a\mathbf{0} = \mathbf{0}$.

(vii) $a(\boldsymbol{v} - \boldsymbol{w}) = a\boldsymbol{v} - a\boldsymbol{w}$.

Proof:

(i) If $\boldsymbol{v} + \boldsymbol{w} = \boldsymbol{v}$, then $-\boldsymbol{v} + \boldsymbol{v} + \boldsymbol{w} = -\boldsymbol{v} + \boldsymbol{v}$; and so using the associative rule, $\mathbf{0} + \boldsymbol{w} = \mathbf{0}$. It follows from Rule 3 that $\mathbf{0} + \boldsymbol{w} = \boldsymbol{w}$, so $\boldsymbol{w} = \mathbf{0}$.

(ii) If $\boldsymbol{v} + \boldsymbol{w} = \mathbf{0}$, then $-\boldsymbol{v} + \boldsymbol{v} + \boldsymbol{w} = -\boldsymbol{v} + \mathbf{0}$; and so $\mathbf{0} + \boldsymbol{w} = -\boldsymbol{v}$. That is, $\boldsymbol{w} = -\boldsymbol{v}$.

(iii) $\boldsymbol{v} + 0\boldsymbol{v} = 1\boldsymbol{v} + 0\boldsymbol{v} = (1 + 0)\boldsymbol{v} = 1\boldsymbol{v} = \boldsymbol{v}$. Thus, $\boldsymbol{v} + 0\boldsymbol{v} = \boldsymbol{v}$; and so $0\boldsymbol{v} = \mathbf{0}$ by part (i).

(iv) $a\boldsymbol{v} + (-a)\boldsymbol{v} = (a - a)\boldsymbol{v} = 0\boldsymbol{v} = \mathbf{0}$. Thus, $a\boldsymbol{v} + (-a)\boldsymbol{v} = \mathbf{0}$; and so $(-a)\boldsymbol{v} = -(a\boldsymbol{v})$ by part (ii).

The proofs of the remaining statements are left for Problems 1. ▮

The vector space in Definition 1-1 is a vector space *over the real numbers.* If the numbers (scalars) mentioned in the definition are complex numbers, then the vector space is "over the complex numbers." If the numbers are rational numbers, then the vector space is "over the rational numbers," and so on. We will use the term "vector space" to mean "vector space over R," where R is the set of real numbers.

PROBLEMS 1

1. The points $P = (1,1)$; $Q = (3,2)$; and $R = (2,3)$ are in a cartesian coordinate plane.
   (a) Find the coordinates of T such that $\boldsymbol{PR} = \boldsymbol{QT}$.
   (b) Compute $(|\boldsymbol{PQ}| + |\boldsymbol{QR}|)$ and $|\boldsymbol{PQ} + \boldsymbol{QR}|$.
   (c) If M is the midpoint of segment QR express $\boldsymbol{PM}$ in terms of PQ and $\boldsymbol{PR}$.
   (d) Find the coordinates of S if $\boldsymbol{PS} = t\boldsymbol{PQ}$.

2. What facts from plane geometry are needed to show that $\boldsymbol{PR} = \boldsymbol{AC}$ in Fig. 1-6?
3. Give a proof that Rule 1 of a vector space holds in case $\boldsymbol{v}$ and $\boldsymbol{w}$ are geometric vectors in a two dimensional plane.
4. Draw a picture showing four points $PQRS$ such that no three are collinear. Let $\boldsymbol{u} = \boldsymbol{PQ}$, $\boldsymbol{v} = \boldsymbol{QR}$, and $\boldsymbol{w} = \boldsymbol{RS}$. Label the arrows that represent $\boldsymbol{u} + \boldsymbol{v}$; $\boldsymbol{v} + \boldsymbol{w}$; $(\boldsymbol{u} + \boldsymbol{v}) + \boldsymbol{w}$; and $\boldsymbol{u} + (\boldsymbol{v} + \boldsymbol{w})$.
5. Suppose that P, Q, and R are three non-collinear points such that $\boldsymbol{v} = \boldsymbol{PQ}$ and $\boldsymbol{w} = \boldsymbol{PR}$. What vector (in terms of $\boldsymbol{v}$ and $\boldsymbol{w}$) does $\boldsymbol{RQ}$ represent?
6. Prove (v) in Theorem 1-1.
7. Prove (vi) in Theorem 1-1.
8. Prove (vii) in Theorem 1-1.
9. Prove that $-(-\boldsymbol{v}) = \boldsymbol{v}$.
10. Is the set R of real numbers a vector space? Is the set of rational numbers a vector space (over R)?

2 THE SPACE R^n. SUBSPACES

In the preceding section we considered some properties of geometric vectors and then defined an abstract vector space. A vector space is also called a *linear space* or a *linear vector space*. In this section we will consider some more examples of vector spaces and introduce some notation.

First, let us consider the set R^2 of all ordered pairs of real numbers. You are familiar with the symbol (x, y) for an element of R^2. We will also use the notation (x^1, x^2) for an ordered pair of real numbers. The "1" and the "2" are superscripts (*not powers*). Thus,

$$R^2 = \{(x^1, x^2): x^1 \text{ and } x^2 \text{ in } R\}$$

where R is the set of real numbers.

If a cartesian coordinate system exists in a plane, an element of R^2 can be interpreted as a point in the plane or as an arrow $\boldsymbol{OP}$ where $O = (0, 0)$ and $P = (x^1, x^2)$. Every arrow represents a geometric vector, so (x^1, x^2) can be considered as a representation of a geometric vector $\boldsymbol{x}$. Conversely, given a geometric vector $\boldsymbol{x}$, there is a unique arrow whose initial point is the origin O that represents $\boldsymbol{x}$. If $\boldsymbol{OP} = \boldsymbol{x}$ and $P = (x^1, x^2)$, then $\boldsymbol{x}$ can be represented by the element (x^1, x^2) in R^2. In short, there is a one-to-one correspondence between R^2 and the set of all geometric vectors in a plane that is established once a coordinate system is fixed. Using the geometric vector representation of elements of R^2 we state the following definition (see Fig. 2-1):

DEFINITION 2-1

Equality: $(x^1, x^2) = (y^1, y^2)$ if, and only if, $x^1 = y^1$ and $x^2 = y^2$.
Addition: $(x^1, x^2) + (y^1, y^2) = (x^1 + y^1, x^2 + y^2)$.
Scalar Multiplication: $c\,(x^1, x^2) = (cx^1, cx^2)$.

These definitions are motivated by the geometric interpretation of R^2 (Fig. 2-1), and the set of plane geometric vectors form a vector space in the sense of Definition 1-1. Hence, it is not surprising that *R^2 with Definition 2-1 is a vector space.* To verify this fact we first note that R^2 is closed with respect to addition and to scalar multiplication because $(x^1 + y^1, x^2 + y^2)$ and (cx^1, cx^2) are elements of R^2 (Why?). The verification of the basic eight rules is straightforward. For example, the equations

$$(x^1, x^2) + (y^1, y^2) = (x^1 + y^1, x^2 + y^2) = (y^1 + x^1, y^2 + x^2) = (y^1, y^2) + (x^1, x^2)$$

show that Rule 1 is valid. In particular, we see that $(0, 0)$ is the zero vector and $-(x^1, x^2) = (-x^1, -x^2)$. The rest of the detailed verification of the basic rules is left to you.

Because R^2 is a vector space, we will use a vector symbol to denote an

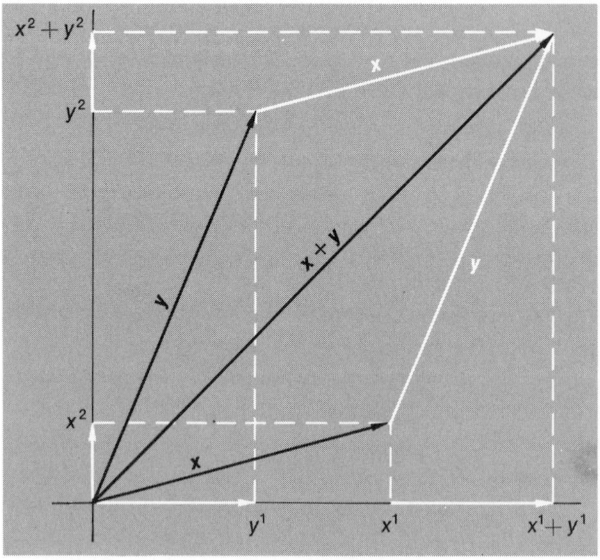

Figure 2-1

element of R^2. Thus, we write $\boldsymbol{x} \in R^2$ for the element (x^1, x^2), and so on. For short, we write $\boldsymbol{x} = (x^1, x^2)$; $\boldsymbol{y} = (y^1, y^2)$; $\boldsymbol{z} = (z^1, z^2)$; and so on.

Just as R^2 can be considered as a geometric plane, so too R^3 can be interpreted as a three-dimensional space. More precisely, a one-to-one correspondence between R^3 and the set of three-dimensional geometric vectors can be established by introducing a coordinate system (see Fig. 2-2). The element $(x^1, x^2, x^3) \in R^3$ corresponds to the geometric vector represented by the arrow from the origin (0, 0, 0) to the point (x^1, x^2, x^3), and conversely. The definitions of equality, addition, and scalar multiplication suggested by the geometry are the same as those suggested by Definition 2-1; namely

$$(x^1, x^2, x^3) = (y^1, y^2, y^3) \text{ if, and only if, } x^1 = y^1, x^2 = y^2, \text{ and } x^3 = y^3;$$

$$(x^1, x^2, x^3) + (y^1, y^2, y^3) = (x^1 + y^1, x^2 + y^2, x^3 + y^3);$$

$$c(x^1, x^2, x^3) = (cx^1, cx^2, cx^3).$$

Again, it is a straightforward matter to verify that R^3 with these definitions is a vector space. Again, we use the notation $\boldsymbol{x} = (x^1, x^2, x^3)$, and so on.

Now let us consider R^n for $n > 3$. It certainly makes sense to talk about R^4, R^5, and so on. Even though we no longer have a picture to guide us, it seems

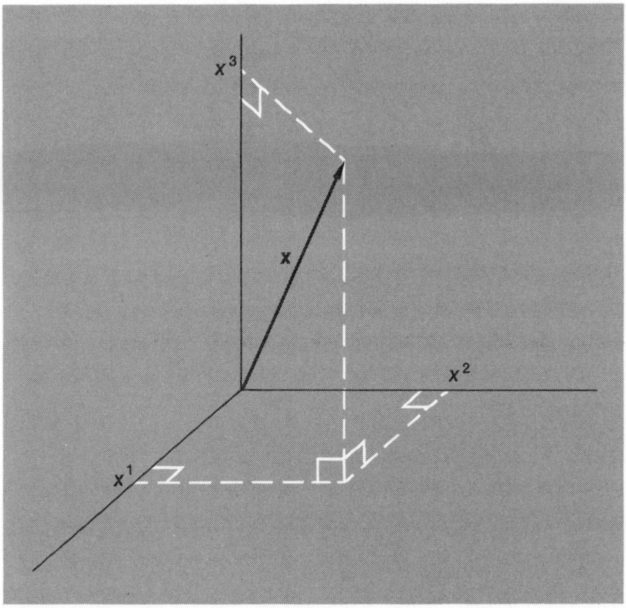

Figure 2-2

reasonable on the basis of our experience with R^2 and R^3 to make the following definition:

DEFINITION 2-2

(i) $(x^1, x^2, \ldots, x^n) = (y^1, y^2, \ldots, y^n)$ if, and only if, $x^1 = y^1$; $x^2 = y^2; \ldots; x^n = y^n$.
(ii) $(x^1, x^2, \ldots, x^n) + (y^1, y^2, \ldots, y^n) = (x^1 + y^1, \ldots, x^n + y^n)$.
(iii) $c\,(x^1, x^2, \ldots, x^n) = (cx^1, cx^2, \ldots, cx^n)$.

It is plain to see that R^n is closed with respect to addition and to scalar multiplication by these definitions. The verification of the eight basic rules for any particular n is carried out just like it is in the case of $n = 2$. Thus, we have the following basic fact: *If **n** is any positive integer, $\boldsymbol{R^n}$ with Definition 2-2 is a vector space.*

Normally we omit the reference to Definition 2-2 and just say that R^n is a vector space. However, Problem 2-1 shows us that this definition is a vital part of the statement that R^n is a vector space. Also, we see that R^1 and R can be identified in an obvious way.

Some subsets of three-dimensional geometric spaces are linear spaces and some are not. A plane that contains the origin is not only a sub*set* of three-dimensional space, but is a vector space itself; that is, a sub*space*. We formally define a subspace as follows:

DEFINITION 2-3

A non-empty subset U of a vector space V is called a *subspace* of V if, and only if, $\boldsymbol{v} + \boldsymbol{w}$ and $c\boldsymbol{v}$ belong to U whenever $\boldsymbol{v}$ and $\boldsymbol{w}$ are in U.

In other words, if a non-empty subset U is closed with respect to the vector space operations, then U is a subspace. We note that:

If $\boldsymbol{u} \in U$, then $(-1)\boldsymbol{u} = -\boldsymbol{u} \in U$, and $\boldsymbol{u} + (-\boldsymbol{u}) = \boldsymbol{0} \in U$. Also, the basic eight rules hold in U because they hold in V. Thus, U is itself a vector space. We could have defined a subspace of V as a subset that was itself a vector space with respect to the operations in V.

Example 2-1 Show that $U = \{(x, x) : x \in R\}$ is a subspace of R^2.

Solution: U is clearly a subset of R^2. Furthermore, for any (v, v) and (w, w) in U, the vector $c(v, v) = (cv, cv)$ and the vector $(v, v) + (w, w) = (v + w, v + w)$ also will be in U. Fig. 2-3 shows a picture of U when R^2 is pictured geometrically.

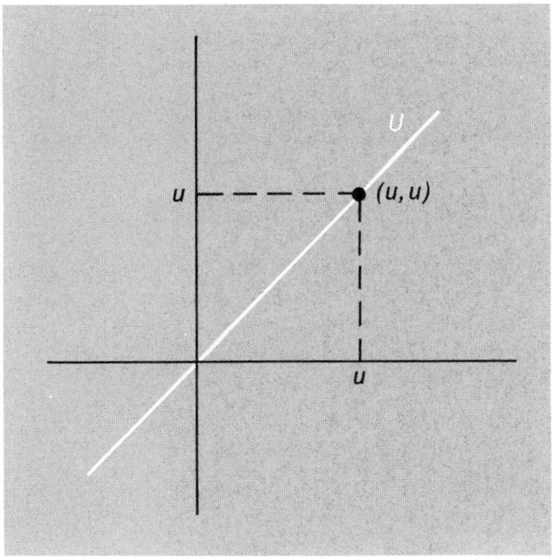

Figure 2-3

Example 2-2 Is $U = \{(x, 2x + 1) : x \in R\}$ a subspace of R^2?

Solution: NO; the vector $(0,1) \in U$, but $2(0,1) = (0,2) \notin U$.

Any vector space V is a subspace of itself, and the subset consisting of the zero vector alone, $\{\mathbf{0}\}$, is a subspace. Also, if $\boldsymbol{v}$ is any vector in V, then $\{c\boldsymbol{v} : c \in R\}$ is a subspace (see Problem 2-2). It is a simple exercise for you to show that it is the "smallest" subspace that contains $\boldsymbol{v}$. We say it is *generated* by $\boldsymbol{v}$ or that $\boldsymbol{v}$ is the generator of that subspace. Some authors use the phrase "span of $\boldsymbol{v}$" for the space generated by $\boldsymbol{v}$. We will use the notation Sp $\{\boldsymbol{v}\}$ for the space generated by $\boldsymbol{v}$.

Now suppose that there are two vectors, $\boldsymbol{v}_1$ and $\boldsymbol{v}_2$, in V, and we want to find the smallest subspace that contains $\boldsymbol{v}_1$ and $\boldsymbol{v}_2$; that is, the subspace generated by $\boldsymbol{v}_1$ and $\boldsymbol{v}_2$. Because it is to be a subspace, the vectors $a\boldsymbol{v}_1 + b\boldsymbol{v}_2$ must be in it. So as a minimum it must contain the set $U = \{a\boldsymbol{v}_1 + b\boldsymbol{v}_2 : a \text{ and } b \text{ any real numbers}\}$. On the other hand, if $\boldsymbol{w} = a\boldsymbol{v}_1 + b\boldsymbol{v}_2$ and $\boldsymbol{x} = c\boldsymbol{v}_1 + d\boldsymbol{v}_2$ are vectors in U, then $\boldsymbol{w} + \boldsymbol{x}$ and $k\boldsymbol{w}$ are also in U. Thus, U is a subspace of V, and we say U is generated by $\boldsymbol{v}_1$ and $\boldsymbol{v}_2$. We write:

$$\text{Sp}\,\{\boldsymbol{v}_1, \boldsymbol{v}_2\} = \{a\boldsymbol{v}_1 + b\boldsymbol{v}_2 : a, b \text{ in } R\}.$$

Example 2-3 Let $\boldsymbol{v}_1 = (1,1,2)$ and $\boldsymbol{v}_2 = (-1,2,1)$. Find Sp $\{\boldsymbol{v}_1, \boldsymbol{v}_2\}$ and give a geometric description of it.

Solution:
$$\text{Sp}\,\{\boldsymbol{v}_1, \boldsymbol{v}_2\} = \{a(1,1,2) + b(-1,2,1) : (a, b) \text{ in } R^2\}$$
$$= \{(a - b, a + 2b, 2a + b) : (a, b) \text{ in } R^2\}.$$

The parametric equations of the set of points making up Sp $\{\boldsymbol{v}_1, \boldsymbol{v}_2\}$ are

$$x^1 = a - b, \quad x^2 = a + 2b, \quad x^3 = 2a + b.$$

A non-parametric equation is $x^1 + x^2 - x^3 = 0$. Thus, Sp $\{\boldsymbol{v}_1, \boldsymbol{v}_2\}$ is a plane containing the origin.

The vector $a\boldsymbol{v}_1 + b\boldsymbol{v}_2$ is a *linear combination* of $\boldsymbol{v}_1$ and $\boldsymbol{v}_2$. Thus, Sp $\{\boldsymbol{v}_1, \boldsymbol{v}_2\}$ is the set of all linear combinations of $\boldsymbol{v}_1$ and $\boldsymbol{v}_2$. If there are k numbers, $a^1, \ldots, a^k$, such that

(2-1) $$\boldsymbol{w} = a^1\boldsymbol{v}_1 + \cdots + a^k\boldsymbol{v}_k,$$

then we say that $\boldsymbol{w}$ is a *linear combination* of $\boldsymbol{v}_1, \ldots, \boldsymbol{v}_k$.

DEFINITION 2-4

The subspace generated by $\boldsymbol{v}_1, \ldots, \boldsymbol{v}_k$ is the set of all linear combinations of $\boldsymbol{v}_1, \ldots, \boldsymbol{v}_k$ and is denoted by Sp $\{\boldsymbol{v}_1, \ldots, \boldsymbol{v}_k\}$. Thus,

$$\text{Sp}\,\{\boldsymbol{v}_1, \cdots, \boldsymbol{v}_k\} = \{a^1\boldsymbol{v}_1 + \cdots + a^k\boldsymbol{v}_k : (a^1, \ldots, a^k) \text{ in } R^k\}.$$

If U is any finite subset of V, then Sp U is a subspace, not just a subset. The proof of that fact is similar to the informal proof given above in the case in which U contained two vectors $\boldsymbol{v}_1$ and $\boldsymbol{v}_2$.

If a subspace is generated by n vectors and $\boldsymbol{u}$ is a linear combination of these n vectors, then the subspace generated by enlarging the set of generators by including $\boldsymbol{u}$ is the same subspace as before. This fact is the subject of the following theorem.

THEOREM 2-1

If $\boldsymbol{u}$ is a linear combination of $\boldsymbol{e}_1, \ldots, \boldsymbol{e}_n$; then

$$\text{Sp}\,\{\boldsymbol{u}, \boldsymbol{e}_1, \ldots, \boldsymbol{e}_n\} = \text{Sp}\,\{\boldsymbol{e}_1, \ldots, \boldsymbol{e}_n\}.$$

Proof: Because it is obviously true that

$$\text{Sp}\,\{\boldsymbol{e}_1, \ldots, \boldsymbol{e}_n\} \subset \text{Sp}\,\{\boldsymbol{u}, \boldsymbol{e}_1, \ldots, \boldsymbol{e}_n\},$$

we need only show that

$$\text{Sp}\,\{\boldsymbol{u}, \boldsymbol{e}_1, \ldots, \boldsymbol{e}_n\} \subset \text{Sp}\,\{\boldsymbol{e}_1, \ldots, \boldsymbol{e}_n\}.$$

Suppose that $\boldsymbol{x}$ is in Sp $\{\boldsymbol{u}, \boldsymbol{e}_1, \ldots, \boldsymbol{e}_n\}$. Then there are numbers such that

$$\boldsymbol{x} = c\boldsymbol{u} + b^1\boldsymbol{e}_1 + \cdots + b^n\boldsymbol{e}_n.$$

But

$$\boldsymbol{u} = a^1\boldsymbol{e}_1 + \cdots + a^n\boldsymbol{e}_n,$$

so

$$\begin{aligned} \boldsymbol{x} &= c\,(a^1\boldsymbol{e}_1 + \cdots + a^n\boldsymbol{e}_n) + b^1\boldsymbol{e}_1 + \cdots + b^n\boldsymbol{e}_n \\ &= (ca^1 + b^1)\boldsymbol{e}_1 + \cdots + (ca^n + b^n)\boldsymbol{e}_n. \end{aligned}$$

Thus, $\boldsymbol{x}$ is in Sp $\{\boldsymbol{e}_1, \ldots, \boldsymbol{e}_n\}$. ∎

PROBLEMS 2

1. Suppose that V is the set of all number pairs with definitions of equality and scalar multiplication as given in Definition 2-1, and the sum $(x^1, x^2) + (y^1, y^2)$ is defined as follows. Which definitions make V a vector space?

   (a) $(2x^1 + 2y^1, x^2 + y^2)$ (b) $(2x^1 + y^1, 2x^2 + y^2)$

   (c) $(x^1 - y^1, x^2 - y^2)$ (d) $(x^1 + y^2, x^2 + y^1)$

   (e) (x^1y^1, x^2y^2) (f) $(x^1 + y^1, 0)$

2. Prove that $\{c\boldsymbol{v} : c \in R\}$ for a fixed $\boldsymbol{v} \in V$ is a subspace of V.
3. Let U and W be subspaces of V.
   (a) Is $U \cap W$ a subspace?
   (b) Is $U \cup W$ a subspace?
4. Is $\{a + b, a - 2b, 3a) : (a, b, c) \in R^3\}$ a subspace of R^3?
   (b) Is $\{(a + b - 1, a - b, a + b) : (a, b, c) \in R^3\}$ a subspace of R^3?
5. Find two vectors $\boldsymbol{v}_1, \boldsymbol{v}_2$ in R^3 that generate the subspace $U = \{(2a - b, a - 3b, -4a + b)\}$. Can you find three vectors such that Sp $\{\boldsymbol{v}_1, \boldsymbol{v}_2, \boldsymbol{v}_3\} = U$? Can you find one vector such that Sp $\{\boldsymbol{v}_1\} = U$?
6. Let $U = \{\boldsymbol{u}_1, \boldsymbol{u}_2\}$ and $W = \{\boldsymbol{w}_1, \boldsymbol{w}_2, \boldsymbol{w}_3\}$ be subsets of a vector space V. Prove that if $U \subset$ Sp W, then Sp $U \subset$ Sp W.
7. Find a vector that generates the subspace $U \cap W$ if U is the space in Problem 5 and $W =$ Sp $\{\boldsymbol{w}_1, \boldsymbol{w}_2\}$ where $\boldsymbol{w}_1 = (0,4,1)$ and $\boldsymbol{w}_2 = (2,5,0)$.
8. Prove that

$$\text{Sp}\,\{(1,1,1), (2,2,3), (5,5,7)\} = \text{Sp}\,\{(1,1,1), (2,2,3)\}.$$

3 FUNCTION SPACES. INDEPENDENCE AND DEPENDENCE

There are some very important examples of vector spaces whose elements are functions. Let us denote by $C(I)$ the set of all real valued functions that are continuous in an interval I. In particular, $C(R)$ stands for the set of functions that are continuous for all x. If f and g are in $C(I)$, we state the following definition:

DEFINITION 3-1

Equality: $f = g$ if, and only if, $f(x) = g(x)$ for all $x \varepsilon I$.
Addition: $(f + g)(x) = f(x) + g(x)$.
Scalar Multiplication: $(af)(x) = af(x)$.

This definition states that $f + g$ is the function h whose value at x is $h(x) = f(x) + g(x)$, and that af is the function k whose value at x is $k(x) = af(x)$, for all x in I. For example, if $s(x) = \sin x$ and $c(x) = \cos x$, then s and c are in $C(R)$. The functions $s + c$ and $2s$ are defined by the equations

$$(s + c)(x) = \sin x + \cos x$$
$$(2s)(x) = 2 \sin x.$$

The sum of two continuous functions is a continuous function, and if we multiply a continuous function by a number, we get a continuous function. Thus, $C(I)$ is closed with respect to the operations in Definition 3-1. Furthermore,

$$f(x) + g(x) = g(x) + f(x) \text{ for all } x \varepsilon I,$$
$$f + g = g + f;$$

and hence, Rule 1 for vector spaces holds. It is easy to verify that the other rules hold too. In particular, the *zero function* is the function whose value is the number 0 for all $x \varepsilon I$, and $(-f)(x) = -f(x)$. Thus, $C(I)$ with Definition 3-1 is a vector space.

If n is a positive integer, we let $C^n(I)$ denote the set of all real valued functions that have a continuous n^{th} derivative in I. If f has derivatives of all orders in I, we say f is in $C^\infty(I)$. If we use Definition 3-1 for functions in $C^n(I)$ or $C^\infty(I)$, then the eight vector space rules still hold. To see that $C^n(I)$ or $C^\infty(I)$ is closed with respect to the operations in Definition 3-1, recall that $(f + g)' = f' + g'$ and that $(cf)' = cf'$ where the primes denote differentiation. Thus, if f

and g have continuous derivatives, then so do $f + g$ and cf. Then, if f' and g' have continuous derivatives, so do $(f + g)'$ and $(cf)'$, and so on. If we identify $C^0(I)$ with $C(I)$, then $C^n(I)$ with Definition 3-1 is a vector space, where n can be replaced with 0, 1, 2, . . . or ∞.

The space C^n(I) is an example of a function space. Another example is the set of *all* functions whose domain is I with Definition 3-1 (see Problem 3-1). When we think of functions as elements of a vector space, it is natural to use a vector symbol to denote a function. Thus, we might write $\boldsymbol{s}(x) = \sin x$ to suggest that $\boldsymbol{s}$ is a "vector" in the space $C^\infty(R)$, even though $\boldsymbol{s}(x)$ is a number. In particular, let us consider a polynomial function. If

$$p(x) = 2x^3 - x^2 + 3 \text{ (x^3 means "x cubed" here!)}, \tag{3-1}$$

then p can be represented as a sum of multiples of power functions. Let $\boldsymbol{e}_n$ denote the nth power function (exponent of x is n); that is, $\boldsymbol{e}_n(x) = x^n$. Then the function (vector) $\boldsymbol{p}$ in Equation 3-1 can be written as

$$p = 2\boldsymbol{e}_3 - \boldsymbol{e}_2 + 3\boldsymbol{e}_0. \tag{3-2}$$

The set P_4 of all polynomial functions of degree less than 4 is simply the function space generated by $\{\boldsymbol{e}_0, \boldsymbol{e}_1, \boldsymbol{e}_2, \boldsymbol{e}_3\}$. Thus, we write

$$P_4 = \text{Sp}\,\{\boldsymbol{e}_0, \boldsymbol{e}_1, \boldsymbol{e}_2, \boldsymbol{e}_3\}.$$

Equation 3-2 says that $\boldsymbol{p}$ is a linear combination of the functions $\boldsymbol{e}_0$, $\boldsymbol{e}_2$, and $\boldsymbol{e}_3$. The space P_k of all polynomial functions of degree less than k is the set of all linear combinations of the power functions $\boldsymbol{e}_0, \boldsymbol{e}_1, \ldots, \boldsymbol{e}_{k-1}$.

In any set of k vectors $\boldsymbol{v}_1, \ldots, \boldsymbol{v}_k$ in a vector space V, there is one linear combination of them that is equal to the zero vector; namely, the *zero linear combination* $0\boldsymbol{v}_1 + 0\boldsymbol{v}_2 + \cdots + 0\boldsymbol{v}_k$. There may, or may not, be some other linear combination of these vectors that is equal to the zero vector. We distinguish between these two cases by saying that a set of k vectors is dependent or independent according to the following definition:

DEFINITION 3-2

A set of k vectors $\{\boldsymbol{v}_1, \ldots, \boldsymbol{v}_k\}$ is
(a) ***dependent*** if there is a non-zero linear combination of the vectors that is equal to the zero vector;
(b) ***independent*** if the only linear combination of the vectors that is equal to the zero vector is the zero linear combination.

Remark 3-1. We frequently say that the vectors are dependent or independent instead of saying that the set of vectors is dependent or independent.

Example 3-1 Describe two dependent geometric vectors.

Solution: Suppose $\boldsymbol{v}$ and $\boldsymbol{w}$ are dependent. Then there are numbers a and b, not both zero, such that $a\boldsymbol{v} + b\boldsymbol{w} = 0$. If $a \neq 0$, then $\boldsymbol{v} = (-b/a)\boldsymbol{w}$, and if $b \neq 0$, then $\boldsymbol{w} = (-a/b)\boldsymbol{v}$. Thus, either $\boldsymbol{v}$ is a multiple of $\boldsymbol{w}$ or $\boldsymbol{w}$ is a multiple of $\boldsymbol{v}$. In either case if $\boldsymbol{v}$ and $\boldsymbol{w}$ are represented by arrows with a common initial point, these arrows lie in a line. For this reason the phrase "linearly dependent" is also used where we have used the word "dependent."

Remark 3-2. A single vector is independent unless it is the zero vector, and the zero vector is dependent because $c\mathbf{0}$ with $c \neq 0$ is a non-zero linear combination of $\mathbf{0}$ equal to $\mathbf{0}$. Any set of vectors that contains the zero vector is a dependent set.

Example 3-2 Let $\boldsymbol{e}_1 = (1,0)$ and $\boldsymbol{e}_2 = (0,1)$. Show that $\boldsymbol{e}_1$ and $\boldsymbol{e}_2$ are independent vectors in R^2.

Solution: If $a^1\boldsymbol{e}_1 + a^2\boldsymbol{e}_2 = \mathbf{0}$, then

$$a^1(1,0) + a^2(0,1) = (0,0).$$

Hence,

$$(a^1,0) + (0,a^2) = (0,0),$$

so

$$(a^1,a^2) = (0,0),$$

from which we conclude that $a^1 = a^2 = 0$. In other words, if a linear combination of $\boldsymbol{e}_1$ and $\boldsymbol{e}_2$ is equal to $\mathbf{0}$, then the coefficients are both zero; that is, it is the zero linear combination.

Example 3-3 Let $\boldsymbol{s}$ and $\boldsymbol{c}$ be the sine and cosine functions. Show that $\boldsymbol{s}$ and $\boldsymbol{c}$ are independent vectors in $C^\infty(R)$.

Solution: The equation $a\boldsymbol{s} + b\boldsymbol{c} = \mathbf{0}$ means that

$$a \sin x + b \cos x = 0$$

for all x. Differentiation yields

$$a \cos x - b \sin x = 0$$

for all x. Multiply our first equation by $\sin x$ and our second equation by $\cos x$ and add to get $a = 0$. Multiply our first equation by $\cos x$ and our second equation by $-\sin x$ and add to get $b = 0$. Thus, if $a\boldsymbol{s} + b\boldsymbol{c} = \mathbf{0}$, then $a = b = 0$. In other words $\boldsymbol{s}$ and $\boldsymbol{c}$ are independent.

It is possible to extend the definition of independence to infinite sets of vectors as well.

DEFINITION 3-3

If S is any subset of a vector space U, then S is an independent set if, and only if, each set of k vectors in the set are independent. If S is not an independent set, it is called a dependent set.

Example 3-4 The infinite set of power functions $\boldsymbol{e}_0, \boldsymbol{e}_1, \ldots$ is an independent set.

Solution: A linear combination of k vectors from the set $\boldsymbol{e}_0, \boldsymbol{e}_1, \boldsymbol{e}_2, \ldots$ is simply a polynomial function of some fixed degree n, say $\boldsymbol{p}_n(x) = a_n x^n + \cdots + a_r x^r$. But $a_n x^n + \cdots + a_r x^r = 0$ for all x if, and only if, all the coefficients are zero.

The next theorem tells us something about the number of independent vectors in a subspace generated by n vectors.

THEOREM 3-1

Let $\boldsymbol{e}_1, \ldots, \boldsymbol{e}_n$ be vectors in V, and let $U = \text{Sp}\{\boldsymbol{e}_1, \ldots, \boldsymbol{e}_n\}$. Then there are at most n independent vectors in U. In other words, if $m > n$, any set of m vectors is dependent.

Proof: Let $W = \{\boldsymbol{w}_1, \ldots, \boldsymbol{w}_m\}$ be a set of m independent vectors in U. Since $\boldsymbol{w}_1 \neq \mathbf{0}$ (why?), $\boldsymbol{w}_1$ is a non-zero linear combination of $\boldsymbol{e}_1, \ldots, \boldsymbol{e}_n$; say

$$\boldsymbol{w}_1 = b^1\boldsymbol{e}_1 + \cdots + b^n\boldsymbol{e}_n. \tag{3-3}$$

Now apply Theorem 2-1. Replacing $\boldsymbol{u}$ with $\boldsymbol{w}_1$ in the notation of Theorem 2-1 we get

$$U = \text{Sp}\{\boldsymbol{e}_1, \ldots, \boldsymbol{e}_n\} = \text{Sp}\{\boldsymbol{w}_1, \boldsymbol{e}_1, \ldots, \boldsymbol{e}_n\}. \tag{3-4}$$

We can suppose that $b^1 \neq 0$. (If $b^1 = 0$ and $b^2 \neq 0$, for example, we can simply re-label the vectors $\boldsymbol{e}_1$ and $\boldsymbol{e}_2$.) Then

$$e_1 = \frac{1}{b^1}(w_1 - b^2 e_2 - \cdots - b^n e_n).$$

Because e_1 is a linear combination of $w_1, e_2, \ldots, e_n$, we can apply Theorem 2-1 again (this time replacing u with e_1, and e_1 with w_1) to get

$$\text{(3-5)} \qquad \text{Sp}\,\{w_1, e_1, \ldots, e_n\} = \text{Sp}\,\{w_1, e_2, \ldots, e_n\}.$$

From Equations 3-4 and 3-5 we see that

$$\text{(3-6)} \qquad U = \text{Sp}\,\{w_1, e_2, e_3, \ldots, e_n\}.$$

Now we repeat the argument with e_1 replaced by w_1 and w_1 replaced by w_2.

First we write

$$w_2 = c^1 w_1 + c^2 e_2 + \cdots + c^n e_n.$$

The right side of this equation cannot be the zero linear combination, and in fact $c^j \neq 0$ for some $j > 1$; otherwise W is a dependent set. Now we can proceed as above to get

$$\text{(3-7)} \qquad U = \text{Sp}\,\{w_1, w_2, e_3, \ldots, e_n\}.$$

It is clear that we can keep repeating the argument as long as there are vectors in W we have not used, and when we have used n vectors from W we arrive at the equation

$$\text{(3-8)} \qquad U = \text{Sp}\,\{w_1, \ldots, w_n\}.$$

Now we claim that there can be no vectors in W that we have not used. For suppose that there were one, say w_{n+1}. Then, since $w_{n+1} \in U$, it would be a non-zero linear combination of $w_1, \ldots, w_n$; say $w_{n+1} = d^1 w_1 + \cdots + d^n w_n$. But then $d^1 w_1 + \cdots + d^n w_n - w_{n+1}$ is a non-zero linear combination of vectors in W that is equal to the zero vector, contradicting the assumption that W is an independent set. ∎

Example 3-5 Show that an independent set of vectors in R^2 contains at most two vectors.

Solution: Any vector $x = (x^1, x^2)$ is a linear combination of $e_1 = (1,0)$ and $e_2 = (0,1)$ because

$$(x^1, x^2) = x^1(1,0) + x^2(0,1).$$

Thus, we see that Sp $\{e_1, e_2\} = R^2$. Theorem 3-1 tells us that any set of three or more vectors is a dependent set.

Examples 3-2 and 3-5 tell us that we can find an independent set containing two vectors, but not more than two, in R^2. It is for this reason that we say R^2 is two dimensional. In the next section we will put our idea of dimension on a firm basis.

THEOREM 3-2

Let $\{\boldsymbol{v}_1, \ldots, \boldsymbol{v}_k\}$ be an independent set of vectors in V. If Sp $\{\boldsymbol{v}_1, \ldots, \boldsymbol{v}_k\} \neq V$, then there is a vector $\boldsymbol{v}_{k+1}$ such that $\{\boldsymbol{v}_1, \ldots, \boldsymbol{v}_k, \boldsymbol{v}_{k+1}\}$ is an independent set.

Proof: If Sp $\{\boldsymbol{v}_1, \ldots, \boldsymbol{v}_k\} \neq V$, then there is a vector $\boldsymbol{v}_{k+1}$ that is not a linear combination of $\boldsymbol{v}_1, \ldots, \boldsymbol{v}_k$. Now suppose that

$$a^1\boldsymbol{v}_1 + \cdots + a^k\boldsymbol{v}_k + a^{k+1}\boldsymbol{v}_{k+1} = \boldsymbol{0}. \tag{3-9}$$

Then $a^{k+1} = 0$, for if a^{k+1} were not zero, we could solve Equation 3-9 for $\boldsymbol{v}_{k+1}$ and conclude that it is a linear combination of $\boldsymbol{v}_1, \ldots, \boldsymbol{v}_k$, contrary to our assumption that it is not. Thus, we conclude that if Equation 3-9 holds, then

$$a^1\boldsymbol{v}_1 + \cdots + a^k\boldsymbol{v}_k = \boldsymbol{0}.$$

But this equation implies $a^1 = \cdots = a^k = 0$ because $\{\boldsymbol{v}_1, \ldots, \boldsymbol{v}_k\}$ is an independent set. Thus, Equation 3-9 implies that all the coefficients are zero, so $\{\boldsymbol{v}_1, \ldots, \boldsymbol{v}_k, \boldsymbol{v}_{k+1}\}$ is an independent set. ∎

PROBLEMS 3

1. Show that the set of all functions whose domain is an interval I is a vector space if we use Definition 3-1.
2. Let P be the space of polynomial functions. For which n and I is P a subspace of $C^n(I)$?
3. Is $C^1(I)$ a subspace of $C(I)$? Is $C(I)$ a subspace of $C^1(I)$? Make a general statement about $C^n(I)$ and $C^{n+k}(I)$.
4. Let $I = [-1,1]$; and consider the set of all real valued functions on I. Determine which of the following subsets are subspaces.

   (a) $\{f : f(0) = 0\}$.
   (b) $\{f : f(1) = 0\}$.
   (c) $\{f : f(0) = 1\}$.

5. Let $D(I)$ be the set of real valued discontinuous functions in I. Is $D(\mathrm{I})$ a vector space?
6. Show that (1,3) and (1,4) are independent vectors in R^2.
7. Determine whether the following vectors in R^4 are dependent or independent.
   (a) (1,2,0,4); (−1,0,5,1); (1,6,10,14).
   (b) (0,1,0,1); (1,0,1,0); (2,3,4,5).
8. Let $\boldsymbol{v}_1 = (0,1,1)$ and $\boldsymbol{v}_2 = (1,0,1)$.
   (a) Show that $\{\boldsymbol{v}_1, \boldsymbol{v}_2\}$ is an independent set.
   (b) Show that $\mathrm{Sp}\,\{\boldsymbol{v}_1, \boldsymbol{v}_2\} \neq R^3$.
   (c) Verify that Theorem 3-2 is true for this example by finding a vector $\boldsymbol{v}_3$ such that $\{\boldsymbol{v}_1, \boldsymbol{v}_2, \boldsymbol{v}_3\}$ is an independent set.
9. Let $\boldsymbol{e}_1 = (1,0,0)$; $\boldsymbol{e}_2 = (0,1,0)$; and $\boldsymbol{e}_3 = (0,0,1)$. Prove that:
   (a) $\boldsymbol{e}_1, \boldsymbol{e}_2$, and $\boldsymbol{e}_3$ are independent vectors in R^3.
   (b) $R^3 = \mathrm{Sp}\,\{\boldsymbol{e}_1, \boldsymbol{e}_2, \boldsymbol{e}_3\}$.
   (c) Any 4 vectors in R^3 are dependent.
10. Supply a solution to Example 3-3 that does not utilize differentiation.
11. Let $s_k(x) = \sin kx$. Show that s_1 and s_2 are independent vectors in $C^\infty(R)$.
12. Let $\boldsymbol{f}(x) = e^x$ and $\boldsymbol{g}(x) = e^{-x}$. Are $\boldsymbol{f}$ and $\boldsymbol{g}$ independent vectors in $C'(R)$?
13. Suppose that a, b, and c are three distinct numbers and let $f_1(x) = \sin(x + a)$; $f_2(x) = \sin(x + b)$; and $f_3(x) = \sin(x + c)$.
   (a) Show that $f_2 \in \mathrm{Sp}\,\{\boldsymbol{s}, \boldsymbol{c}\}$ if $\boldsymbol{s}$ and $\boldsymbol{c}$ are the sine and cosine functions.
   (b) Show that f_1, f_2, f_3 are dependent vectors in $C^\infty(R)$.
14. The homogeneous system of the linear equations

$$\begin{aligned} ax + by &= 0 \\ cx + dy &= 0 \end{aligned}$$

can be written as a single equation in R^2; namely,

$$x(a,c) + y\,(b,d) = (0,0).$$

That is,

$$x\boldsymbol{v} + y\boldsymbol{w} = \mathbf{0}.$$

Use vector space language to state a condition that is necessary and sufficient if the homogeneous system is to have a non-trivial solution (that is, a solution other than (0,0)).

4 BASIS VECTORS. COORDINATES. DIMENSION

Choose a fixed point in a geometric plane. Any vector in a two-dimensional geometric vector space can be represented by an arrow from this fixed point in the plane. If $\{e_1, e_2\}$ is an independent set of vectors, then neither e_1 nor e_2 is the zero vector and the arrows representing them do not lie in a line. It is geometrically clear that every two-dimensional geometric vector can be represented by an arrow that is a linear combination of the arrows for e_1 and e_2 (see Fig. 4-1). We say that $\{e_1, e_2\}$ is a *basis* for the two-dimensional geometric vector space.

If $e_1 = (1,0)$ and $e_2 = (0,1)$, we have seen that e_1 and e_2 are independent vectors in R^2 and that every v in R^2 can be represented as a linear combination of e_1 and e_2. We say that $\{e_1, e_2\}$ is a basis for R^2. If $x = x^1 e_1 + x^2 e_2$, then x^1 and x^2 are the *coordinates* (or components) of x *with respect to* the basis $\{e_1, e_2\}$.

Let e_0 and e_1 be power functions; $e_0(x) = x^0 = 1$ and $e_1(x) = x^1 = x$. Then every first degree polynomial function can be written as a linear combination of the independent vectors e_0 and e_1 (see Example 3-4). We say that $\{e_0, e_1\}$ is a basis for the space P_2. If $p(x) = a + bx$, the coordinates of p with respect to the basis $\{e_0, e_1\}$ are a and b. Our formal definition of a basis for a vector space is:

DEFINITION 4-1

A set of vectors E is a ***basis*** for V if
(i) E is an independent set
(ii) $\text{Sp } E = V$.

Condition (ii) of our definition can be rephrased to say that every vector in V is a linear combination of vectors in E.

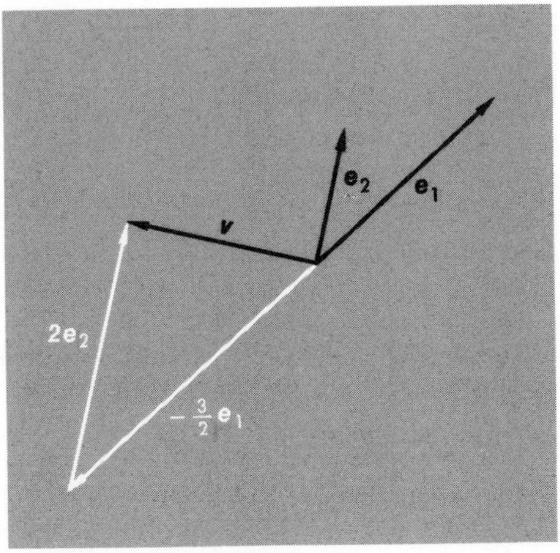

Figure 4-1

Example 4-1 Let $e_1 = (1,0,\ldots,0)$; $e_2 = (0,1,0,\ldots,0)$; . . . ; and $e_n = (0,0,\ldots,0,1)$. Then $E = \{e_1,\ldots,e_n\}$ is a basis for R^n.

Solution: We have examined this situation for $n = 2$ and $n = 3$ (see Problem 3-9). The extension to any positive integer $n > 3$ is straightforward.

Example 4-2 Consider the subspace Sp $\{s, c\}$ of $C^\infty(R)$ where s and c are the sine and cosine functions. Show that $\{s, c\}$ is a basis for this space.

Solution: By definition, if $f \varepsilon$ Sp $\{s, c\}$, then f is a linear combination of s and c; and we proved that s and c are independent in Example 3-3.

Example 4-3 The set of power functions $\{e_0,e_1,e_2,\ldots\} = E$ is a basis for the space P of all polynomials.

Solution: Clearly, any p in P is a linear combination of power functions, and E is an independent set (Example 3-4).

Looking at the two-dimensional geometric vector space and the space R^2 suggests that the dimension of a vector space be defined to be the number of vectors in a basis. Before that can be done we must satisfy ourselves that every basis for V has the same number of vectors in it.

THEOREM 4-1

If V has a basis $E = \{e_1,\ldots,e_n\}$ with n vectors in it, then every basis has n vectors in it.

Proof: If $\{a_1,\ldots,a_m\}$ is a basis for V, then it is an independent set of vectors in Sp $\{e_1,\ldots,e_n\}$. Theorem 3-1 tells us that $m \leqq n$. On the other hand $\{e_1,\ldots,e_n\}$ is an independent set in Sp $\{a_1,\ldots,a_m\}$. Theorem 3-1 says that $n \leqq m$. We conclude that $m = n$. ∎

DEFINITION 4-2

If V has a basis E with n vectors ($n \geqq 1$), then V is ***finite dimensional***, and the dimension of V is n. We write dim $V = n$. In the degenerate case $V = \{\mathbf{0}\}$, we say that dim $V = 0$.

The space R^n is n-dimensional (Example 4-1). The space Sp $\{s, c\}$ in Example 4-2 is two dimensional. The polynomial space P in Example 4-3 is not finite dimensional.

THEOREM 4-2

Any set of n independent vectors is a basis in an n-dimensional space V.

Proof: The proof of this theorem is contained in the proof of Theorem 3-1. There we saw that if $w_1, \ldots, w_n$ were n independent vectors in Sp $\{e_1, \ldots, e_n\}$, then (see Equation 3-7)

$$\text{Sp}\,\{w_1, \ldots, w_n\} = \text{Sp}\,\{e_1, \ldots, e_n\}.$$

Our theorem follows when $\{e_1, \ldots, e_n\}$ is a basis for V. ∎

Example 4-4 Show that $B = \{(1,1), (-1,1)\}$ is a basis for R^2. Find the coordinates of the vector (2,4) in R^2 in the basis B.

Solution: Since dim $R^2 = 2$, we need only show that our vectors are independent. Now $a(1,1) + b(-1,1) = (0,0)$ means that a and b must satisfy the following system of equations:

$$a - b = 0$$

$$a + b = 0.$$

We easily find that both a and b must be zero, so (1,1) and $(-1,1)$ are independent. To find the coordinates of (2,4) we must find x^1 and x^2 such that $(2,4) = x^1(1,1) + x^2(-1,1) = (x^1 - x^2, x^1 + x^2)$. Thus, we must solve the system:

$$x^1 - x^2 = 2$$

$$x^1 + x^2 = 4.$$

Solving, we get $x^1 = 3$ and $x^2 = 1$. The geometric situation is shown in Fig. 4-2.

Example 4-5 Let $p_1(x) = x + 1$ and $p_2(x) = x - 1$. Show that $\{p_1, p_2\}$ is a basis for P_2. What are the coordinates of the power functions e_0 and e_1 with respect to this basis?

Solution: Because P_2 is a two-dimensional space, we need only show that p_1 and p_2 are independent vectors. If

$$a^1 p_1 + a^2 p_2 = \mathbf{0},$$

then

$$a^1(x + 1) + a^2(x - 1) = 0 \text{ for all } x.$$

Let $x = 1$ and then $x = -1$ to find that $a^1 = a^2 = 0$, so that $\{p_1, p_2\}$ is an indepen-

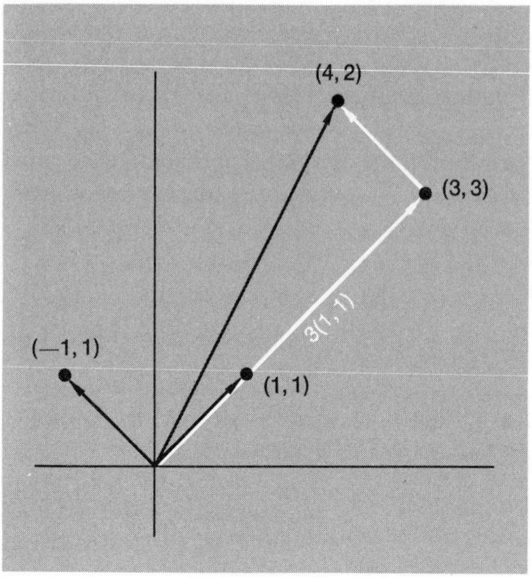

Figure 4-2

dent set. Now, to find the coordinates of $\boldsymbol{e}_0$ and $\boldsymbol{e}_1$ with respect to the basis $\{\boldsymbol{p}_1, \boldsymbol{p}_2\}$ we must find numbers a, b, c, and d such that

$$\boldsymbol{e}_0 = a\boldsymbol{p}_1 + b\boldsymbol{p}_2$$
$$\boldsymbol{e}_1 = c\boldsymbol{p}_1 + d\boldsymbol{p}_2.$$

These equations signify that for all x,

$$1 = a(x + 1) + b(x - 1) = (a + b)x + (a - b)$$
$$x = c(x + 1) + d(x - 1) = (c + d)x + (c - d).$$

Thus, we must solve the following equations:

$$a + b = 0 \qquad c + d = 1$$
$$a - b = 1 \qquad c - d = 0.$$

When we solve these equations, we find that $a = c = d = 1/2$ and $b = -1/2$.

If $\{\boldsymbol{e}_1, \ldots, \boldsymbol{e}_n\}$ is a basis in V, then it follows from Theorem 3-1 that no set of independent vectors contains more than n vectors. Thus, if W is a subspace of V, then $\dim W \leqq n$. If W consists of the zero vector alone, $\dim W = 0$. Suppose that $W \neq \{\boldsymbol{0}\}$ and that $\boldsymbol{w}_1$ is a zon-zero vector in W. If $\operatorname{Sp}\{\boldsymbol{w}_1\} = W$, then $\{\boldsymbol{w}_1\}$ is a basis for W and $\dim W = 1$. If $\text{Sp}\{w_1\} \neq W$, then there is a vector w_2 such that $\{w_1, w_2\}$ is an independent set (see Theorem 3-2). If $\text{Sp}\{w_1, w_2\} = W$, then $\dim W = 2$. If $\text{Sp}\{w_1, w_2\} \neq W$, then we can find w_3 such that $\{w_1, w_2, w_3\}$ is an independent set, and so on. We can continue in this way until we have found an independent set $\{w_1, \ldots, w_k\}$ that is a basis for W. Of course, $k \leqq n$. Our next theorem says that we can extend this basis of W to a basis for V.

THEOREM 4-3

If $\dim V = n$ and $\{w_1, \ldots, w_k\}$ is an independent set, then there exist $n - k$ vectors $v_{k+1}, \ldots, v_n$ such that $\{w_1, \ldots, w_k, v_{k+1}, \ldots, v_n\}$ is a basis for V. In particular, if W is a subspace of V and $\{w_1, \ldots, w_k\}$ is a basis for W, then the basis for W can be extended to a basis for V.

Proof: The process of extending the set of vectors $\{w_1, \ldots, w_k\}$ to a basis follows the pattern we used in our discussion above to pick out a basis for a subspace. If $\text{Sp}\{w_1, \ldots, w_k\} = V$, then $\{w_1, \ldots, w_k\}$ is a basis for V. Hence, $k = n$, and we are finished. If $\text{Sp}\{w_1, \ldots, w_k\} \neq V$, then there is a vector v_{k+1} that is not a linear combination of $w_1, \ldots, w_k$. It follows from Theorem 3-2 that $\{w_1, \ldots, w_k, v_{k+1}\}$ is an independent set. If the space generated by this independent set is V, then that set is a basis, and we are finished. If not, we can find a vector v_{k+2} that is not a linear combination of $w_1, \ldots, w_k, v_{k+1}$, and (Theorem 3-2) $\{w_1, \ldots, w_k, v_{k+1}, v_{k+2}\}$ is an independent set. Because $\dim V = n$, we can continue this process until we have an independent set of n vectors that generates V. Thus, we can extend our set of k vectors to a basis. ∎

The remaining part of this section will be devoted to some notational matters. The first of these is the *summation convention*. As we have seen in our work up to this point, there are many times when we must consider a linear combination of vectors. In many cases it is convenient to use the summation symbol Σ. Thus,

$$\sum_{\alpha=1}^{n} a^\alpha v_\alpha = a^1 v_1 + \cdots + a^n v_n.$$

The idea of abbreviating a sum will now be carried one step further. We will omit the Σ sign too! Thus, an expression with a *Greek letter superscript and a subscript that is the same Greek letter* indicates that we are to form a sum. Usually the range of the summation index will be indicated by the context surrounding the equation, but if there is any doubt about the range of the index, we will indicate it explicitly. Thus, we write

$$a^\alpha \boldsymbol{v}_\alpha (\alpha = 1, \ldots, n)$$

to mean

$$a^1 \boldsymbol{v}_1 + \cdots + a^n \boldsymbol{v}_n.$$

Using this convention we write:

"If $\{\boldsymbol{e}_1, \boldsymbol{e}_2, \boldsymbol{e}_3\}$ is a basis for R^3, then $\boldsymbol{x} = x^\alpha \boldsymbol{e}_\alpha$."

It is understood that $\alpha = 1, 2, 3$. To illustrate the summation notation we will use it to write the proof of the next theorem. You should write out each equation involving the summation convention until you are sure you understand its usage.

THEOREM 4-4

If $E = \{\boldsymbol{e}_1, \ldots, \boldsymbol{e}_n\}$ is a basis for V, then the coordinates of any vector $\boldsymbol{v}$ with respect to E are unique.

Proof: We are to show that if $\boldsymbol{v} = x^\alpha \boldsymbol{e}_\alpha$ and $\boldsymbol{v} = y^\alpha \boldsymbol{e}_\alpha$, then $x^1 = y^1$, $x^2 = y^2, \ldots, x^n = y^n$. Now $x^\alpha \boldsymbol{e}_\alpha = y^\alpha \boldsymbol{e}_\alpha$ implies that $(x^\alpha - y^\alpha)\boldsymbol{e}_\alpha = \boldsymbol{0}$. So $x^1 - y^1 = 0, \ldots, x^n - y^n = 0$ because E is an independent set. ▮

As we have said, if $E = \{\boldsymbol{e}_1, \ldots, \boldsymbol{e}_n\}$ is a basis for V and $\boldsymbol{v} = x^\alpha \boldsymbol{e}_\alpha$, then the numbers $x^1, \ldots, x^n$ are the *coordinates* of $\boldsymbol{v}$ with respect to E. We will write these n coordinate numbers in a column using the following notation:

$$[\boldsymbol{v}]_E = \begin{bmatrix} x^1 \\ \cdot \\ \cdot \\ \cdot \\ x^n \end{bmatrix}.$$

This column of numbers is a *column matrix*. Notice that the x^k is in the kth row of our column matrix. We say that the upper index is a "row-index." To illustrate this notation, look at Example 4-4. If

$$E = \{(1,1), (-1,1)\} \text{ and } \boldsymbol{v} = (2,4),$$

then

$$[\boldsymbol{v}]_E = [(2,4)]_E = \begin{bmatrix} 3 \\ \\ 1 \end{bmatrix}.$$

In Example 4-5 if we let $E = \{p_1, p_2\}$, we found that

$$[e_0]_E = \begin{bmatrix} \frac{1}{2} \\ -\frac{1}{2} \end{bmatrix} \quad \text{and} \quad [e_1]_E = \begin{bmatrix} \frac{1}{2} \\ \frac{1}{2} \end{bmatrix}.$$

Now let us look at the situation in R^2 when the basis $E = \{(1,0), (0,1)\}$. In that case

$$[(x^1, x^2)]_E = \begin{bmatrix} x^1 \\ x^2 \end{bmatrix}.$$

For example,

$$[(2,3)]_E = \begin{bmatrix} 2 \\ 3 \end{bmatrix}.$$

The basis $\{(1,0), (0,1)\}$ is the most natural basis for R^2. The ***natural basis*** for R^n is

$$\{(1,0,\ldots,0), (0,1,0,\ldots,0), \ldots, (0,\ldots,0,1)\}.$$

Whenever the natural basis for $\boldsymbol{R^n}$ *is used, we omit the subscript referring to the basis in our coordinate notation.* Thus, if $\boldsymbol{v}$ is in R^n, then $[\boldsymbol{v}]$ stands for the column matrix of n numbers that make up $\boldsymbol{v}$. For example

$$[(1,2,3)] = \begin{bmatrix} 1 \\ 2 \\ 3 \end{bmatrix}.$$

There might seem to be little point in making such a fuss about notation at this stage of the development of our subject. It will turn out to be useful later, however, and now is a good time to practice using it.

PROBLEMS 4

1. Let O be the origin of a rectangular cartesian coordinate system in the plane, and let (2,1) and (−1,2), respectively, be the coordinates of points B_1 and B_2. The geometric vectors $\boldsymbol{b}_1 = \boldsymbol{OB}_1$ and $\boldsymbol{b}_2 = \boldsymbol{OB}_2$ are linearly independent and $B = \{\boldsymbol{b}_1, \boldsymbol{b}_2\}$ is a basis for the geometric vector space. If $\boldsymbol{v} = \boldsymbol{OP}$, find $[\boldsymbol{v}]_B$ if the coordinates of P are:
(a) (3,4) (b) (1,0) (c) (2, −1) (d) (1,1)

2. Determine which of the following sets are bases for R^3.
   (a) $\{(2,-1,1), (1,-2,3), (3,0,-1)\}$
   (b) $\{(1,1,2), (3,1,-2), (4,-1,3), (2,1,-1)\}$
   (c) $\{(2,-1,1), (1,3,2), (1,-4,-1)\}$
   (d) $\{(6,-1,2), (3,0,-1)\}$
3. Prove that E is a basis for R^2 and find $[(1,3)]_E$.
   (a) $E = \{(0,-1), (-1,0)\}$
   (b) $E = \{(1,3), (-2,1)\}$
   (c) $E = \{(1,1), (0,2)\}$
   (d) $E = \{(1,1), (-2,1)\}$
4. Let $B = \{(1,2,0), (3,-2,1), (-4,3,2)\}$.
   (a) Prove that B is a basis for R^3.
   (b) Find $[v]_B$ if $v = (3,6,9)$.
   (c) Find $[e_2]_B$ if $\{e_1, e_2, e_3\}$ is the natural basis for R^3.
5. (a) Show that $\{p_1, p_2, p_3\} = B$ is a basis for P_3 if $p_1(x) = x^2 + x + 1$, $p_2(x) = x + 1$, $p_3(x) = 1$.
   (b) Find $[e_2]_B$ if $e_2(x) = x \cdot x$.
6. Let $W = \text{Sp}\,\{(1,1,1)\}$. Find a basis for W and extend that basis to a basis for R^3.
7. Let $W = \text{Sp}\,\{(1,2,1), (2,3,0)\}$. Find a basis for W and extend that basis to a basis for R^3.
8. Let $U = \text{Sp}\,\{(1,2)\}$ and $W = \text{Sp}\,\{(-1,1)\}$. Show that every vector in R^2 can be written in a unique way as the sum of a vector in U and a vector in W.
9. Let $V = \text{Sp}\,\{s, c\}$ where s and c are the sine and cosine functions. Then $\{s, c\} = E$ is a basis for V. Find $[f]_E$ if:
   (a) $f(x) = \sin(x + a)$ (b) $f(x) = \cos(x + a)$
10. If p is a polynomial in the space P of all polynomials and if E is the set $\{e_0, e_1, e_2, \ldots\}$ of all power functions, give a reasonable interpretation of the symbol $[p]_E$.

Two

Linear Maps and Matrices

The idea of a function is a basic concept in mathematics. The notion of a function involves a set called the domain of the function, a set called the range of the function, and a rule that assigns to each element of the domain an element of the range. Most of the functions with which you have been concerned have been functions whose domains and ranges were sets of real numbers. In this chapter we will again be studying functions, but the domains and ranges will be vector spaces.

In calculus, and in other elementary mathematics, a good deal of time is spent studying the properties of functions that are defined by formulas that specify the rules of correspondences. Here we will reverse the procedure. We will single out certain kinds of functions by means of some properties and call them linear maps. Then we will ask, "What is the formula that defines such a function?" In answering this question we are led to a study of matrices. The relationship between a matrix and a linear map is studied in great detail since it forms the bridge between the geometric and algebraic interpretation of a linear map. The material that is discussed in this chapter sets the stage for much of our later work, so you should do your best to understand the basic ideas presented here.

5 LINEAR MAPS. ISOMORPHIC SPACES

Suppose that $E = \{e_1, \ldots, e_n\}$ is a basis for V. If

$$v = x^1 e_1 + \cdots + x^n e_n = x^\alpha e_\alpha$$

is any vector in V, then

$$[v]_E = \begin{bmatrix} x^1 \\ \cdot \\ \cdot \\ \cdot \\ x^n \end{bmatrix}.$$

It is natural to associate the element $x = (x^1, \ldots, x^n)$ in R^n with the vector $v = x^\alpha e_\alpha$ in V. In other words, there is a natural way of defining a *function* F whose domain is V and whose range is R^n. We will write

$$F: V \to R^n$$

to mean that the domain and range of F are V and R^n, respectively. A function is also called a *transformation*, or a *mapping*, or for short, a ***map***. The vector $F(v) = x$ is called the *image of* v in the map F.

Example 5-1 Let $E = \{e_0, e_1, e_2\}$ be the usual basis for P_3, that is, $e_0(x) = 1$, $e_1(x) = x$, $e_2(x) = x \cdot x$. Define $F: P_3 \to R^3$ as indicated in the preceding paragraph. Find $F(p)$ if $p(x) = 3x^2 - 2x + 1$.

Solution: Since $p = e_0 - 2e_1 + 3e_2$, we see that $F(p) = (1, -2, 3)$.

Let us look at some of the properties of the map F that we defined above. Suppose that $v = x^\alpha e_\alpha$ and $w = y^\alpha e_\alpha$ and let $x = (x^1, \ldots, x^n)$ and $y = (y^1, \ldots, y^n)$. Then $F(v) = x$ and $F(w) = y$. Furthermore,

$$F(v + w) = F(x^\alpha e_\alpha + y^\alpha e_\alpha) = F((x^\alpha + y^\alpha)e_\alpha) = x + y,$$

and

$$F(cv) = F(cx^\alpha e_\alpha) = cx.$$

In other words

(5-1) $$F(\boldsymbol{v} + \boldsymbol{w}) = F(\boldsymbol{v}) + F(\boldsymbol{w}) \quad \text{and} \quad F(c\boldsymbol{v}) = cF(\boldsymbol{v}).$$

We also see that if $\boldsymbol{v} \neq \boldsymbol{w}$, then $\boldsymbol{x} \neq \boldsymbol{y}$. That is,

(5-2) $$\text{if } \boldsymbol{v} \neq \boldsymbol{w}, \text{ then } F(\boldsymbol{v}) \neq F(\boldsymbol{w}).$$

It can also be seen that every element of R^n is the image of some vector in V, for if $z = (z^1, \ldots, z^n)$, then $z^\alpha \boldsymbol{e}_\alpha$ is mapped onto z. Hence,

(5-3) $$\text{for any } z \text{ in } R^n, \text{ there is a } \boldsymbol{u} \text{ in } V \text{ such that } F(\boldsymbol{u}) = z.$$

This last condition can be succinctly expressed by the equation $F(V) = R^n$, where $F(V)$ is the set of all images of vectors in V. In short,

$$F(V) = \{F(\boldsymbol{v}) : \boldsymbol{v} \in V\}.$$

We will be concerned with maps (functions) from one vector space V to another vector space. Let us denote the second vector space by $\hat{V}$, read "vee-hat." Then,

$$F : V \to \hat{V}$$

means the domain to F is V and the range of F is the space $\hat{V}$. Sometimes we will draw a picture such as the one shown in Fig. 5-1 to illustrate the situation.

Most of our work will be with maps that have the properties expressed in Equations 5-1, and many important maps also have one or both of the properties described in Equations 5-2 and 5-3. Thus, we will give names to these properties.

DEFINITION 5-1

Let $F : V \to \hat{V}$. If F has the properties listed in Equations 5-1, we say that F is a ***linear map***. The two conditions expressed in Equations 5-1 can be restated in a single equation (see Problem 5-2) as

(5-4) $$F(c\boldsymbol{v} + \boldsymbol{w}) = cF(\boldsymbol{v}) + F(\boldsymbol{w}).$$

If F has Property 5-2, which is equivalent to the statement:

(5-5) $$F(\boldsymbol{v}) = F(\boldsymbol{w}) \quad \text{implies} \quad \boldsymbol{v} = \boldsymbol{w},$$

then F is said to be ***injective*** or ***one-to-one***.

If $F(V) = \hat{V}$, then F is said to be ***surjective*** or ***onto***.

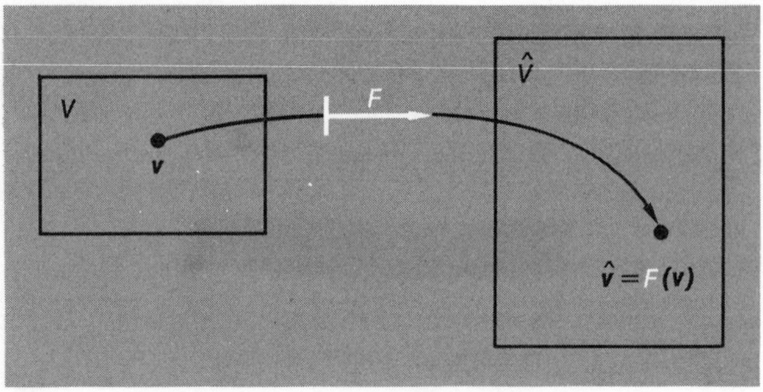

Figure 5-1

In the following example we consider a map $F: R^2 \to R^1$. The image of a vector $\boldsymbol{x} = (x^1, x^2)$ in R^2 is the vector $F(\boldsymbol{x}) = F((x^1, x^2))$. We will use the abbreviated notation

$$F(x^1, x^2) \quad \text{for} \quad F((x^1, x^2)),$$

and we will use such an abbreviation whenever the domain of F is R^n.

Example 5-2 Define $F: R^2 \to R^1$ by the rule $F(x^1, x^2) = x^1 - x^2$. Show that F is linear. Is F injective? Is F surjective?

Solution: If $\boldsymbol{x} = (x^1, x^2)$ and $\boldsymbol{y} = (y^1, y^2)$, then

$$\begin{aligned} F(c\boldsymbol{x} + \boldsymbol{y}) &= F(cx^1 + y^1, cx^2 + y^2) \\ &= (cx^1 + y^1) - (cx^2 + y^2) \\ &= c(x^1 - x^2) + (y^1 - y^2) \\ &= cF(\boldsymbol{x}) + F(\boldsymbol{y}). \end{aligned}$$

Thus, F is linear.

Since $F(1,1) = F(2,2)$, we see that F is not injective.

Given any number t, the vector $(t,0)$ in R^2 has t for its image because $F(t,0) = t$. Of course, there are many vectors in R^2 whose image is t, but we need only find one vector for each t in order to say that F is surjective.

Example 5-3 Let $F: R^2 \to R^1$ be defined as in Example 5-2. Let $K = \text{Sp}\,\{(1,1)\}$. Find $F(K)$. Sketch a diagram showing $\{\boldsymbol{x}: F(\boldsymbol{x}) = k, k \text{ an integer}\}$.

Solution: If $\boldsymbol{x}$ is in K, then $\boldsymbol{x} = (x,x)$. Thus, $F(\boldsymbol{x}) = 0$ for all $\boldsymbol{x}$ in K. In other words $F(K) = 0$. If $F(\boldsymbol{x}) = k$, then

$$x^1 - x^2 = k,$$

so that

$$x^2 = x^1 - k.$$

The set $\{\boldsymbol{x} : x^2 = x^1 - k\}$ is a set of lines, each with slope 1, as shown in Fig. 5-2.

Example 5-4 Let $D: P \to P$ be the derivative map defined by the rule $D(\boldsymbol{p}) = \boldsymbol{p}'$. Is D linear? Injective? Surjective?

Solution: The map D is linear because of the differentiation rule

$$(a\boldsymbol{p} + \boldsymbol{q})' = a\boldsymbol{p}' + \boldsymbol{q}'.$$

If $\boldsymbol{q}(x) = \boldsymbol{p}(x) + c$, then $\boldsymbol{q}'(x) = \boldsymbol{p}'(x)$. Thus, if $c \neq 0$, we have found a $\boldsymbol{q} \neq \boldsymbol{p}$ such that $D(\boldsymbol{q}) = D(\boldsymbol{p})$, and so D is not injective.

Given any $\boldsymbol{p}$, if

$$\boldsymbol{q}(x) = \int_0^x \boldsymbol{p}(t)\,dt,$$

we see that $\boldsymbol{q}$ is a polynomial and $D(\boldsymbol{q}) = \boldsymbol{p}$. Thus, D is a surjective map.

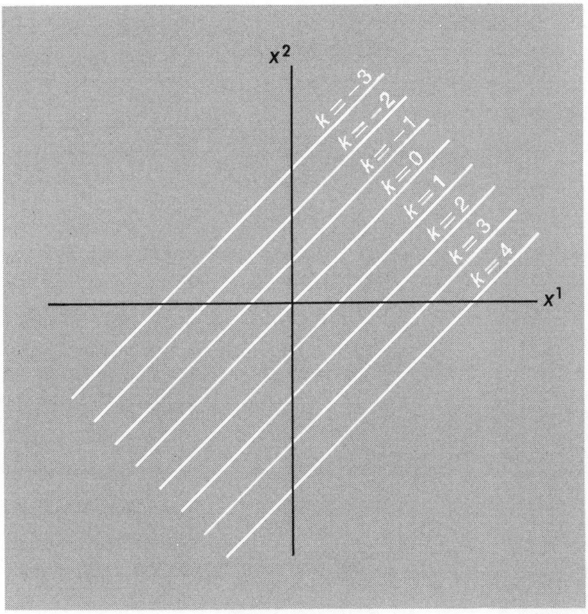

Figure 5-2

As we have seen, the map $F: V \to R^n$ defined by

$$F(x^\alpha e_\alpha) = (x^1, \ldots, x^n)$$

is linear, injective, and surjective. A map with all three of these properties is called a *vector space isomorphism*, and we say V is ***isomorphic*** to R^n. Our observations above tell us that *every n-dimensional vector space is isomorphic to* $\boldsymbol{R^n}$.

If $F: V \to \hat{V}$ is both injective and surjective (one-to-one and onto), F is called an ***invertible*** map. The name "invertible" comes from the fact that we can "invert" the map F in this case to obtain a map $F^{-1}: \hat{V} \to V$ that is called the *inverse* of F. The map F^{-1} is defined as follows:

If $\hat{\boldsymbol{v}} \in \hat{V}$, then $F^{-1}(\hat{\boldsymbol{v}}) = \boldsymbol{v}$ where $\boldsymbol{v}$ is the unique vector such that $F(\boldsymbol{v}) = \hat{\boldsymbol{v}}$.

Notice that F^{-1} is well-defined because the fact that F is invertible means that for each $\hat{\boldsymbol{v}}$ there is exactly one $\boldsymbol{v}$ such that $F(\boldsymbol{v}) = \hat{\boldsymbol{v}}$. A schematic diagram of the situation is shown in Fig. 5-3.

If F^{-1} exists; that is, if F is invertible, then F^{-1} is also an invertible map and

$$(F^{-1})^{-1} = F. \tag{5-6}$$

We leave the proof of these facts to you in the problems and turn to the rest of the proof of the following theorem.

THEOREM 5-1

If $F: V \to \hat{V}$ is an invertible linear map, then $F^{-1}: \hat{V} \to V$ is also an invertible linear map.

Proof: We will prove that F^{-1} is linear. Suppose that

$$F(\boldsymbol{v}) = \hat{\boldsymbol{v}} \quad \text{and} \quad F(\boldsymbol{w}) = \hat{\boldsymbol{w}}.$$

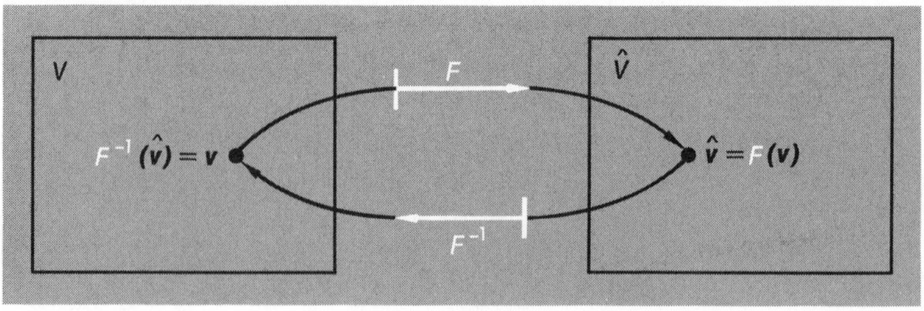

Figure 5-3

Then

$$\boldsymbol{v} = F^{-1}(\hat{\boldsymbol{v}}), \quad \boldsymbol{w} = F^{-1}(\hat{\boldsymbol{w}}), \quad \text{and} \quad F(c\boldsymbol{v} + \boldsymbol{w}) = c\hat{\boldsymbol{v}} + \hat{\boldsymbol{w}}.$$

Thus,

$$F^{-1}(c\hat{\boldsymbol{v}} + \hat{\boldsymbol{w}}) = c\boldsymbol{v} + \boldsymbol{w} = cF^{-1}(\hat{\boldsymbol{v}}) + F^{-1}(\hat{\boldsymbol{w}}).$$ ∎

Example 5-5 Suppose that $F: R^2 \to R^2$ is defined by the equation

$$F(\boldsymbol{x}) = (x^1 + x^2, x^1 - x^2).$$

Show that F is an invertible linear map and find $F^{-1}(\boldsymbol{x})$.

Solution: The map F is a linear map because

$$\begin{aligned} F(c\boldsymbol{x} + \boldsymbol{y}) &= F(cx^1 + y^1, cx^2 + y^2) \\ &= (cx^1 + y^1 + cx^2 + y^2, cx^1 + y^1 - cx^2 - y^2) \\ &= c(x^1 + x^2, x^1 - x^2) + (y^1 + y^2, y^1 - y^2) \\ &= cF(\boldsymbol{x}) + F(\boldsymbol{y}). \end{aligned}$$

If $F(\boldsymbol{x}) = F(\boldsymbol{y})$, then $x^1 + x^2 = y^1 + y^2$ and $x^1 - x^2 = y^1 - y^2$. Thus,

$$\begin{aligned} (x^1 - y^1) + (x^2 - y^2) &= 0 \\ (x^1 - y^1) - (x^2 - y^2) &= 0. \end{aligned}$$

By adding and subtracting these equations we find that $x^1 = y^1$ and $x^2 = y^2$. Thus, if $F(\boldsymbol{x}) = F(\boldsymbol{y})$, then $\boldsymbol{x} = \boldsymbol{y}$, which is equivalent to Property 5-2. Hence, F is injective.

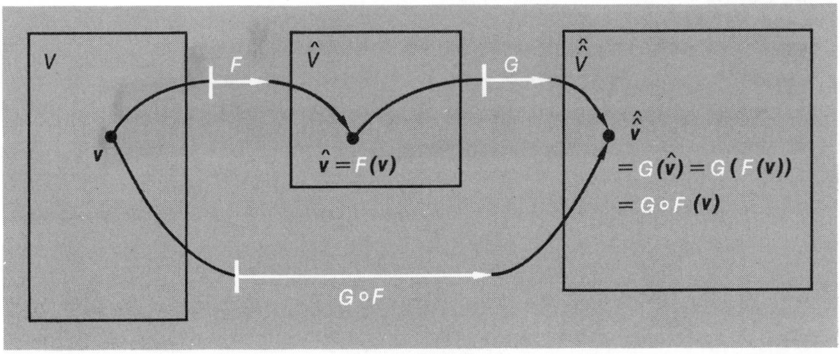

Figure 5-4

Given z, $F(\boldsymbol{x}) = z$ if

$$x^1 + x^2 = z^1 \qquad (5\text{-}7)$$
$$x^1 - x^2 = z^2.$$

Solving, we find that

$$x^1 = \tfrac{1}{2}(z^1 + z^2) \qquad (5\text{-}8)$$
$$x^2 = \tfrac{1}{2}(z^1 - z^2).$$

In other words $F(\frac{1}{2}(z^1 + z^2), \frac{1}{2}(z^1 - z^2)) = (z^1, z^2)$. Given any z, there is a vector in R^2 whose image is z, so F is surjective.

Equations 5-7 and 5-8 are statements of the vector equations $F(\boldsymbol{x}) = z$ and $\boldsymbol{x} = F^{-1}(z)$. In other words

$$F^{-1}(z) = \tfrac{1}{2}(z^1 + z^2, z^1 - z^2)$$

or

$$F^{-1}(\boldsymbol{x}) = \tfrac{1}{2}F(\boldsymbol{x}).$$

As a result of Theorem 5-1, we see that if $F: V \to \hat{V}$ is an isomorphism, then $F^{-1}: \hat{V} \to V$ is also an isomorphism. Thus, we can say that V and $\hat{V}$ are isomorphic whenever we can establish an isomorphism map either from V onto $\hat{V}$ or from $\hat{V}$ onto V.

Now suppose that both $F: V \to \hat{V}$ and $G: \hat{V} \to \hat{\hat{V}}$ are isomorphisms. Our next theorem tells us that the map $H: V \to \hat{\hat{V}}$ defined by the equation $H(\boldsymbol{v}) = G(F(\boldsymbol{v}))$ is an isomorphism. We say H is a ***composite*** map and write $\boldsymbol{H = G \circ F}$.

THEOREM 5-2

Let $F: V \to \hat{V}$ and $G: \hat{V} \to \hat{\hat{V}}$, so that $(G \circ F): V \to \hat{\hat{V}}$.
(a) If F and G are linear maps, then $G \circ F$ is a linear map.
(b) If F and G are injective maps, then $G \circ F$ is an injective map.
(c) If F and G are surjective maps, then $G \circ F$ is a surjective map.

Proof: Part (a). $(G \circ F)(c\boldsymbol{v} + \boldsymbol{w}) = G(F(c\boldsymbol{v} + \boldsymbol{w})) = G(cF(\boldsymbol{v}) + F(\boldsymbol{w})) = c(G \circ F)(\boldsymbol{v}) + (G \circ F)(\boldsymbol{w})$.

Part (b). If $\boldsymbol{v} \neq \boldsymbol{w}$, then $F(\boldsymbol{v}) \neq F(\boldsymbol{w})$, so $G(F(\boldsymbol{v})) \neq G(F(\boldsymbol{w}))$. Thus, if $\boldsymbol{v} \neq \boldsymbol{w}$, $(G \circ F)(\boldsymbol{v}) \neq (G \circ F)(\boldsymbol{w})$.

Part (c). For any vector $\hat{\hat{\boldsymbol{v}}}$ there is a vector $\hat{\boldsymbol{v}}$ such that $G(\hat{\boldsymbol{v}}) = \hat{\hat{\boldsymbol{v}}}$, and for any vector $\hat{\boldsymbol{v}}$ there is a vector $\boldsymbol{v}$ such that $F(\boldsymbol{v}) = \hat{\boldsymbol{v}}$. Thus, there is a vector $\boldsymbol{v}$ such that

$$G(F(\boldsymbol{v})) = (G \circ F)(\boldsymbol{v}) = \hat{\hat{\boldsymbol{v}}}.$$

In other words,

$$(G \circ F)(V) = \hat{\hat{V}}. \quad \blacksquare$$

As a particular application of the preceding theorem, we see that if V is isomorphic to $\hat{V}$ and $\hat{V}$ is isomorphic to $\hat{\hat{V}}$, then V is isomorphic to $\hat{\hat{V}}$. As a special case, if $\dim V = \dim \hat{V} = n$, then V and $\hat{V}$ are both isomorphic to R^n. Thus, V and $\hat{V}$ are isomorphic. In other words:

*All **n**-dimensional vector spaces are isomorphic to one another.*

Thus, as far as finite dimensional vector spaces are concerned, there is really only one vector space of a given dimension. It would then seem reasonable to restrict our study to R^n. We could do this, but then we would have to show that our results did not depend on the choice of a basis, since the isomorphism from V onto R^n was defined in terms of a choice of basis. By and large, we will study V directly because the "coordinate free" approach is more likely to be applicable to the case when V is not finite dimensional.

PROBLEMS 5

1. Prove that if $F: V \to \hat{V}$ is a linear map, then
   (a) $F(\mathbf{0}) = \hat{\mathbf{0}}$.
   (b) $\{\boldsymbol{v} : \boldsymbol{v} \in V, F(\boldsymbol{v}) = \hat{\mathbf{0}}\}$ is a subspace of V.
2. Show that Equations 5-1 and Equation 5-4 express equivalent conditions.
3. Let $F: R^1 \to R^1$ be a linear map. Write a formula for $F(x)$. Give a geometric description of $\{(x, F(x))\}$. Discuss the possibilities for $F(R^1)$. How can you tell from a picture of $\{(x, F(x))\}$ whether or not F is injective?
4. Let $F: R^3 \to R^2$ be defined by the equation $F(x^1, x^2, x^3) = (x^1, 0)$.
   (a) Prove that F is a linear map.
   (b) Is F injective?
   (c) Is F surjective?
   (d) Is F invertible?
5. Suppose that the map $F: V \to \hat{V}$ is defined by the rule "$F(\boldsymbol{v}) = \hat{\mathbf{0}}$ for all $\boldsymbol{v}$ in V." Is F a linear map?
6. Show that if F is an invertible map, then F^{-1} is also an invertible map and $(F^{-1})^{-1} = F$.
7. Determine if $F: R^2 \to R^1$ is a linear map if $F(x^1, x^2)$ is equal to
   (a) $3x^1 - x^2$ (b) $x^1 + 4x^2 + 6$ (c) x^1 (d) x^1/x^2
8. Suppose that $F: V \to \hat{V}$ is a linear map and that the image of both $\boldsymbol{v}_1$ and $\boldsymbol{v}_2$ is $\hat{\mathbf{0}}$. Let $W = \text{Sp}\,\{\boldsymbol{v}_1, \boldsymbol{v}_2\}$. Describe $F(W)$.

9. Let $F: R^1 \to R^2$ such that $F(t) = (x^1, x^2)$. In this case there are two functions $F^1: R^1 \to R^1$ and $F^2: R^1 \to R^1$ such that $x^1 = F^1(t)$ and $x^2 = F^2(t)$.
   (a) Show that if F^1 and F^2 are linear maps, then so is F.
   (b) Show that if F is a linear map, then F^1 and F^2 are linear maps.
10. Let $F: C[0,\pi] \to R^1$ be defined by the equation

$$F(f) = \int_0^\pi f(t)dt.$$

   (a) Find $F(\boldsymbol{s})$ and $F(\boldsymbol{c})$ where $\boldsymbol{s}$ and $\boldsymbol{c}$ are the sine and cosine functions.
   (b) Is F a linear map?
   (c) What is $F(W)$ if $W = \text{Sp}\{\boldsymbol{s}, \boldsymbol{c}\}$?
   (d) Is F injective? Surjective?
11. Let $F: C(R) \to C(R)$ be defined by $F(f) = g$ where

$$g(x) = \int_0^x f(t)dt.$$

   (a) Is F linear?
   (b) Is F injective?
   (c) Is F surjective?

6 PROPERTIES OF LINEAR MAPS

To define a function we must state the rule of correspondence in some way. For example, in calculus a function is usually defined by a formula such as $f(t) = t \sin t$. In this section we begin our effort to find the formula that defines a linear map $F: V \to \hat{V}$ in the case where V is finite dimensional. First, we must gather together some basic properties of linear maps.

In Problem 5-1b we asked you to show that if $F: V \to \hat{V}$ is linear, then the set of vectors mapped onto zero is a subspace of V. This subspace is called the ***kernel** of **F*** or the ***null space** of **F***. We will use the notation ***K(F)*** for this subspace. Thus,

$$K(F) = \{\boldsymbol{v} \text{ in } V: F(\boldsymbol{v}) = \hat{\boldsymbol{0}} \text{ in } \hat{V}\}.$$

(We will write $\boldsymbol{0}$ instead of $\hat{\boldsymbol{0}}$ if it is clear which zero we mean.) Of course, the kernel of F may consist of the zero subspace $\{\boldsymbol{0}\}$. In fact, this situation occurs precisely when F is an injective linear map. To grasp this fact, notice that if F is injective, then $F(\boldsymbol{v}) = F(\boldsymbol{0}) = \hat{\boldsymbol{0}}$ implies $\boldsymbol{v} = \boldsymbol{0}$; and conversely, if $K(F) = \{\boldsymbol{0}\}$, then $F(\boldsymbol{v}_1) = F(\boldsymbol{v}_2)$ implies $F(\boldsymbol{v}_1 - \boldsymbol{v}_2) = \hat{\boldsymbol{0}}$, which in turn implies $\boldsymbol{v}_1 = \boldsymbol{v}_2$. Thus,

***F** is injective if, and only if, **K(F)** = {**0**}.*

Example 6-1 Let $F: R^2 \to R^1$ be defined by the equation $F(x^1, x^2) = x^1 - x^2$. Find $K(F)$.

Solution: $F(x^1, x^2) = 0$ if, and only if, $x^1 = x^2$. Thus, $K(F) = \text{Sp}\,\{(1,1)\} = \{(k,k): k \in R^1\}$. Notice that $K(F)$ is a subspace of dimension 1.

Example 6-2 Let $D: P \to P$ be the derivative map. What is $K(D)$?

Solution: If $D(\boldsymbol{p}) = \mathbf{0}$, the zero polynomial, then $\boldsymbol{p}$ is a "constant polynomial."

Suppose that W is a subspace of V and that $F: V \to \hat{V}$ is a linear map. If F is surjective; that is, if $F(V) = \hat{V}$, then $F(V)$ is a vector space. Also, $F(\mathbf{0}) = \mathbf{0}$, so that $F(W)$ is a vector space if W is the zero subspace. $K(F)$ is a subspace, and of course, $F(K(F)) = \{\mathbf{0}\}$. Thus, the image of a subspace W is a subspace in certain particular cases. Let us now look at $F(W)$ in the general case.

If $\hat{\boldsymbol{w}}_1 = F(\boldsymbol{w}_1)$ and $\hat{\boldsymbol{w}}_2 = F(\boldsymbol{w}_2)$ are vectors in $F(W)$, then

$$c\hat{\boldsymbol{w}}_1 + \hat{\boldsymbol{w}}_2 = cF(\boldsymbol{w}_1) + F(\boldsymbol{w}_2) = F(c\boldsymbol{w}_1 + \boldsymbol{w}_2).$$

Since W is a subspace, $c\boldsymbol{w}_1 + \boldsymbol{w}_2 = \boldsymbol{w}$ is in W, and so $c\hat{\boldsymbol{w}}_1 + \hat{\boldsymbol{w}}_2 = F(\boldsymbol{w})$. Thus, $c\hat{\boldsymbol{w}}_1 + \hat{\boldsymbol{w}}_2$ is in $F(W)$. In other words:

If $F: V \to \hat{V}$ is linear and W is a subspace of V, then $F(W)$ is a subspace of $\hat{V}$.

Example 6-3 Let $W = \text{Sp}\,\{(2,1)\}$, and suppose that F is the map defined in Example 6-1. Find $F(W)$.

Solution: If $\boldsymbol{w} = c(2,1) = (2c, c)$, then $F(2c, c) = c$. Thus, $F(W) = R^1$, which is certainly a subspace of R^1.

Example 6-4 Let $W = P_2$, a subspace of P, and let D be the derivative map. Find $D(W)$.

Solution: If $\boldsymbol{p}$ is in W, then $\boldsymbol{p}(x) = ax + b$ and $D(\boldsymbol{p}) = a$. Thus, $D(W)$ is the space of "constant polynomials."

Now we turn to the problem of defining a linear map in the finite dimensional case. Suppose that V has a basis $E = \{\boldsymbol{e}_1, \ldots, \boldsymbol{e}_n\}$ and that $\boldsymbol{v} = x^1\boldsymbol{e}_1 + \cdots + x^n\boldsymbol{e}_n$. Then if $F: V \to \hat{V}$ is a linear map

$$\begin{aligned} F(\boldsymbol{v}) &= F(x^1\boldsymbol{e}_1 + \cdots + x^n\boldsymbol{e}_n) \\ &= F(x^1\boldsymbol{e}_1) + \cdots + F(x^n\boldsymbol{e}_n) \\ &= x^1F(\boldsymbol{e}_1) + \cdots + x^nF(\boldsymbol{e}_n). \end{aligned}$$

In short, using the summation notation, then

$$F(\boldsymbol{v}) = F(x^\alpha \boldsymbol{e}_\alpha) = x^\alpha F(\boldsymbol{e}_\alpha).$$

Given $\boldsymbol{v}$, we can find $[\boldsymbol{v}]_E$, the coordinates of $\boldsymbol{v}$. Thus, to find $F(\boldsymbol{v})$ we need only know the n values $F(\boldsymbol{e}_1), \ldots, F(\boldsymbol{e}_n)$. With a given linear map F, we can certainly find these n values. Now the question arises, can another linear map G have the same values as F at the basis vectors? If it does, then

$$G(\boldsymbol{v}) = G(x^\alpha \boldsymbol{e}_\alpha) = x^\alpha G(\boldsymbol{e}_\alpha) = x^\alpha F(\boldsymbol{e}_\alpha) = F(x^\alpha \boldsymbol{e}_\alpha) = F(\boldsymbol{v}).$$

In other words, if G has the same values as F at the basis vectors, then G has the same value as F at every vector $\boldsymbol{v}$, and so $G = F$. Thus, *a linear map is uniquely defined by giving its values at the basis vectors.* In fact, a particular linear map is often defined just this way.

Example 6-5 Let $F: R^2 \to R^2$ be the linear map defined by the equation $F(1,0) = (1,1)$ and $F(0,1) = (1,-1)$. Find $K(F)$.

Solution:
$$\begin{aligned} F(x^1, x^2) &= F(x^1(1,0) + x^2(0,1)) \\ &= x^1 F(1,0) + x^2 F(0,1) \\ &= x^1(1,1) + x^2(1,-1) \\ &= (x^1 + x^2, x^1 - x^2). \end{aligned}$$

Map F is the same map we considered in Example 5-5. There we saw that F was injective. Thus, $K(F) = \{\mathbf{0}\}$.

In the preceding example we saw that $\{(1,0), (0,1)\}$ is a basis for $V = R^2$ and that $\{F(1,0), F(0,1)\}$ is a basis for $\hat{V} = R^2$. This need not be the case in general. But since

$$F(\boldsymbol{v}) = F(x^\alpha \boldsymbol{e}_\alpha) = x^\alpha F(\boldsymbol{e}_\alpha),$$

we see that every vector in $F(V)$ is a linear combination of the n vectors $F(\boldsymbol{e}_1), \ldots, F(\boldsymbol{e}_n)$. In other words

(6-1) $$\text{Sp}\{F(\boldsymbol{e}_1), \ldots, F(\boldsymbol{e}_n)\} = F(V).$$

Thus, $\{F(\boldsymbol{e}_1), \ldots, F(\boldsymbol{e}_n)\}$ is a basis for $F(V)$ if, and only if, this set is an independent set. To test this set for independence we set

$$c^1 F(\boldsymbol{e}_1) + \cdots + c^n F(\boldsymbol{e}_n) = \mathbf{0}$$

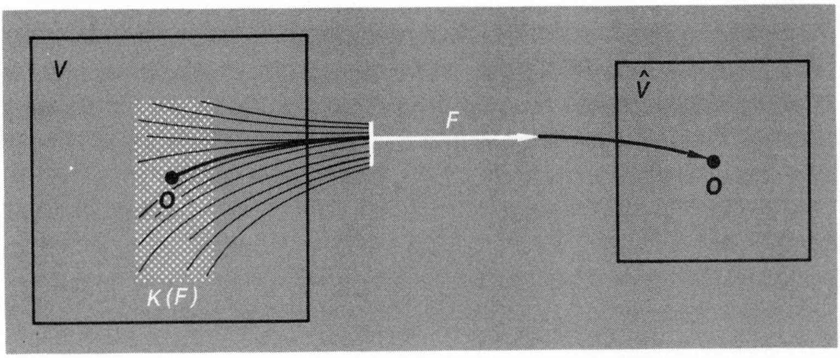

Figure 6-1

and see if this equation implies that each of the coefficients $c^1, \ldots, c^n$ is equal to zero. But, because F is linear,

$$c^\alpha F(\boldsymbol{e}_\alpha) = \mathbf{0} \quad \text{implies that} \quad F(c^\alpha \boldsymbol{e}_\alpha) = \mathbf{0}.$$

If $K(F) = \{\mathbf{0}\}$; that is, if F is injective, then $F(c^\alpha \boldsymbol{e}_\alpha) = \mathbf{0}$ implies that $c^1\boldsymbol{e}_1 + \cdots + c^n\boldsymbol{e}_n = \mathbf{0}$, which in turn implies that

$$c^1 = c^2 = \cdots = c^n = 0$$

because $\{\boldsymbol{e}_1, \ldots, \boldsymbol{e}_n\}$ is an independent set. Thus, we have the following useful fact:

> If $K(F) = \{\mathbf{0}\}$ and $\{\boldsymbol{e}_1, \ldots, \boldsymbol{e}_n\}$ is a basis for V, then $\{F(\boldsymbol{e}_1), \ldots, F(\boldsymbol{e}_n)\}$ is a basis for $F(V)$.

Now what happens if $K(F) \neq \{\mathbf{0}\}$? Because $K(F)$ is a subspace (Problem 5-1b), it has a basis, say $\{\boldsymbol{e}_1, \ldots, \boldsymbol{e}_k\}$, where $1 \leq k \leq n$. According to Theorem 4-3 in Chapter 1 this basis can be extended to a basis of V, say $\{\boldsymbol{e}_1, \ldots, \boldsymbol{e}_k, \boldsymbol{e}_{k+1}, \ldots, \boldsymbol{e}_n\}$. We know that the images of these vectors span $F(V)$ (Equation 6-1). But $F(\boldsymbol{e}_1) = \cdots = F(\boldsymbol{e}_k) = \mathbf{0}$, so

$$\text{Sp}\,\{F(\boldsymbol{e}_{k+1}), \ldots, F(\boldsymbol{e}_n)\} = F(V).$$

To see that $\{F(\boldsymbol{e}_{k+1}), \ldots, F(\boldsymbol{e}_n)\}$ is an independent set we write

$$c^{k+1}F(\boldsymbol{e}_{k+1}) + \cdots + c^nF(\boldsymbol{e}_n) = \mathbf{0}.$$

Again, using the fact that F is a linear map we can write the preceding equation as

$$F(c^{k+1}\boldsymbol{e}_{k+1} + \cdots + c^n\boldsymbol{e}_n) = \mathbf{0}.$$

But this equation says $c^{k+1}e_{k+1} + \cdots + c^n e_n$ is in $K(F)$. Because $\{e_1, \ldots, e_k\}$ is a basis for $K(F)$, there are k numbers $c^1, \ldots, c^k$ such that

$$c^{k+1}e_{k+1} + \cdots + c^n e_n = c^1 e_1 + \cdots + c^k e_k.$$

Thus,

$$c^1 e_1 + \cdots + c^k e_k - c^{k+1}e_{k+1} - \cdots - c^n e_n = \mathbf{0}.$$

Because $\{e_1, \ldots, e_n\}$ is an independent set, each coefficient in this linear combination is zero. In particular, $c^{k+1} = \cdots = c^n = 0$. Thus, $\{F(e_{k+1}), \ldots, F(e_n)\}$ is independent set, and hence, a basis for $F(V)$. We now have finished the difficult part of the proof of the following theorem.

THEOREM 6-1

Let $\dim V = n$ and let $F: V \to \hat{V}$ be a linear map. Then

$$\dim F(V) + \dim K(F) = \dim V.$$

In particular, if $K(F) = \{\mathbf{0}\}$, the images of the basis vectors for V form a basis for $F(V)$.

Proof: If $K(F) = \{\mathbf{0}\}$, we agreed that $\dim K(F) = 0$; and $\dim F(V) = n = \dim V$, as we saw above. If $\dim K(F) = k$, our discussion preceding the statement of the theorem tells us that $\dim F(V) = n - k = \dim V - \dim K(F)$. ∎

Example 6-6 Let $F: R^2 \to R^1$ be linear. Prove that $\dim K(F) \geq 1$.

Solution: $\dim K(F) = \dim R^2 - \dim F(R^2) = 2 - \dim F(R^2)$. Because $\dim F(R^2) \leq 1$ in this case, $\dim K(F) \geq 1$. Notice that in Example 6-1 $\dim K(F) = 1$ and $\dim F(R^2) = 1$.

Now suppose that $F: V \to \hat{V}$ is linear and that $\dim V = \dim \hat{V}$. Then $\dim F(V) = \dim \hat{V} - \dim K(F)$. Because $F(V) = \hat{V}$ if, and only if, $\dim F(V) = \dim \hat{V}$, we see that in this case F is surjective if, and only if, F is injective ($K(F) = \{\mathbf{0}\}$). Hence, if $\dim V = \dim \hat{V}$, the words "injective," "surjective," and invertible" really mean the same thing for a linear map. More precisely, a linear map F is injective if, and only if, F is surjective; and F is surjective if, and only if, F is invertible. One very important special case in which $\dim V = \dim \hat{V}$ is when $V = \hat{V}$. In fact, if $\dim V = \dim \hat{V}$, then V and $\hat{V}$ are isomorphic, and hence, in one sense "equal." The case in which V and $\hat{V}$ are equal will occupy a great deal of our attention in later sections; F in that case is called an operator in a space.

follow up on p. 39

DEFINITION 6-1

If $F: V \to V$ is a linear map, F is called a ***linear operator*** *in* V.

We summarize our discussion above in the following theorem.

THEOREM 6-2

If F is a linear operator in a finite dimensional vector space V, then the following statements are equivalent:
(i) F is invertible (F^{-1} exists).
(ii) F is injective $\left(K(F) = \{\mathbf{0}\}\right)$.
(iii) F is surjective $\left(F(V) = V\right)$.

Example 6-7 Does Theorem 6-2 hold if V is not finite dimensional?

Solution: NO. The derivative operator in the space of polynomials is surjective, but not injective (see Example 5-4).

PROBLEMS 6

1. Determine if F is linear and find $K(F)$.
   (a) $F: R^1 \to R^2$, $F(x) = (x, x)$
   (b) $F: R^1 \to R^2$, $F(x) = (x, \sqrt{x})$
   (c) $F: R^2 \to R^3$, $F(x^1, x^2) = (x^1 + x^2, x^1 - x^2, 2x^1)$
   (d) $F: R^3 \to R^2$, $F(x^1, x^2, x^3) = (x^1 - x^2, x^1 - x^3)$
   (e) $F: C[0,1] \to R$, $F(\boldsymbol{f}) = \boldsymbol{f}(0)$
   (f) $F: P \to P$, $F(\boldsymbol{p}) = \boldsymbol{p}'(0)$.
2. Let $F: R^3 \to R^2$ be the linear map defined by the equations $F(1,0,0) = (1,1)$; $F(0,1,0) = (-1,1)$; $F(0,0,1) = (-1,-1)$.
   (a) Find $F(x^1,x^2,x^3)$.
   (b) Find a non-zero vector in $K(F)$.
   (c) Find a basis for $K(F)$.
   (d) What is dim $K(F)$? Is F injective? surjective?
3. Let $F: R^3 \to R^2$ be the linear map defined by the equations $F(1,0,0) = F(0,1,0) = F(0,0,1) = (1,0)$.
   (a) Find a non-zero vector in $K(F)$.
   (b) What is dim $K(F)$?
   (c) Find a basis for $K(F)$.
   (d) Give a geometric description of $F(R^3)$.
4. Let $\boldsymbol{e}_n$ be the nth power function and define the linear operator in P by the equation $F(\boldsymbol{e}_n) = \boldsymbol{e}_{n+1}$ for $n = 0, 1, \ldots$. Find $K(F)$. Find $F(P_2)$.
5. Suppose that $\{\boldsymbol{e}_1, \boldsymbol{e}_2\}$ is a basis in V and that $\hat{\boldsymbol{v}}$ is a fixed vector in $\hat{V}$. Define a

linear map $F: V \to \hat{V}$ by the equations $F(\boldsymbol{e}_1) = F(\boldsymbol{e}_2) = \hat{\boldsymbol{v}}$. Discuss dim $K(F)$ and dim $F(V)$.

6. Define a linear map $F: R^3 \to R^2$ by the equations $F(1,0,0) = (1,0)$; $F(0,1,0) = (0,1)$; and $F(0,0,1) = (0,0)$. Find $F(1,2,3)$. Find dim $K(F)$ and dim $F(R^3)$. Is F injective? Is F surjective? Interpret this map geometrically.
7. Show that if $F: R^2 \to R^1$ is linear, then the equation defining F is $F(x^1, x^2) = ax^1 + bx^2$, where a and b are some fixed numbers.
8. Show that if $F: R^1 \to R^2$ is linear, then there is a fixed vector (x^1, x^2) such that $F(c) = c(x^1, x^2)$ for all $c \in R^1$.
9. If $\boldsymbol{s}$ and $\boldsymbol{c}$ are the sine and cosine functions, show that the derivative operator D is a linear operator in Sp $\{\boldsymbol{s}, \boldsymbol{c}\}$. Find $K(D)$.
10. Show that R^m is not isomorphic to R^n if $m \neq n$.
11. In each of the following give a geometric description of the linear operator defined in R^2 by interpreting R^2 as a coordinate plane. Determine if F is invertible and, if it is, find F^{-1}.
    (a) $F(1,0) = (0,1)$ and $F(0,1) = (1,0)$
    (b) $F(1,0) = (1,0)$ and $F(0,1) = (0,-1)$
    (c) $F(1,0) = (-1,0)$ and $F(0,1) = (0,-1)$
    (d) $F(1,0) = (1,0)$ and $F(0,1) = (0,0)$.
12. Interpret R^2 as a coordinate plane. Describe geometrically the set $S = \{\boldsymbol{x} : \boldsymbol{x} = \boldsymbol{u} + c\boldsymbol{v}\}$ where $\boldsymbol{u}$ and $\boldsymbol{v}$ are fixed vectors in R^2. Is S a subspace? Give a geometric description of $F(S)$ if F is a linear operator in R^2.
13. Let $D: P_3 \to P_2$ be the derivative map. Choose the usual power functions as bases in P_3 and P_2. Describe D by giving its values on the basis vectors in P_3.

7 REPRESENTING LINEAR MAPS BY MATRICES. COORDINATE CHANGES

In Problem 6-7 we asked you to show that the formula defining a linear map $F: R^2 \to R^1$ is $F(\boldsymbol{x}) = ax^1 + bx^2$. In that case F is determined by two numbers, a and b. In this section we will see that a linear map $F: R^n \to R^m$ is determined by $m \cdot n$ numbers. First, let us generalize the result of Problem 6-7 to the case of a linear map $F: R^n \to R^1$. If $E = \{\boldsymbol{e}_1, \ldots, \boldsymbol{e}_n\}$ is the natural basis for R^n, then

$$F(\boldsymbol{x}) = F(x^\alpha \boldsymbol{e}_\alpha) = x^\alpha F(\boldsymbol{e}_\alpha).$$

The numbers $a_1, \ldots, a_n$ defined as $a_j = F(\boldsymbol{e}_j)$ determine F:

$$F(\boldsymbol{x}) = a_\alpha x^\alpha.$$

We will obtain this number from a product of a row of numbers, or *row matrix*, times a column matrix. Thus, we define

$$[a_1 \ . \ . \ . \ a_n] \cdot \begin{bmatrix} x^1 \\ \cdot \\ \cdot \\ \cdot \\ x^n \end{bmatrix} = [a_1 x^1 + \cdots + a_n x^n] = [a_\alpha x^\alpha]. \tag{7-1}$$

Notice that the right side of this equation is merely a number with a bracket around it. It is the coordinate of $F(x)$ in the natural basis of R^1.

We have encountered this column matrix before. It is the coordinate matrix of $\boldsymbol{x}$ with respect to the basis E that we have written $[\boldsymbol{x}]$ (the E subscript is omitted here because the natural basis was chosen for R^n). The numbers $a_1, \ldots, a_n$ depend on F and on the bases we choose for R^n and R^1. (It seems strange to consider anything other than 1 as a basis for R^1, but it can be done!) We will write

$$[F] = [a_1 \ . \ . \ . \ a_n].$$

Notice that the *lower index* is now a *column index*; that is, a_k is the number in the kth column of the row matrix. Thus, in this special case,

$$[F][\boldsymbol{x}] = [F(\boldsymbol{x})].$$

Now let us look at the situation when we consider a linear map $F: R^2 \to R^2$. As a matter of fact, it is just as easy to consider a linear map $F: V \to \hat{V}$ where $\dim V = \dim \hat{V} = 2$. Let $E = \{\boldsymbol{e}_1, \boldsymbol{e}_2\}$ and $\hat{E} = \{\hat{\boldsymbol{e}}_1, \hat{\boldsymbol{e}}_2\}$ be bases for V and $\hat{V}$. As we know, F is completely determined by its values at $\boldsymbol{e}_1$ and $\boldsymbol{e}_2$. Suppose, for example, that

$$\begin{aligned} F(\boldsymbol{e}_1) &= 2\hat{\boldsymbol{e}}_1 - 3\hat{\boldsymbol{e}}_2 \\ F(\boldsymbol{e}_2) &= 4\hat{\boldsymbol{e}}_1 + 5\hat{\boldsymbol{e}}_2. \end{aligned} \tag{7-2}$$

The four numbers 2, -3, 4, and 5 define F once the bases are chosen:

$$\begin{aligned} F(\boldsymbol{v}) &= F(x^1\boldsymbol{e}_1 + x^2\boldsymbol{e}_2) \\ &= x^1F(\boldsymbol{e}_1) + x^2F(\boldsymbol{e}_2) \\ &= x^1(2\hat{\boldsymbol{e}}_1 - 3\hat{\boldsymbol{e}}_2) + x^2(4\hat{\boldsymbol{e}}_1 + 5\hat{\boldsymbol{e}}_2) \\ &= (2x^1 + 4x^2)\hat{\boldsymbol{e}}_1 + (-3x^1 + 5x^2)\hat{\boldsymbol{e}}_2. \end{aligned} \tag{7-3}$$

Thus, if F is defined by Equation 7-2, the vector $\boldsymbol{v}$ is mapped into a vector $\hat{\boldsymbol{v}}$

whose $\hat{E}$-coordinates are the coefficients of $\hat{e}_1$ and $\hat{e}_2$ given in Equation 7-3. Symbolically,

$$[v]_E = \begin{bmatrix} x^1 \\ x^2 \end{bmatrix} \overset{F}{\longmapsto} \begin{bmatrix} 2x^1 + 4x^2 \\ -3x^1 + 5x^2 \end{bmatrix} = [\hat{v}]_{\hat{E}}.$$

In view of the definition in Equation 7-1 the first and second rows of $[\hat{v}]_{\hat{E}}$ are, respectively, the products

$$[2 \quad 4] \cdot \begin{bmatrix} x^1 \\ x^2 \end{bmatrix} \quad \text{and} \quad [-3 \quad 5] \cdot \begin{bmatrix} x^1 \\ x^2 \end{bmatrix}.$$

This observation suggests that we write

$$\begin{bmatrix} 2x^1 + 4x^2 \\ -3x^1 + 5x^2 \end{bmatrix} = \begin{bmatrix} 2 & 4 \\ -3 & 5 \end{bmatrix} \cdot \begin{bmatrix} x^1 \\ x^2 \end{bmatrix}. \tag{7-4}$$

The table of four numbers on the right of this equation is the *matrix of **F** relative to the bases **E** and **Ê***, and we write

$$[F]_{\hat{E}}^{E} = \begin{bmatrix} 2 & 4 \\ -3 & 5 \end{bmatrix}.$$

Notice that $[F(e_1)]_{\hat{E}}$ is the first *column*, and $[F(e_2)]_{\hat{E}}$ is the second column, of $[F]_{\hat{E}}^{E}$. If we define the product of a matrix times a column matrix so that Equation 7-4 is true, we can write

$$[F(v)]_{\hat{E}} = [F]_{\hat{E}}^{E} \cdot [v]_E.$$

Now we will consider the general finite dimensional case. It follows the pattern we have seen above. First, we will explain the notation we use for a matrix that has ***m*** *rows* and ***n*** *columns*. An ***m*** *by* ***n*** *matrix* contains m · n numbers. When we display it as a table, the number a_j^i is put in the ith row and j^{th} column. For example, a 3 by 4 matrix is written

$$\begin{bmatrix} a_1^1 & a_2^1 & a_3^1 & a_4^1 \\ a_1^2 & a_2^2 & a_3^2 & a_4^2 \\ a_1^3 & a_2^3 & a_3^3 & a_4^3 \end{bmatrix}.$$

If $F: V \to \hat{V}$ is a linear map with $E = \{\boldsymbol{e}_1, \ldots, \boldsymbol{e}_n\}$ a basis for V and $\hat{E} = \{\hat{\boldsymbol{e}}_1, \ldots, \hat{\boldsymbol{e}}_m\}$ a basis for $\hat{V}$, then the *matrix of* ***F*** *with respect to* ***E*** *and* $\hat{\boldsymbol{E}}$ is the m by n matrix denoted by $[F]^E_{\hat{E}}$ and defined as follows (using summation notation with $\alpha = 1, \ldots, m$): If $F(\boldsymbol{e}_j) = a^\alpha_j \hat{\boldsymbol{e}}_\alpha (j = 1, \ldots, n)$, then

(7-5)
$$[F]^E_{\hat{E}} = \begin{bmatrix} a^1_1 & \cdots & a^1_n \\ \vdots & & \\ a^m_1 & \cdots & a^m_n \end{bmatrix}.$$

The first column of this matrix is $[F(\boldsymbol{e}_1)]_{\hat{E}}$, the second column is $[F(\boldsymbol{e}_2)]_{\hat{E}}$, and so on. To remind us of this fact we write

(7-6)
$$[F]^E_{\hat{E}} = [F(\boldsymbol{e}_1) \ldots F(\boldsymbol{e}_n)]_{\hat{E}}.$$

The indices E and $\hat{E}$ are omitted in the notation for the matrix of F when natural bases are used or when the context indicates which bases are used. We write these indices in order to state a formula explicitly or to ask a question concisely, but as a matter of actual practice we do not often use them in working problems.

Example 7-1 Let $F: R^2 \to R^3$ be defined by $F(x^1, x^2) = (x^1 + x^2, x^1 - x^2, x^1)$. Find $[F]$.

Solution: Bases are not mentioned so we assume that the natural bases for R^2 and R^3 are to be used. Then

$$F(1,0) = (1,1,1) = 1(1,0,0) + 1(0,1,0) + 1(0,0,1)$$
$$F(0,1) = (1,-1,0) = 1(1,0,0) - 1(0,1,0) + 0(0,0,1).$$

Thus,

$$F(\boldsymbol{e}_1) = 1\hat{\boldsymbol{e}}_1 + 1\hat{\boldsymbol{e}}_2 + 1\hat{\boldsymbol{e}}_3$$
$$F(\boldsymbol{e}_2) = 1\hat{\boldsymbol{e}}_1 - 1\hat{\boldsymbol{e}}_2 + 0\hat{\boldsymbol{e}}_3,$$

and

$$[F] = \begin{bmatrix} 1 & 1 \\ 1 & -1 \\ 1 & 0 \end{bmatrix}.$$

Example 7-2 Use the same F as in Example 7-1, but substitute the basis $E = \{(1,1), (1,-1)\}$ for R^2 and let $\hat{E}$ be the natural basis for R^3. Find $[F]^E_{\hat{E}}$.

Solution:
$$F(1,1) = (2,0,1) = 2\hat{\boldsymbol{e}}_1 + \hat{\boldsymbol{e}}_3$$
$$F(1,-1) = (0,2,1) = 2\hat{\boldsymbol{e}}_2 + \hat{\boldsymbol{e}}_3.$$

Thus,

$$[F]_{\hat{E}}^{E} = \begin{bmatrix} 2 & 0 \\ 0 & 2 \\ 1 & 1 \end{bmatrix}.$$

Example 7-3 Find the matrix representing the derivative map $D: P_3 \rightarrow P_2$ if the usual power function bases are used.

Solution: Because $D_x 1 = 0$, $D_x x = 1$, *and* $D_x x^2 = 2x$,

$$D(\boldsymbol{e}_0) = \boldsymbol{0},\ D(\boldsymbol{e}_1) = \boldsymbol{e}_0, \quad \text{and} \quad D(\boldsymbol{e}_2) = 2\boldsymbol{e}_1.$$

Thus,

$$[D] = \begin{bmatrix} 0 & 1 & 0 \\ & & \\ 0 & 0 & 2 \end{bmatrix}.$$

Let us return to the problem of finding $[F(\boldsymbol{v})]_{\hat{E}}$ if we know $[\boldsymbol{v}]_E$ and $[F]_{\hat{E}}^{E}$, where $F: V \rightarrow \hat{V}$, $E = \{\boldsymbol{e}_1, \ldots, \boldsymbol{e}_n\}$, and $\hat{E} = \{\hat{\boldsymbol{e}}_1, \ldots, \hat{\boldsymbol{e}}_m\}$. Our procedure is to carry out the computations of Equation 7-3 in the general case (using the summation notation) and to use Equation 7-5. That is,

$$F(\boldsymbol{v}) = F(x^\beta \boldsymbol{e}_\beta) = x^\beta F(\boldsymbol{e}_\beta) = x^\beta a_\beta^\alpha \hat{\boldsymbol{e}}_\alpha.$$

Thus, F maps $\boldsymbol{v}$ onto $\hat{\boldsymbol{v}}$ with coordinate matrix

$$\begin{bmatrix} a_\beta^1 x^\beta \\ \vdots \\ a_\beta^m x^\beta \end{bmatrix}.$$

We define

$$\begin{bmatrix} a_1^1 & \ldots & a_n^1 \\ \vdots & & \vdots \\ a_1^m & \ldots & a_n^m \end{bmatrix} \cdot \begin{bmatrix} x^1 \\ \vdots \\ x^n \end{bmatrix} = \begin{bmatrix} a_1^1 x^1 + \cdots + a_n^1 x^n \\ \vdots \\ a_1^m x^1 + \cdots + a_n^m x^n \end{bmatrix}. \tag{7-7}$$

For example,

$$\begin{bmatrix} 1 & 2 & 3 \\ & & \\ 4 & 5 & 6 \end{bmatrix} \cdot \begin{bmatrix} 7 \\ 8 \\ 9 \end{bmatrix} = \begin{bmatrix} 7 + 16 + 27 \\ \\ 28 + 40 + 54 \end{bmatrix} = \begin{bmatrix} 50 \\ \\ 122 \end{bmatrix}.$$

The product of a matrix times a column matrix is defined only if the number of columns of the matrix is equal to the number of rows of the column matrix. As a special case, our definition in Equation 7-7 gives the same result as Equation 7-1. Using the definition in Equation 7-7 we can now write a basic result:

$$[F(\mathbf{v})]_{\hat{E}} = [F]^{E}_{\hat{E}}[\mathbf{v}]_{E}. \tag{7-8}$$

Example 7-4 Let F be defined as in Example 7-1. Use matrix multiplication to find $F(2,3)$.

Solution:

$$[F(2,3)] = \begin{bmatrix} 1 & 1 \\ 1 & -1 \\ 1 & 0 \end{bmatrix} \cdot \begin{bmatrix} 2 \\ 3 \end{bmatrix} = \begin{bmatrix} 5 \\ -1 \\ 2 \end{bmatrix}.$$

Thus,

$$F(2,3) = (5,-1,2).$$

Example 7-5 Use the matrix in Example 7-2 to find $F(2,3)$.

Solution: In the notation of Example 7-2 $[(2,3)]_E = \begin{bmatrix} \frac{5}{2} \\ -\frac{1}{2} \end{bmatrix}.$

Thus,

$$[F(2,3)] = \begin{bmatrix} 2 & 0 \\ 0 & 2 \\ 1 & 1 \end{bmatrix} \cdot \begin{bmatrix} \frac{5}{2} \\ -\frac{1}{2} \end{bmatrix} = \begin{bmatrix} 5 \\ -1 \\ 2 \end{bmatrix}.$$

Again we find that $F(2,3) = (5,-1,2)$.

A linear map $F: V \to \hat{V}$ is represented by an m by n matrix if $\dim V = n$ and $\dim \hat{V} = m$. As an important special case, let us consider a linear *operator* F in V (that is, $\hat{V} = V$). Then the matrix representing F is an n by n *square matrix*. It is still possible to express $\mathbf{v}$ in terms of the vectors in a basis E and to express $F(\mathbf{v})$ in terms of the vectors in another basis $\hat{E}$. Thus, we may still write Equation 7-8 in the case of a linear operator $F: V \to V$. It would seem to be silly to change bases just to compute $F(\mathbf{v})$, and in general it is not done. In one very special case it is very useful to consider E and $\hat{E}$ as different bases; namely, when F is the identity operator I.

DEFINITION 7-1

The identity operator I in a vector space V is defined by the rule $I(\mathbf{v}) = \mathbf{v}$ for all $\mathbf{v} \in V$.

If E is any basis for V and I is the identity operator in V, then

$$[I]_E^E = \begin{bmatrix} 1 & 0 & \cdots & 0 \\ 0 & 1 & \cdots & 0 \\ \vdots & \vdots & & \vdots \\ 0 & 0 & \ldots 1 & 0 \\ 0 & 0 & \ldots 0 & 1 \end{bmatrix}.$$

Now if $E = \{e_1, \ldots, e_n\}$ and $\hat{E} = \{\hat{e}_1, \ldots, \hat{e}_n\}$ are two bases of V and if $e_1 = I(e_1) = a_1^\beta \hat{e}_\beta$, $e_2 = I(e_2) = a_2^\beta \hat{e}_\beta$, and so on, then

$$[I]_{\hat{E}}^E = \begin{bmatrix} a_1^1 & \ldots & a_n^1 \\ \vdots & & \vdots \\ a_1^n & \cdots & a_n^n \end{bmatrix}.$$

Since $I(v) = v$, then $[I(v)]_{\hat{E}} = [v]_{\hat{E}}$, the coordinates of v in the basis $\hat{E}$. Thus, using Equation 7-8 we have the *coordinate transformation equation*

(7-9) $$[v]_{\hat{E}} = [I]_{\hat{E}}^E [v]_E.$$

The kth column of $[I]_{\hat{E}}^E$ consists of the "hat coordinates" of e_k. We write the following to remind us of that fact (see Equation 7-6):

(7-10) $$[I]_{\hat{E}}^E = [e_1 \ldots e_n]_{\hat{E}}.$$

Example 7-6 Let $V = R^2$, let E be the standard basis, and let $\hat{E} = \{(3,2), (3,-2)\}$. Write the coordinate transformation equations for this case.

Solution:

$$\hat{e}_1 = 3e_1 + 2e_2$$
$$\hat{e}_2 = 3e_1 - 2e_2.$$

Solving, we find

$$e_1 = \tfrac{1}{6}\hat{e}_1 + \tfrac{1}{6}\hat{e}_2$$
$$e_2 = \tfrac{1}{4}\hat{e}_1 - \tfrac{1}{4}\hat{e}_2.$$

Thus,

$$[I]_{\hat{E}}^E = \begin{bmatrix} \frac{1}{6} & \frac{1}{4} \\ \frac{1}{6} & -\frac{1}{4} \end{bmatrix} \quad \text{and} \quad [I]_E^{\hat{E}} = \begin{bmatrix} 3 & 3 \\ 2 & -2 \end{bmatrix}.$$

The coordinate transformation equation is

$$\begin{bmatrix} \hat{x}^1 \\ \\ \hat{x}^2 \end{bmatrix} = \begin{bmatrix} \frac{1}{6} & \frac{1}{4} \\ \\ \frac{1}{6} & -\frac{1}{4} \end{bmatrix} \cdot \begin{bmatrix} x^1 \\ \\ x^2 \end{bmatrix}.$$

In other words

$$\hat{x}^1 = \tfrac{1}{6}x^1 + \tfrac{1}{4}x^2$$
$$\hat{x}^2 = \tfrac{1}{6}x^1 - \tfrac{1}{4}x^2.$$

The result expressed in Equation 7-9 can be written, using summation notation, as

$$\hat{x}^j = a^j_\alpha x^\alpha \quad (j = 1, \ldots, n)$$

where

$$\boldsymbol{e}_k = a^\beta_k \hat{\boldsymbol{e}}_\beta \quad (k = 1, \ldots, n)$$

and

$$\boldsymbol{v} = x^\alpha \boldsymbol{e}_\alpha = \hat{x}^\beta \hat{\boldsymbol{e}}_\beta.$$

Let us conclude this section by examining the change of coordinates in a cartesian coordinate plane that results from a rotation of the axes through an angle of ϕ. Using simple trigonometry (see Fig. 7-1), if $\hat{\boldsymbol{e}}_1$ and $\hat{\boldsymbol{e}}_2$ represent the "rotated" unit vectors, then

$$\hat{\boldsymbol{e}}_1 = (\cos\phi)\boldsymbol{e}_1 + (\sin\phi)\boldsymbol{e}_2$$
$$\hat{\boldsymbol{e}}_2 = \left(\cos\left(\phi + \frac{\pi}{2}\right)\right)\boldsymbol{e}_1 + \left(\sin\left(\phi + \frac{\pi}{2}\right)\right)\boldsymbol{e}_2$$
$$= (-\sin\phi)\boldsymbol{e}_1 + (\cos\phi)\boldsymbol{e}_2.$$

We solve these equations to get

$$I(\boldsymbol{e}_1) = \boldsymbol{e}_1 = (\cos\phi)\hat{\boldsymbol{e}}_1 - (\sin\phi)\hat{\boldsymbol{e}}_2$$
$$I(\boldsymbol{e}_2) = \boldsymbol{e}_2 = (\sin\phi)\hat{\boldsymbol{e}}_1 + (\cos\phi)\hat{\boldsymbol{e}}_2.$$

Thus,

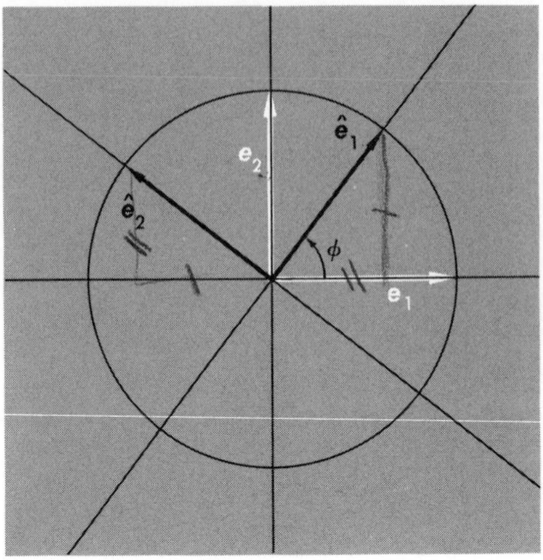

Figure 7-1

$$[I]_{\hat{E}}^{E} = \begin{bmatrix} \cos\phi & \sin\phi \\ -\sin\phi & \cos\phi \end{bmatrix}. \tag{7-11}$$

If P is any point in the coordinate plane, its E-coordinates and its $\hat{E}$-coordinates relative to the rotated axes are related by the equation

$$\begin{bmatrix} \hat{x}^1 \\ \hat{x}^2 \end{bmatrix} = \begin{bmatrix} \cos\phi & \sin\phi \\ -\sin\phi & \cos\phi \end{bmatrix} \cdot \begin{bmatrix} x^1 \\ x^2 \end{bmatrix}.$$

In the usual notation of (x, y) for the coordinates of a point in the plane,

$$\hat{x} = x\cos\phi + y\sin\phi$$
$$\hat{y} = -x\sin\phi + y\cos\phi.$$

PROBLEMS 7

1. Let $F: R^1 \to R^2$ be defined by $F(t) = (t, 2t)$. What is $[F]$?
2. Let $F: V \to \hat{V}$ be a linear map defined by the rule $F(\mathbf{v}) = \mathbf{0}$ for all $\mathbf{v}$. Find $[F]$, regardless of what bases are used.
3. Find $[F]$ if F is defined as in:
(a) Problem 6-2. (b) Problem 6-3.

4. Let $F : R^3 \to R^2$ be given by the rule $F((x^1, x^2, x^3)) = (x^1 - x^2, x^1 - x^3)$. Find $[F]_{\hat{E}}^{E}$ if:
   (a) E and $\hat{E}$ are the natural bases.
   (b) $E = \{(1,1,0), (0,1,0), (0,0,1)\}$ and $\hat{E}$ is the natural basis.
   (c) E is the natural basis and $\hat{E} = \{(1,1), (1,-1)\}$.
   (d) E is the basis in (b) and $\hat{E}$ is the basis in (c).

5. Find the following products:

$$\text{(a)} \quad \begin{bmatrix} 3 & 0 & 1 & 0 \\ 0 & 2 & 0 & 4 \end{bmatrix} \cdot \begin{bmatrix} 1 \\ -1 \\ 1 \\ -1 \end{bmatrix} \qquad \text{(b)} \quad \begin{bmatrix} 6 & 5 \\ 4 & 3 \\ 2 & 1 \end{bmatrix} \cdot \begin{bmatrix} 1 \\ -1 \end{bmatrix}$$

6. Find n and $F(1,2,3)$ if $F : R^3 \to R^n$ and $[F]$ is the matrix:

$$\text{(a)} \quad \begin{bmatrix} 3 & -1 & 2 \\ -1 & 0 & 3 \end{bmatrix} \qquad \text{(b)} \quad \begin{bmatrix} 4 & 5 & 6 \end{bmatrix}$$

$$\text{(c)} \quad \begin{bmatrix} 1 & 0 & 1 \\ 0 & 1 & 1 \\ 1 & 1 & 0 \end{bmatrix} \qquad \text{(d)} \quad \begin{bmatrix} 1 & 1 & 0 \\ -1 & 0 & -1 \\ 2 & -3 & 4 \\ 3 & -4 & 5 \end{bmatrix}$$

7. Let $\hat{E} = \{(0,1), (2,2)\}$ and let E be the natural basis for R^2. Find $[I]_{E}^{\hat{E}}$ and $[I]_{\hat{E}}^{E}$.

8. Define the linear operator in R^2 by the equation $F(x^1, x^2) = (x^1 + 2x^2, 2x^1 - x^2)$. Let $\boldsymbol{v} = (1,2)$. Find $[F]_{\hat{E}}^{E}$ and $[F(\boldsymbol{v})]_{\hat{E}}$ in each case:
   (a) $\hat{E} = E$, the natural basis.
   (b) $\hat{E} = E = \{(1,2), (2,-1)\}$.
   (c) E is the natural basis and $\hat{E}$ is as in (b).

9. Let I be the identity operator in R^2. Find $[I]_{\hat{E}}^{E}$ in each of the cases in Problem 8.

10. Find $[F]_{E}^{\hat{E}}$ for part (c) of Problem 8.

11. Let $[a_j^i] = \begin{bmatrix} 1 & 1 \\ -1 & 1 \end{bmatrix}$. Suppose that $[a_j^i]$ is the matrix of a linear operator F in R^2 relative to the natural basis E. Find $F((2,4))$. Now interpret $[a_j^i]$ as $[I]_{\hat{E}}^{E}$. Find $[(2,4)]_{\hat{E}}$. Interpret your results in terms of a coordinate plane.

12. Let $E = \{\boldsymbol{e}_1, \ldots, \boldsymbol{e}_k\}$ be a basis for W, a subspace of V. Suppose that E is extended to a basis $\hat{E}$ for V.
    (a) Define the linear map $F : W \to V$ by the rule $F(\boldsymbol{w}) = \boldsymbol{w}$. Describe $[F]_{\hat{E}}^{E}$.
    (b) Define the linear map $F : V \to W$ by the rule $F(\boldsymbol{e}_j) = \boldsymbol{e}_j$ for $j = 1, \ldots, k$ and $F(\boldsymbol{e}_j) = \boldsymbol{0}$ for $j = k + 1, \ldots, n$. Describe $[F]_{E}^{\hat{E}}$.

8 MATRIX ALGEBRA

The definition of the product of a matrix times a column matrix in Equation 7-7 was motivated by the desire to make Equation 7-8 valid. The motivation for the definition of the product of a matrix times another matrix (not necessarily a column matrix) comes from the following situation.

Let $F : V \to \hat{V}$ and $G : \hat{V} \to \hat{\hat{V}}$ be linear maps. As we have seen, the composite map $H = G \circ F$ is also a linear map (Theorem 5-2). Suppose that $E = \{e_1, \ldots, e_n\}$, $\hat{E} = \{\hat{e}_1, \ldots, \hat{e}_m\}$, and $\hat{\hat{E}} = \{\hat{\hat{e}}_1, \ldots, \hat{\hat{e}}_q\}$ are bases in V, $\hat{V}$, and $\hat{\hat{V}}$. Suppose that the matrix representations of the maps F and G are

$$[F]^E_{\hat{E}} = \begin{bmatrix} a^1_1 & \cdots & a^1_n \\ \vdots & & \vdots \\ a^m_1 & \cdots & a^m_n \end{bmatrix} \quad \text{and} \quad [G]^{\hat{E}}_{\hat{\hat{E}}} = \begin{bmatrix} b^1_1 & \cdots & b^1_m \\ \vdots & & \vdots \\ b^q_1 & \cdots & b^q_m \end{bmatrix}.$$

To find $[H]^E_{\hat{\hat{E}}} = [G \circ F]^E_{\hat{\hat{E}}}$, we see that the following equations are valid for each $k = 1, \ldots, n$ (using summation notation)

$$\text{(8-1)} \qquad H(e_k) = G(F(e_k)) = G(a^\alpha_k \hat{e}_\alpha) = a^\alpha_k G(\hat{e}_\alpha) = a^\alpha{}_k b^\beta_\alpha \hat{\hat{e}}_\beta.$$

Since column k of the matrix of H consists of the numbers that are the coordinates of $H(e_k)$, we see that column k of the matrix of H is

$$\begin{bmatrix} b^1_\alpha a^\alpha_k \\ \vdots \\ b^q_\alpha a^\alpha_k \end{bmatrix} = \begin{bmatrix} b^1_1 a^1_k + \cdots + b^1_m a^m_k \\ \vdots \\ b^q_1 a^1_k + \cdots + b^q_m a^m_k \end{bmatrix}.$$

Hence, the matrix of H is a q by n matrix, each of whose entries is a sum:

$$[H]^E_{\hat{\hat{E}}} = \begin{bmatrix} b^1_\alpha a^\alpha_1 & \cdots & b^1_\alpha a^\alpha_n \\ \vdots & & \vdots \\ b^q_\alpha a^\alpha_1 & \cdots & b^q_\alpha a^\alpha_n \end{bmatrix}.$$

We now define the product of a matrix $[A]$ and a matrix $[B]$ so as to make the matrix of H equal to the product of the matrix of G times the matrix of F.

DEFINITION 8-1

Let $[A]$ be an m by n matrix and $[B]$ be a q by m matrix. We define

$$[B]\cdot[A] = \begin{bmatrix} b^1_\alpha a^\alpha_1 & \cdots & b^1_\alpha a^\alpha_n \\ \vdots & & \vdots \\ b^q_\alpha a^\alpha_1 & \cdots & b^q_\alpha a^\alpha_n \end{bmatrix},$$

where a^j_k is the number in row j and column k of matrix $[A]$ and where b^j_k is the number in row j and column k of matrix $[B]$. Thus, the number in row j and column k of the matrix $[B]\cdot[A]$ is $b^j_\alpha a^\alpha_k = b^j_1 a^1_k + \cdots + b^j_m a^m_k$.

Let us illustrate this definition by computing some products.

(8-2)
$$\begin{bmatrix} 1 & 2 & 0 \\ -1 & 0 & 4 \end{bmatrix} \cdot \begin{bmatrix} 0 & 2 & -1 \\ 1 & 0 & 4 \\ 3 & 5 & 2 \end{bmatrix} = \begin{bmatrix} 2 & 2 & 7 \\ 12 & 18 & 9 \end{bmatrix}.$$

The number 12 in the first column, second row, was computed as follows:

1st matrix, second row

$$(-1)\cdot 0 + 0\cdot 1 + 4\cdot 3 = 12.$$

2nd matrix, first column

Some more examples are

(8-3)
$$\begin{bmatrix} 1 & 5 \\ 2 & 10 \end{bmatrix} \cdot \begin{bmatrix} 2 & -1 \\ -4 & 2 \end{bmatrix} = \begin{bmatrix} -18 & 9 \\ -36 & 18 \end{bmatrix}$$

and

(8-4)
$$\begin{bmatrix} 2 & -1 \\ -4 & 2 \end{bmatrix} \cdot \begin{bmatrix} 1 & 5 \\ 2 & 10 \end{bmatrix} = \begin{bmatrix} 0 & 0 \\ 0 & 0 \end{bmatrix} = [O].$$

If the product $[A]\cdot[B]$ is defined, the product $[B]\cdot[A]$ is not necessarily defined. Equations 8-3 and 8-4 show us that even if both products are defined, we cannot conclude that they are equal. Thus,

$$[A]\cdot[B]=[C] \quad \textit{does not imply} \quad [B]\cdot[A]=[C].$$

Equation 8-4 also shows us that

$$[A]\cdot[B]=[O] \quad \textit{does not imply} \quad [A]=[O] \text{ or } [B]=[O],$$

where $[O]$ is the matrix with the number zero in each position.

We will now state the fact regarding the matrix of a composite map that is a result of the definition of matrix multiplication. Because we will refer to it later, we will state it as a theorem. The proof of the theorem is contained in our discussion and definitions.

THEOREM 8-1

Let $F: V \to \hat{V}$ and $G: \hat{V} \to \hat{\hat{V}}$ be linear maps. Let E, $\hat{E}$, and $\hat{\hat{E}}$ be bases for the finite dimensional spaces V, $\hat{V}$, and $\hat{\hat{V}}$. Then

$$[G\circ F]^{E}_{\hat{\hat{E}}} = [G]^{\hat{E}}_{\hat{\hat{E}}}\cdot[F]^{E}_{\hat{E}}.$$

The situation described in Theorem 8-1 is illustrated in Fig. 8-1 for the case in which dim $V = 4$, dim $\hat{V} = 2$, and dim $\hat{\hat{V}} = 3$.

Example 8-1 Let $F: R^3 \to R^3$ and $G: R^3 \to R^2$ be defined by $F(x^1, x^2, x^3) = (2x^2 - x^3, x^1 + 4x^3, 3x^1 + 5x^2 + 2x^3)$ and $G(x^1, x^2, x^3) = (x^1 + 2x^2, -x^1 + 4x^3)$. Find the matrix of the composite map $G\circ F: R^3 \to R^2$ with natural bases.

Solution: The first matrix on the left of Equation 8-2 is $[G]$ and the second is $[F]$. Thus,

$$[G\circ F] = [G]\cdot[F] = \begin{bmatrix} 2 & 2 & 7 \\ 12 & 18 & 9 \end{bmatrix}.$$

Also, it follows that

$$(G\circ F)(x^1, x^2, x^3) = (2x^1 + 2x^2 + 7x^3, 12x^1 + 18x^2 + 9x^3).$$

Example 8-2 Let F and G be the linear operators in R^2 defined by $F(1,0) = (2,-4)$; $F(0,1) = (-1,2)$; and $G(1,0) = (1,2)$; $G(0,1) = (5,10)$. Discuss the composite operators $G\circ F$ and $F\circ G$.

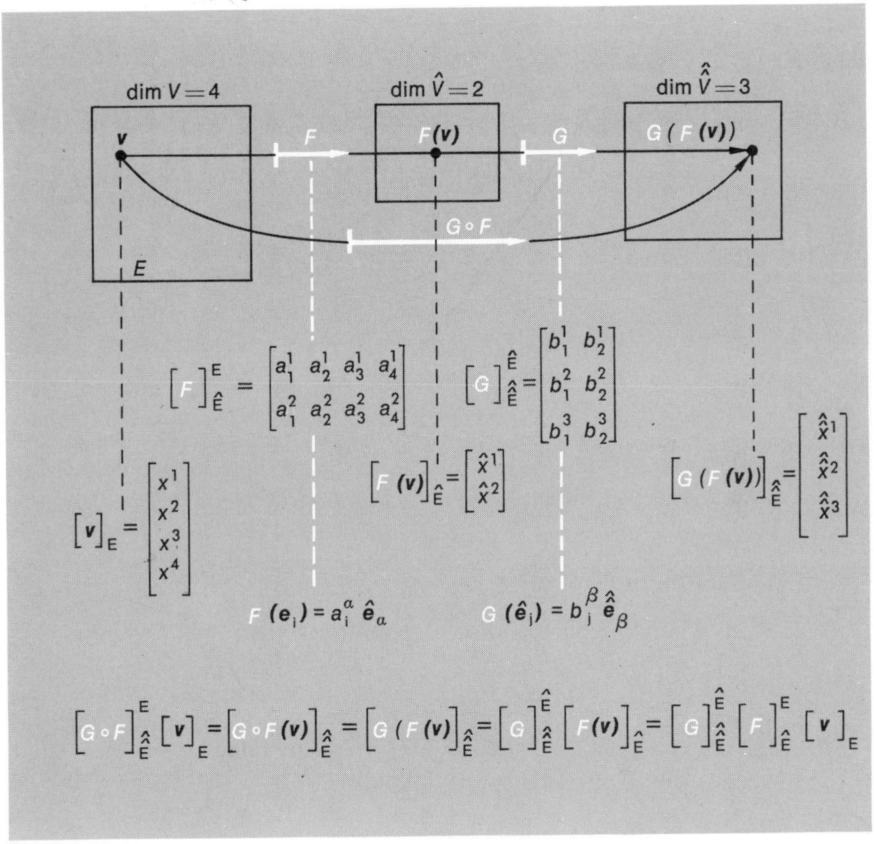

Figure 8-1

Solution: Using the natural basis in R^2 we see from Equations 8-3 and 8-4 that

$$[G \circ F] = [G] \cdot [F] = \begin{bmatrix} -18 & 9 \\ -36 & 18 \end{bmatrix} \quad \text{and} \quad [F \circ G] = [O].$$

Thus, $F \circ G$ is the zero map, but neither F nor G is the zero map. This fact is not surprising if we look at it geometrically by considering R^2 as a coordinate plane. The operator G maps all points of the plane into a line containing the origin and the point (1,2), as you can see by computing $G(\mathbf{x}) = (x^1 + 5x^2)(1,2)$. Thus, $G(R^2) = \text{Sp}\,\{(1,2)\}$. Because $F(\mathbf{x}) = (2x^1 - x^2)(1,-2)$, we see that $K(F) = \text{Sp}\,\{(1,2)\}$. Thus,

$$G(R^2) \subset K(F).$$

This means that $F(G(R^2)) = \{\mathbf{0}\}$; that is, $(F \circ G)(R^2) = \{\mathbf{0}\}$. A geometric picture of the situation is shown in Fig. 8-2.

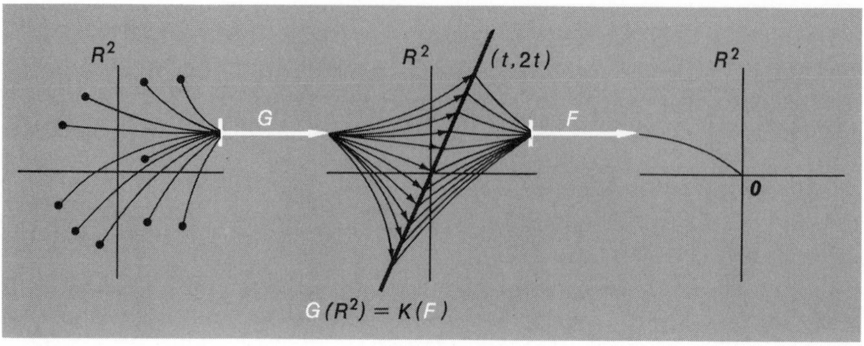

Figure 8-2

Now that we have defined multiplication for matrices we will define addition of two matrices and the multiplication of a matrix by a number.

> **DEFINITION 8-2**
>
> If $[A]$ and $[B]$ are both m by n matrices, then
>
> $$[A] = [B] \text{ if, and only if, } a^j_k = b^j_k;$$
> $$[A] + [B] = [C] \text{ where } c^j_k = a^j_k + b^j_k;$$
> $$c[A] = [D] \text{ where } d^j_k = ca^j_k;$$
>
> for each $j = 1, \ldots, m$; $k = 1, \ldots, n$.

For example,

$$\begin{bmatrix} 1 & 2 \\ 3 & 4 \\ 5 & 6 \end{bmatrix} + \begin{bmatrix} 2 & 3 \\ 4 & 5 \\ -1 & 0 \end{bmatrix} = \begin{bmatrix} 3 & 5 \\ 7 & 9 \\ 4 & 6 \end{bmatrix} \quad \text{and} \quad 2 \cdot \begin{bmatrix} 1 & 2 \\ 3 & 4 \\ 0 & -1 \end{bmatrix} = \begin{bmatrix} 2 & 4 \\ 6 & 8 \\ 0 & -2 \end{bmatrix}.$$

We will now list the basic rules governing the arithmetic of matrices:

$$[A] + [B] = [B] + [A]$$
$$([A] + [B]) + [C] = [A] + ([B] + [C])$$
$$[A] + [O] = [O] + [A] = [A]$$
$$[A] + (-1[A]) = [O]$$

(8-5)

$$(a + b)[A] = a[A] + b[A]$$
$$a([A] + [B]) = a[A] + a[B]$$
$$(ab)[A] = a(b[A])$$
$$1[A] = [A].$$

It is a straightforward matter to verify these rules. For example, the first one is valid because the equation $a_k^j + b_k^j = b_k^j + a_k^j$ is true for each j,k since it is simply an equality between sums of numbers.

Hopefully, you have noticed that the eight properties that are listed in Equations 8-5 are merely the basic eight vector space properties. Thus, the set of all m by n matrices with Definition 8-2 forms a vector space. In fact, we see that we can find a basis for this space rather easily and, hence, determine its dimension. Let $[E]_j^k$ be the m by n matrix that contains all zero entries except for a 1 in row j and column k. For example, if $m = 3$ and $n = 4$,

$$[E]_2^3 = \begin{bmatrix} 0 & 0 & 0 & 0 \\ 0 & 0 & 1 & 0 \\ 0 & 0 & 0 & 0 \end{bmatrix}.$$

It is easy to see that the set of these E-matrices span our matrix space because

$$[A] = a_\beta^\alpha [E]_\alpha^\beta \quad \text{(double sum!)}.$$

For example, in the 2 by 2 case,

$$\begin{bmatrix} 1 & 2 \\ 3 & 4 \end{bmatrix} = 1 \cdot \begin{bmatrix} 1 & 0 \\ 0 & 0 \end{bmatrix} + 2 \cdot \begin{bmatrix} 0 & 1 \\ 0 & 0 \end{bmatrix} + 3 \cdot \begin{bmatrix} 0 & 0 \\ 1 & 0 \end{bmatrix} + 4 \cdot \begin{bmatrix} 0 & 0 \\ 0 & 1 \end{bmatrix}.$$

Furthermore, the matrices form an independent set because

$$c_\beta^\alpha [E]_\alpha^\beta = [O] \quad \text{implies} \quad [C] = [O];$$

that is, $c_k^j = 0$ for each j,k. Thus, the E-matrices do form a *natural basis* for the space of m by n matrices, and because there are $m \cdot n$ E-matrices, the dimension of our space is $m \cdot n$. We summarize these facts in a theorem.

THEOREM 8-2

The set of all m by n matrices with Definition 8-2 is a vector space of dimension $m \cdot n$.

In addition to the rules in Equation 8-5 you can easily verify that the following rules are valid (assuming all products that are written are defined):

$$\begin{aligned} &[A]([B] + [C]) = [A][B] + [A][C] \\ &[A](c[B]) = (c[A])[B] = c([A][B]). \end{aligned} \tag{8-6}$$

The problem with multiplication in the space of m by n matrices is that it is not defined if $m \neq n$. In the space of square n by n matrices we see that the space is closed with respect to multiplication and that the rules in Equation 8-6 apply. Furthermore, there is a matrix that plays a very special role in matrix multiplication. The n by n matrix with 1's on the main diagonal from the upper left-hand corner to the lower right-hand corner is called the *identity matrix* and is denoted by $[I]$. For example, if $n = 3$,

$$[I] = \begin{bmatrix} 1 & 0 & 0 \\ 0 & 1 & 0 \\ 0 & 0 & 1 \end{bmatrix}.$$

If we use the "delta symbol" δ^j_k defined by

$$\delta^j_k = \begin{cases} 1 & \text{if} \quad j = k \\ 0 & \text{if} \quad j \neq k, \end{cases}$$

it is easy to see that

$$[A][I] = \begin{bmatrix} a^1_\alpha \delta^\alpha_1 & \cdots & a^1_\alpha \delta^\alpha_n \\ \vdots & & \\ a^n_\alpha \delta^\alpha_1 & \cdots & a^n_\alpha \delta^\alpha_n \end{bmatrix} = [A],$$

and similarly, that

$$[I][A] = [A].$$

(Write this out for $n = 3$ to help you see what is going on.)

The matrix $[I]$ plays the role of a "1" as far as multiplication goes. We have defined addition (and subtraction) and multiplication of matrices. What about division? Even in the case of numbers we cannot always divide (division by zero is not permitted), so it is reasonable to expect that there are some matrices that will be outlawed in our discussion of division. The quotient a/b of two numbers can be thought of as the product of a and the reciprocal or inverse of b; namely, $a/b = ab^{-1}$. We will discuss division of matrices by considering the idea of the inverse of a matrix.

DEFINITION 8-3

A square matrix $[A]$ is said to be *invertible*, or to have an inverse, if there is a matrix called the *inverse of* $[A]$ and written $[A]^{-1}$ such that

$$[A][A]^{-1} = [A]^{-1}[A] = [I].$$

As we have suggested, not all matrices are invertible. For example, you can easily convince yourself that $[O]$ is not invertible, because for any matrix $[B]$

$$[B][O] = [O] \neq [I].$$

But if $[A]^{-1}$ does exist, then *it is unique*. For if $[A][B] = [I]$, then

$$[A]^{-1}[A][B] = [A]^{-1}[I];$$

so

$$[I][B] = [A]^{-1}$$

from which it follows that $[B] = [A]^{-1}$.

We have used the word "invertible" to describe two different things—an operator or map (see the discussion before Theorem 5-1) and a matrix. We also know that in the finite dimensional case a linear operator is represented by a matrix once a basis is chosen. A natural question that arises is, "Is an invertible operator represented by an invertible matrix?" The answer is yes, and it is a direct corollary to Theorem 8-1 with the right interpretation.

THEOREM 8-3

Let E and $\hat{E}$ be two bases in a finite dimensional vector space, V, and let F be an invertible linear operator on V. Then $[F]^{E}_{\hat{E}}$ is an invertible matrix and

$$[F]^{E\,-1}_{\hat{E}} = [F^{-1}]^{\hat{E}}_{E}.$$

Proof: Let $\hat{V} = \hat{\hat{V}} = V$ and $G = F^{-1}$ in Theorem 8-1. Then if $\hat{\hat{E}} = E$, we have

$$[F^{-1} \circ F]^{E}_{E} = [F^{-1}]^{\hat{E}}_{E}[F]^{E}_{\hat{E}}. \tag{8-7}$$

But $F^{-1} \circ F = I$, the identity operator, and for any basis E, $[I]_E^E = [I]$. Thus,

$$[F^{-1}]_{\hat{E}}^{\hat{E}}[F]_{\hat{E}}^{E} = [I]. \tag{8-8}$$

Now we can also make the following substitutions. In Theorem 8-1 replace F with F^{-1}, G with F, E with $\hat{E}$, $\hat{E}$ with E, and $\hat{\hat{E}}$ with $\hat{E}$. We then get

$$[F \circ F^{-1}]_{\hat{E}}^{\hat{E}} = [F]_{\hat{E}}^{E}[F^{-1}]_{E}^{\hat{E}}. \tag{8-9}$$

Again $F \circ F^{-1} = I$ and $[I]_{\hat{E}}^{\hat{E}} = [I]$, so

$$[F]_{\hat{E}}^{E}[F^{-1}]_{E}^{\hat{E}} = [I]. \tag{8-10}$$

Our result follows from the definition of the inverse of a matrix and Equations 8-8 and 8-10. ∎

As a special case of the preceding theorem, suppose that F is the identity operator I. Of course, $I^{-1} = I$ also, so we see that

$$[I]_{E}^{\hat{E}} = ([I]_{\hat{E}}^{E})^{-1}. \tag{8-11}$$

Example 8-3 Verify Equation 8-11 for the matrices in Example 7-6.

Solution: From Example 7-6

$$[I]_{\hat{E}}^{E}[I]_{E}^{\hat{E}} = \begin{bmatrix} \frac{1}{6} & \frac{1}{4} \\ \frac{1}{6} & -\frac{1}{4} \end{bmatrix} \cdot \begin{bmatrix} 3 & 3 \\ 2 & -2 \end{bmatrix} = \begin{bmatrix} 1 & 0 \\ 0 & 1 \end{bmatrix}$$

and

$$\begin{bmatrix} 3 & 3 \\ 2 & -2 \end{bmatrix} \cdot \begin{bmatrix} \frac{1}{6} & \frac{1}{4} \\ \frac{1}{6} & -\frac{1}{4} \end{bmatrix} = \begin{bmatrix} 1 & 0 \\ 0 & 1 \end{bmatrix}.$$

Therefore, Equation 8-11 is true in this case.

Example 8-4 Let F be the linear operator on R^2 whose matrix in the natural basis is

$$[F] = \begin{bmatrix} 2 & 1 \\ 1 & 1 \end{bmatrix}.$$

Verify that

$$[F^{-1}] = \begin{bmatrix} 1 & -1 \\ -1 & 2 \end{bmatrix}.$$

Solution: Because

$$\begin{bmatrix} 2 & 1 \\ 1 & 1 \end{bmatrix} \cdot \begin{bmatrix} 1 & -1 \\ -1 & 2 \end{bmatrix} = \begin{bmatrix} 1 & 0 \\ 0 & 1 \end{bmatrix} = \begin{bmatrix} 1 & -1 \\ -1 & 2 \end{bmatrix} \cdot \begin{bmatrix} 2 & 1 \\ 1 & 1 \end{bmatrix},$$

we see that

$$[F]^{-1} = \begin{bmatrix} 1 & -1 \\ -1 & 2 \end{bmatrix}.$$

But because $[F^{-1}] = [F]^{-1}$, we are finished.

Although we have defined the inverse of a matrix and shown that it is unique if it exists, we have not discussed any technique for finding the inverse of a matrix. The problem of computing the inverse of a matrix is an important one; we will reserve discussion of it until a later section.

PROBLEMS 8

1. Compute:

(a) $\begin{bmatrix} 1 & 2 \\ -1 & 3 \end{bmatrix} \cdot \begin{bmatrix} 2 \\ 0 \end{bmatrix}$ (b) $\begin{bmatrix} 1 & 2 \\ -1 & 3 \end{bmatrix} \cdot \begin{bmatrix} 1 \\ 3 \end{bmatrix}$

(c) $\begin{bmatrix} 1 & 2 \\ -1 & 3 \end{bmatrix} \cdot \begin{bmatrix} 2 & 1 \\ 0 & 3 \end{bmatrix}$ (d) $\begin{bmatrix} 2 & 1 \\ 0 & 3 \end{bmatrix} \cdot \begin{bmatrix} 1 & 2 \\ -1 & 3 \end{bmatrix}$.

2. Compute:

(a) $\begin{bmatrix} 2 & 5 & -1 \\ 6 & 0 & 2 \\ 1 & 3 & 4 \end{bmatrix} \cdot \begin{bmatrix} 1 \\ -1 \\ 2 \end{bmatrix}$ (b) $\begin{bmatrix} 2 & 5 & -1 \\ 6 & 0 & 2 \\ 1 & 3 & 4 \end{bmatrix} \cdot \begin{bmatrix} 1 & 0 & 1 \\ -1 & 0 & 0 \\ 2 & 1 & 0 \end{bmatrix}$

(c) $\begin{bmatrix} 1 & 2 & 3 \\ 2 & 4 & 5 \\ 3 & 5 & 6 \end{bmatrix} \cdot \begin{bmatrix} 0 & 0 & 1 \\ 1 & 0 & 0 \\ 0 & 1 & 0 \end{bmatrix}$ (d) $\begin{bmatrix} 0 & 0 & 1 \\ 1 & 0 & 0 \\ 0 & 1 & 0 \end{bmatrix} \cdot \begin{bmatrix} 0 & 1 & 0 \\ 0 & 0 & 1 \\ 1 & 0 & 0 \end{bmatrix}.$

(e) $[1 \quad 2 \quad 3] \cdot \begin{bmatrix} 4 & 7 \\ 5 & 8 \\ 6 & 9 \end{bmatrix}$ (f) $\begin{bmatrix} 1 & 2 & -3 \\ -1 & -2 & 3 \end{bmatrix} \cdot \begin{bmatrix} 0 & 1 & -1 \\ 0 & 1 & 1 \\ 1 & 0 & 2 \end{bmatrix}$

3. Let $[A]^2 = [A][A]$, and so on. Find $[A]^2$ and $[A]^3$ if $[A]$ is the matrix:

(a) $\begin{bmatrix} 0 & 1 & 0 \\ 0 & 0 & 1 \\ 1 & 0 & 0 \end{bmatrix}$ (b) $\begin{bmatrix} 0 & 1 & 2 \\ 0 & 0 & 3 \\ 0 & 0 & 0 \end{bmatrix}$

4. Let $F: R^2 \to R^3$ and $G: R^3 \to R^2$ be given by the equations

$$F(x^1, x^2) = (x^1 + x^2, x^1 - x^2, 2x^1)$$
$$G(x^1, x^2, x^3) = (x^1 + x^2 + x^3, x^1 - x^2 - x^3).$$

(a) Find $F \circ G\,(x^1, x^2, x^3)$
(b) Find $[F \circ G]$.
(c) Find $G \circ F\,(x^1, x^2)$
(d) Find $[G \circ F]$.

5. Show that the following four matrices form a basis for the space of all 2 by 2 matrices:

$$\begin{bmatrix} 1 & 1 \\ 1 & 1 \end{bmatrix};\ \begin{bmatrix} 1 & -1 \\ 1 & 1 \end{bmatrix};\ \begin{bmatrix} 1 & -1 \\ -1 & 1 \end{bmatrix};\ \begin{bmatrix} 1 & -1 \\ -1 & -1 \end{bmatrix}.$$

6. Show that $\begin{bmatrix} 1 & 1 \\ 1 & 1 \end{bmatrix}$ is not an invertible matrix.

7. Let F and G be linear operators in R^3 defined by the equations

$$F(x^1, x^2, x^3) = (x^1 + x^3, x^2 - x^3, x^1 + x^2)$$
$$G(x^1, x^2, x^3) = (x^1 - x^2, x^1 + x^3, x^1 + x^2).$$

Find $[F \circ G]$ and $[G \circ F]$. What is dim $F(R^3)$? $G(R^3)$? What is dim $(F \circ G)(R^3)$?

8. Does $[A][B] = [A][C]$ imply that $[B] = [C]$?

9. Let E be the natural basis for R^2 and let $\hat{E} = \{(0,1), (2,2)\}$. Find $[I]_E^{\hat{E}}$ and $[I]_{\hat{E}}^E$ and multiply one by the other.

9 THE SPACE OF LINEAR MAPS

The idea of a function space was introduced in Section 3 by Definition 3-1. Now let us consider the set of all linear maps from V into $\hat{V}$ together with Definition 3-1. If F and G are linear maps, then

$$\begin{aligned}(F + G)(c\boldsymbol{v} + \boldsymbol{w}) &= F(c\boldsymbol{v} + \boldsymbol{w}) + G(c\boldsymbol{v} + \boldsymbol{w})\\ &= cF(\boldsymbol{v}) + F(\boldsymbol{w}) + cG(\boldsymbol{v}) + G(\boldsymbol{w})\\ &= c(F + G)(\boldsymbol{v}) + (F + G)(\boldsymbol{w}).\end{aligned}$$

Also,

$$\begin{aligned}(aF)(c\boldsymbol{v} + \boldsymbol{w}) &= aF(c\boldsymbol{v} + \boldsymbol{w}) = a(cF(\boldsymbol{v})) + F(\boldsymbol{w})\\ &= c(aF)(\boldsymbol{v}) + (aF)(\boldsymbol{w}).\end{aligned}$$

Thus, $F + G$ and aF are linear maps. The set of all linear maps from V into $\hat{V}$ is closed with respect to addition of maps and multiplication of a map by a number. Furthermore, the eight basic rules of a vector space are easily shown to be valid (the "zero" map is the zero vector). For example, Rule 1-1 is valid because

$$\begin{aligned}(F + G)(\boldsymbol{v}) &= F(\boldsymbol{v}) + G(\boldsymbol{v})\\ &= G(\boldsymbol{v}) + F(\boldsymbol{v}) \quad \text{(Why?)}\\ &= (G + F)(\boldsymbol{v}) \quad \text{for all } \boldsymbol{v} \text{ in } V.\end{aligned}$$

Verification of the other rules is left for the problems. It then follows that the following theorem is valid.

THEOREM 9-1

The set of all linear maps from a vector space V into a vector space $\hat{V}$ is a vector space. In particular, the set of all linear operators in a vector space is a vector space.

Let us consider the situation when V and $\hat{V}$ are finite dimensional. In that case we found that once bases are chosen, any linear map is represented by a matrix. The set of all matrices of a given size is a vector space (see Section 8). The question that naturally arises is "Is the space of maps the same as (isomorphic to) the space of matrices?" The answer is yes, and to prove it we must tell you what the isomorphism (linear, invertible transformation) is. We do this in the proof of the following theorem.

THEOREM 9-2

Let dim $V = n$ and dim $\hat{V} = m$. The space of all linear maps from V into $\hat{V}$ is isomorphic to the space of m by n matrices. In particular, the space of all linear operators in V is isomorphic to the space of square n by n matrices.

Proof: Let $E = \{\boldsymbol{e}_1, \ldots, \boldsymbol{e}_n\}$ and $\hat{E} = \{\hat{\boldsymbol{e}}_1, \ldots, \hat{\boldsymbol{e}}_m\}$ as bases in V and $\hat{V}$. If F and G are linear maps from V into $\hat{V}$, then F is represented by the matrix $[F]^E_{\hat{E}}$, and G is represented by the matrix $[G]^E_{\hat{E}}$. Define the transformation T from the space of linear maps into the space of matrices by the rule

$$T(F) = [F]^E_{\hat{E}}.$$

We must show that T is linear, injective, and surjective.

Suppose that $F(\boldsymbol{e}_j) = a^\alpha_j \hat{\boldsymbol{e}}_\alpha$ for each $j = 1, \ldots, n$. Then

$$[F]^E_{\hat{E}} = \begin{bmatrix} a^1_1 & \cdots & a^1_n \\ \vdots & & \vdots \\ a^m_1 & \cdots & a^m_n \end{bmatrix}.$$

Furthermore, $cF(\boldsymbol{e}_j) = ca^\alpha_j \hat{\boldsymbol{e}}_\alpha$ for each $j = 1, \ldots, n$, so that

$$[cF]^E_{\hat{E}} = \begin{bmatrix} ca^1_1 & \cdots & ca^1_n \\ \vdots & & \vdots \\ ca^m_1 & \cdots & ca^m_n \end{bmatrix} = c\begin{bmatrix} a^1_1 & \cdots & a^1_n \\ \vdots & & \vdots \\ a^m_1 & \cdots & a^m_n \end{bmatrix}.$$

Thus,

$$T(cF) = [cF]^E_{\hat{E}} = c[F]^E_{\hat{E}} = cT(F).$$

In a similar way (we leave it for the problems) it can be shown that

$$T(F + G) = T(F) + T(G),$$

so that T is linear. Furthermore, the kernel of T is the zero map because it is the only map represented by the zero matrix. Thus, T is injective. Finally, T is surjective because if $[C]$ is any m by n matrix, we can define a linear map H by the n equations $H(\boldsymbol{e}_j) = c^\alpha_j \boldsymbol{e}_\alpha$ for $j = 1, \ldots, n$, and then

$[C]$ is the matrix representing H. Thus, $T(H) = [C]$. Hence, T is also surjective, and we have finished our proof. ∎

The preceding theorem can be summarized in an informal way by saying that as far as the finite dimensional case is concerned, *a matrix is a map and a map is a matrix. In particular, an operator is a square matrix and a square matrix is an operator.* Of course, identifying an operator with a matrix is possible only after a basis is chosen, so choosing different bases provides different identifications in general. This situation is completely analogous to the fact that every finite dimensional vector space can be identified with R^n once a basis is chosen. Sometimes it is more profitable to use a "coordinate free" approach and deal with maps or operators and vector spaces directly. At other times it is better to introduce bases and work with R^n and matrices. Most important of all, you should be able to use either approach and understand the relationship between the two. Let us prove a theorem that will be useful when we study the problem of finding the inverse of a matrix by using the identification of matrices and operators.

THEOREM 9-3

If $[A]$ and $[B]$ are n by n matrices and $[A][B] = [I]$, then $[B] = [A]^{-1}$.

Proof: We must show that $[B][A] = [I]$. Consider the linear operators A and B on an n-dimensional space whose matrix representations in a fixed basis are $[A]$ and $[B]$. Then from Theorem 8-1

$$[A \circ B] = [A][B] = [I],$$

so $A \circ B = I$. Now we claim that B is an injective operator. For if $B(x) = B(y)$, then

$$\begin{aligned} A \circ B(x) &= A \circ B(y), \\ I(x) &= I(y), \\ x &= y. \end{aligned}$$

Since an injective operator is invertible according to Theorem 6-2, we see that B is invertible. Furthermore, if $B^{-1}(y) = z$, then $y = B(z)$, and hence

$$A(y) = A \circ B(z) = z.$$

In other words, for each y we have $A(y) = B^{-1}(y)$; that is, $A = B^{-1}$. Thus, $B \circ A = I$, and using Theorem 8-1 again, we get

$$[I] = [B \circ A] = [B][A].$$

It follows from this equation and the hypothesis that $[A][B] = [I]$ and that $[B] = [A]^{-1}$. ∎

The preceding theorem tells us that to find the inverse of a matrix $[A]$ we have to solve a matrix equation, say $[A][X] = [I]$. If you write out this equation in the case of 2 by 2 matrices you will see that this one matrix equation is equivalent to two systems of linear equations of two equations each. Thus, the problem of finding the inverse of a matrix reduces to solving systems of equations. We will pursue this idea again in a later section.

As we have said, identifying maps and matrices hinges on choosing bases. In particular, if a basis is chosen in a finite dimensional space, a linear operator and a square matrix can be identified with each other. In plane geometry you can deal with geometric figures such as lines without reference to a coordinate system, or you may introduce coordinate axes into the plane and talk about equations that describe these figures. The equation that describes a line, for example, depends on which axes you choose. If a coordinate system is chosen so that the origin is a point of the line, then the equation of the line is $ax + by = 0$; whereas the equation is $ax + by + c = 0\,(c \neq 0)$ if the origin is not a point of the line. One equation is "simpler" than the other, so if you have a choice, you would prefer that the origin be a point of the line.

The representation of an operator by a matrix depends on the basis (coordinate system) chosen in a finite dimensional space. It seems reasonable to suppose that the matrix representing a given operator is simpler in some coordinate systems than it is in others.

Example 9-1 Let F be the linear operator in R^2 defined by the formula $F(x^1, x^2) = (x^1 + x^2, 2x^1)$. Find $[F]$ in the natural basis. Find $[F]_{\hat{E}}^{\hat{E}}$ if $\hat{E} = \{(1,1), (1,-2)\}$.

Solution: $F(1,0) = (1,2)$ and $F(0,1) = (1,0)$, so in the natural basis

$$[F] = \begin{bmatrix} 1 & 1 \\ 2 & 0 \end{bmatrix}.$$

Because

$$F(\hat{e}_1) = F(1,1) = (2,2) = 2(1,1) = 2\hat{e}_1 + 0\hat{e}_2$$

$$F(\hat{e}_2) = F(1,-2) = (-1,2) = -1(1,-2) = 0\hat{e}_1 - 1\hat{e}_2,$$

we have

$$[F]_{\hat{E}}^{\hat{E}} = \begin{bmatrix} 2 & 0 \\ 0 & -1 \end{bmatrix}.$$

In the preceding example it is clear that the $\hat{E}$ basis is the one to choose because the matrix of F is simpler in that basis. The question is "Can you always find such a basis, and if so, how?" We will provide some answers to this question later. For the moment we will be content to answer the following question: "How does the change of basis affect the matrix representing an operator?" The answer is in the following theorem.

THEOREM 9-4

Let F be an operator in a finite dimensional vector space V, and let E and $\hat{E}$ be two bases in V. Then

$$[F]_{\hat{E}}^{\hat{E}} = [M]^{-1}[F]_E^E[M]$$

where

$$[M] = [I]_E^{\hat{E}} \quad \text{and} \quad [M]^{-1} = [I]_{\hat{E}}^E.$$

Proof: The equation we want to verify follows directly from our previous work. Using the diagram in Fig. 9-1 to guide us, and noting that $F = I \circ F \circ I$, we can use Theorem 8-1 to write

$$[F]_{\hat{E}}^{\hat{E}} = [I \circ F]_{\hat{E}}^E[I]_E^{\hat{E}} = [I]_{\hat{E}}^E[F]_E^E[I]_E^{\hat{E}}.$$ ∎

The preceding theorem tells us that the problem of finding a basis in which an operator F has a simple matrix representation is equivalent to the question of finding a matrix $[M]$ so that for a given matrix $[F]$, the matrix $[M]^{-1}[F][M]$ is a simple matrix. As we have said, that problem will be treated later (in

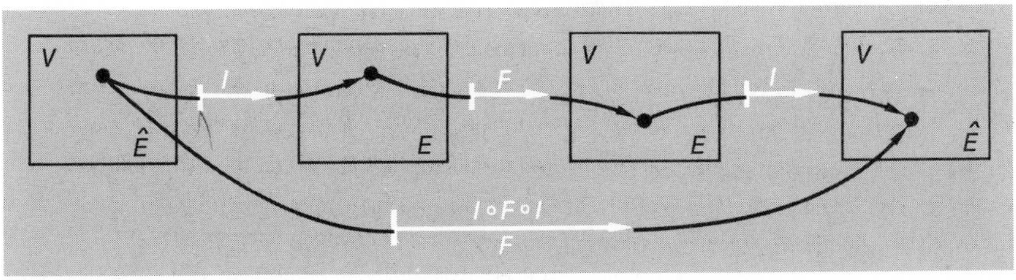

Figure 9-1

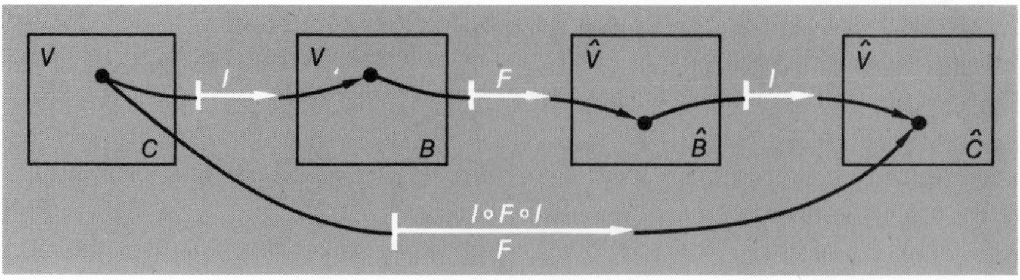

Figure 9-2

Chapter Six). Notice that Theorem 9-4 is really just a special case of the situation in which V and $\hat{V}$ are finite dimensional; $F : V \to \hat{V}$ is a linear map, B and C are bases in V, and $\hat{B}$ and $\hat{C}$ are bases in $\hat{V}$. Then the diagram in Fig. 9-2 leads to the equation

$$[F]^C_{\hat{C}} = [I]^{\hat{B}}_{\hat{C}}[F]^B_{\hat{B}}[I]^C_B.$$

Because we will restrict our use of this result to the special case stated in Theorem 9-4, we supplied an explicit proof, but you can easily write out the proof to cover the general case.

PROBLEMS 9

1. Show that the eight basic rules are valid for the addition of maps and multiplication of maps by numbers.
2. Let T be the transformation defined in the proof of Theorem 9-2. Prove that $T(F + G) = T(F) + T(G)$.
3. Find the matrix $[I]^{\hat{E}}_E$ and verify that Theorem 9-4 is valid for the situation described in Example 9-1.
4. Let $F : R^2 \to R^2$ be defined by the equation

$$F(x^1, x^2) = (x^1 - x^2, x^1 + x^2),$$

and let $\hat{E} = \{(1,1), (1,-1)\}$.
(a) Find $[F]$ in the natural basis.
(b) Find $[F]^{\hat{E}}_{\hat{E}}$.
(c) Find $[I]^E_{\hat{E}}$ and $[I]^{\hat{E}}_E$.
(d) Verify Theorem 9-4 for this example.
(e) Find $[F - I]$.
(f) Find $[F - I]^{\hat{E}}_{\hat{E}}$.

5. Suppose that $[A]$ and $[C]$ are square matrices and that $[B]$ is an invertible matrix such that $[A][B] = [B][C]$. What can you conclude about the linear operators represented by $[A]$ and $[C]$?

6. Given $[I]_{\hat{E}}^{E} = \begin{bmatrix} 2 & 3 \\ 3 & 5 \end{bmatrix}$. Find $[F]_{\hat{E}}^{\hat{E}}$ if $[F]_{E}^{E}$ is the matrix:

(a) $\begin{bmatrix} 1 & 0 \\ 0 & 1 \end{bmatrix}$ (b) $\begin{bmatrix} 10 & 15 \\ -6 & -9 \end{bmatrix}$ (c) $\begin{bmatrix} 8 & 15 \\ -6 & -11 \end{bmatrix}$

7. Let D be the derivative operator on the space P_2 of linear polynomials. Let E be the usual basis consisting of the power functions e_0 and e_1 and let $\hat{E}$ consist of the polynomials $p_1(x) = 1 + x$ and $p_2(x) = 1 - x$. Verify Theorem 9-4.

8. Suppose that F is a linear operator on a two-dimensional vector space whose matrix representation in a fixed basis is $\begin{bmatrix} 2 & 3 \\ 1 & 2 \end{bmatrix}$. Find $[F^2]$ if $F^2 = F \circ F$. Describe the operator $F^2 - 4F + I$.

9. Suppose e_1 and e_2 are unit, perpendicular, geometric vectors in a plane. Then $E = \{e_1, e_2\}$ is a basis. Describe geometrically the basis $\hat{E}$ if $[I]_{\hat{E}}^{E} = \begin{bmatrix} 1 & 1 \\ -1 & 1 \end{bmatrix}$. Suppose that $[F]_{E}^{E} = \begin{bmatrix} 1 & 1 \\ 1 & 1 \end{bmatrix}$. Find $[F]_{\hat{E}}^{\hat{E}}$ and describe F geometrically.

10. Let $\{e_1, \ldots, e_n\}$ be a basis in V and define the linear operator F in V by the equations

$$F(e_1) = e_2, F(e_2) = e_3, \ldots, F(e_n) = e_1.$$

What is the matrix $[F]$ in the given basis? Is F an invertible operator? What is $[F]^n$? What is $K(F^n - I)$?

Three

Inner Product Spaces

The idea of a vector space is a generalization of the concept of an ordinary geometric space. However, up to this point we have been concerned only with certain algebraic properties, and we have not attempted to generalize the ideas of length and angle that are familiar to us in two and three dimensional geometric spaces. In this chapter we are going to extend our ideas of length and angle to the vector space setting. It turns out that for our purposes the most concise way to carry out this extension is to generalize the idea of a scalar product (also called a dot product or an inner product) of two geometric vectors.

Our approach in the beginning of this chapter will remind you of our discussion in Section 1. We will find that the geometric inner product has certain basic properties that can be used as axioms for an abstract inner product, and our subsequent work will be based on those axioms. Much of what we say in the early part of the chapter will be true for any vector space, even if it is not finite dimensional.

However, as we proceed we will concentrate more and more on the finite dimensional case.

10 INNER PRODUCTS. NORMS

Suppose that $\boldsymbol{u}$ and $\boldsymbol{v}$ are geometric vectors in an ordinary two- or three-dimensional geometric space. Both these vectors can be represented by arrows from a fixed point O in space. Let $\boldsymbol{u} = \boldsymbol{OP}$ and $\boldsymbol{v} = \boldsymbol{OQ}$. Let θ be the unique angle, $0 \leqq \theta \leqq \pi$, determined by $\boldsymbol{OP}$ and $\boldsymbol{OQ}$, as shown in Fig. 10-1. The *inner product*, or scalar product, of $\boldsymbol{u}$ and $\boldsymbol{v}$ is the *number* $|\boldsymbol{u}||\boldsymbol{v}|\cos\theta$ where $|\boldsymbol{u}| = |\boldsymbol{OP}|$ and $|\boldsymbol{v}| = |\boldsymbol{OQ}|$. Sometimes the inner product is called the dot product and written $\boldsymbol{u}\cdot\boldsymbol{v}$. We will use the notation $\langle \boldsymbol{u}, \boldsymbol{v}\rangle$. Thus, for geometric vectors

(10-1) $$\langle \boldsymbol{u}, \boldsymbol{v}\rangle = |\boldsymbol{u}||\boldsymbol{v}|\cos\theta.$$

In case either $\boldsymbol{u}$ or $\boldsymbol{v}$ is the zero vector, the angle θ is not defined; but we will say that the inner product is zero in that case, as Equation 10-1 suggests. Even though the reason for defining $\langle \boldsymbol{u}, \boldsymbol{v}\rangle$ is not very evident, we can see that the inner product is related to both the idea of length and angle. Thus,

(10-2) $$|\boldsymbol{u}|^2 = \langle \boldsymbol{u}, \boldsymbol{u}\rangle,$$

so that

(10-3) $$\langle \boldsymbol{u}, \boldsymbol{u}\rangle \text{ is greater than 0 if } \boldsymbol{u} \neq \boldsymbol{0}.$$

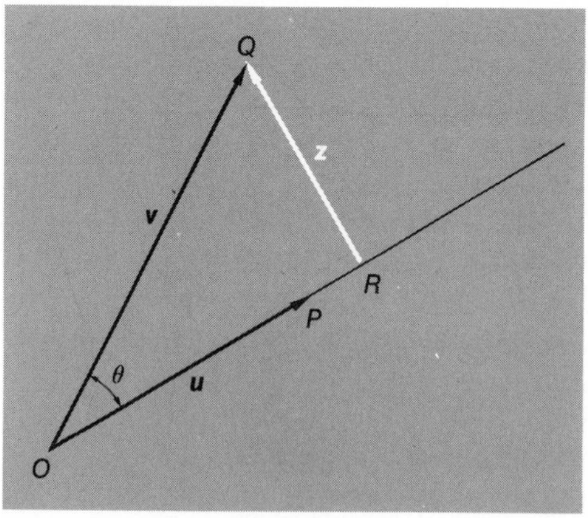

Figure 10-1

Also, we see that

$$\cos\theta = \frac{\langle \boldsymbol{u}, \boldsymbol{v}\rangle}{|\boldsymbol{u}||\boldsymbol{v}|} \tag{10-4}$$

Thus,

$$\langle \boldsymbol{u}, \boldsymbol{v}\rangle = 0 \quad \text{if} \quad \boldsymbol{u} \perp \boldsymbol{v},$$

where $\boldsymbol{u} \perp \boldsymbol{v}$ means $\boldsymbol{u}$ and $\boldsymbol{v}$ are perpendicular, or at right angles. If $\boldsymbol{u} \perp \boldsymbol{v}$, we also say that $\boldsymbol{u}$ and $\boldsymbol{v}$ are orthogonal.

To secure more insight into the geometric meaning of the inner product, let $\boldsymbol{u}$ and $\boldsymbol{v}$ be non-zero vectors as pictured in Fig. 10-1 (θ is an acute angle) or as pictured in Fig. 10-2 (θ is an obtuse angle). Let R be the unique point on line OP such that $\boldsymbol{OR} \perp \boldsymbol{RQ}$ and let $\boldsymbol{z} = \boldsymbol{RQ}$. Then $\boldsymbol{OR}$ is a multiple of $\boldsymbol{u}$, say $c\boldsymbol{u}$, where $c > 0$ if θ is an acute angle and $c < 0$ if θ is an obtuse angle. Furthermore, $\boldsymbol{v} = \boldsymbol{OR} + \boldsymbol{RQ} = c\boldsymbol{u} + \boldsymbol{z}$. If Q is on $\boldsymbol{OP}$, then set $R = Q$, so that $\boldsymbol{z} = \boldsymbol{QQ}$. Thus, every $\boldsymbol{v}$ can be written

$$\boldsymbol{v} = c\boldsymbol{u} + \boldsymbol{z} \quad \text{where} \quad \boldsymbol{z} \perp \boldsymbol{u}. \tag{10-5}$$

The number $|\boldsymbol{v}|\cos\theta = c|\boldsymbol{u}|$ is the *component* of $\boldsymbol{v}$ along $\boldsymbol{u}$. The vector $c\boldsymbol{u}$ is the *orthogonal projection* of $\boldsymbol{v}$ on $\boldsymbol{u}$. We will write

$$P_{\boldsymbol{u}}(\boldsymbol{v}) = c\boldsymbol{u} \quad \text{where} \quad c = \frac{|\boldsymbol{v}|\cos\theta}{|\boldsymbol{u}|} = \frac{\langle \boldsymbol{u}, \boldsymbol{v}\rangle}{|\boldsymbol{u}|^2}. \tag{10-6}$$

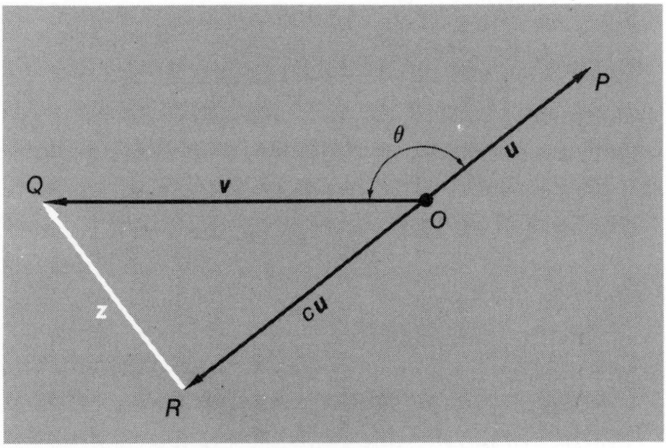

Figure 10-2

We see that

(10-7)) $$\langle \boldsymbol{u}, \boldsymbol{v} \rangle = c|\boldsymbol{u}|^2.$$

Thus, $\langle \boldsymbol{u}, \boldsymbol{v} \rangle$ is the product of the component of $\boldsymbol{v}$ along $\boldsymbol{u}$ times the length of $\boldsymbol{u}$. In Equation 10-1 $\boldsymbol{u}$ and $\boldsymbol{v}$ enter into the definition of the inner product in a "symmetric" way. In short,

(10-8) $$\langle \boldsymbol{u}, \boldsymbol{v} \rangle = \langle \boldsymbol{v}, \boldsymbol{u} \rangle.$$

If we write $\boldsymbol{v}$ as in Equation 10-5, then $a\boldsymbol{v} = ac\boldsymbol{u} + a\boldsymbol{z}$, and $a\boldsymbol{z} \perp \boldsymbol{u}$. Thus, $\langle \boldsymbol{u}, a\boldsymbol{v} \rangle = ac|\boldsymbol{u}|^2 = a\langle \boldsymbol{u}, \boldsymbol{v} \rangle$. Then, using the symmetric property of the inner product,

$$\langle a\boldsymbol{u}, \boldsymbol{v} \rangle = \langle \boldsymbol{v}, a\boldsymbol{u} \rangle = a\langle \boldsymbol{v}, \boldsymbol{u} \rangle = a\langle \boldsymbol{u}, \boldsymbol{v} \rangle.$$

In other words,

(10-9) $$\langle a\boldsymbol{u}, \boldsymbol{v} \rangle = a\langle \boldsymbol{u}, \boldsymbol{v} \rangle.$$

If $\boldsymbol{w} = d\boldsymbol{u} + \boldsymbol{y}$ where $\boldsymbol{y} \perp \boldsymbol{u}$, then $\langle \boldsymbol{u}, \boldsymbol{w} \rangle = d|\boldsymbol{u}|^2$. Then,

$$\boldsymbol{v} + \boldsymbol{w} = (c + d)\boldsymbol{u} + \boldsymbol{z} + \boldsymbol{y}.$$

Now we use the geometric fact that $(\boldsymbol{z} + \boldsymbol{y}) \perp \boldsymbol{u}$ because $\boldsymbol{z} \perp \boldsymbol{u}$ and $\boldsymbol{y} \perp \boldsymbol{u}$ (see Fig. 10-3 for a picture of the three-dimensional case) to write

$$\langle \boldsymbol{u}, \boldsymbol{v} + \boldsymbol{w} \rangle = (c + d)|\boldsymbol{u}|^2 = c|\boldsymbol{u}|^2 + d|\boldsymbol{u}|^2.$$

Thus,

(10-10) $$\langle \boldsymbol{u}, \boldsymbol{v} + \boldsymbol{w} \rangle = \langle \boldsymbol{u}, \boldsymbol{v} \rangle + \langle \boldsymbol{u}, \boldsymbol{w} \rangle.$$

Of course, we also have (using symmetry)

$$\langle \boldsymbol{u} + \boldsymbol{v}, \boldsymbol{w} \rangle = \langle \boldsymbol{u}, \boldsymbol{w} \rangle + \langle \boldsymbol{v}, \boldsymbol{w} \rangle.$$

Now we are in a position similar to the one in which we found ourselves in Section 1. There we listed several properties of vector addition and multiplication by scalars of geometric vectors. To put our development on a firm footing we chose to select some of those properties and treat them as axioms. In so doing we defined an "abstract" vector space. Now we will do the same thing with our notions of length and angle. We will select the properties listed in Equations 10-3, 10-8, and 10-10 as axioms. In so doing we define an "abstract" inner product space.

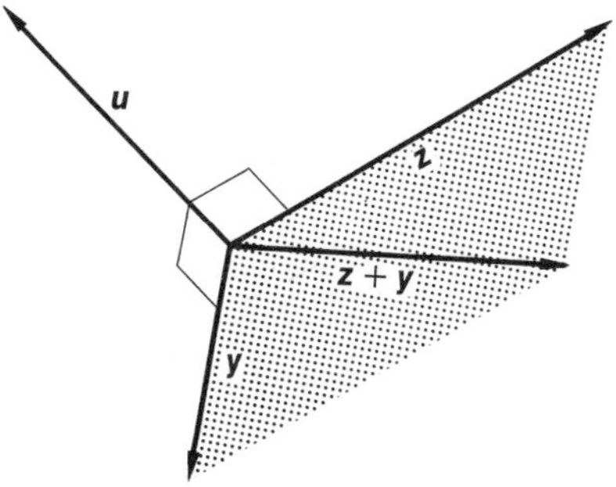

Figure 10-3

DEFINITION 10-1

An ***inner product*** on a vector space V assigns to each pair of vectors $\boldsymbol{u}, \boldsymbol{v}$ a number denoted $\langle \boldsymbol{u}, \boldsymbol{v} \rangle$. This assignment is such that

(i) $\langle \boldsymbol{u}, \boldsymbol{v} \rangle = \langle \boldsymbol{v}, \boldsymbol{u} \rangle$
(ii) $\langle \boldsymbol{u}, \boldsymbol{v} + \boldsymbol{w} \rangle = \langle \boldsymbol{u}, \boldsymbol{v} \rangle + \langle \boldsymbol{u}, \boldsymbol{w} \rangle$
(iii) $\langle a\boldsymbol{u}, \boldsymbol{v} \rangle = a\langle \boldsymbol{u}, \boldsymbol{v} \rangle$
(iv) $\langle \boldsymbol{u}, \boldsymbol{u} \rangle$ is greater than 0 if $\boldsymbol{u} \neq \boldsymbol{0}$.

A vector space with an inner product is called an ***inner product space***. A finite dimensional inner product space is called a ***Euclidean space***.

In view of Property (i) of an inner product space, it is easy to see that Properties (ii) and (iii) are equivalent to

(10-11)
$$\langle \boldsymbol{u} + \boldsymbol{v}, \boldsymbol{w} \rangle = \langle \boldsymbol{u}, \boldsymbol{w} \rangle + \langle \boldsymbol{v}, \boldsymbol{w} \rangle$$
$$\langle \boldsymbol{u}, a\boldsymbol{v} \rangle = a\langle \boldsymbol{u}, \boldsymbol{v} \rangle.$$

DEFINITION 10-2

The ***norm*** or ***length*** of a vector $\boldsymbol{v}$ in an inner product space is denoted by $|\boldsymbol{v}|$ and defined as

$$|\boldsymbol{v}| = \sqrt{\langle \boldsymbol{v}, \boldsymbol{v} \rangle}.$$

The vector $\boldsymbol{u}$ is ***orthogonal*** or perpendicular to $\boldsymbol{v}$, and we write $\boldsymbol{u} \perp \boldsymbol{v}$, if $\langle \boldsymbol{u}, \boldsymbol{v} \rangle = 0$.

As we have seen, the scalar product in a geometric vector space as defined by Equation 10-1 is an example of an inner product in a vector space. Let us look at another example.

Example 10-1 Let $\boldsymbol{x}$ and $\boldsymbol{y}$ be in R^2. Show that the following definition makes R^2 an inner product space:

$$\langle \boldsymbol{x}, \boldsymbol{y} \rangle = x^1 y^1 + x^2 y^2.$$

Solution: We verify that the four properties of Definition 10-1 hold.

(i) $\langle \boldsymbol{y}, \boldsymbol{x} \rangle = y^1 x^1 + y^2 x^2 = x^1 y^1 + x^2 y^2 = \langle \boldsymbol{x}, \boldsymbol{y} \rangle.$

(ii) $\langle \boldsymbol{x}, \boldsymbol{y} + \boldsymbol{z} \rangle = x^1(y^1 + z^1) + x^2(y^2 + z^2)$

$= x^1 y^1 + x^2 y^2 + x^1 z^1 + x^2 z^2$

$= \langle \boldsymbol{x}, \boldsymbol{y} \rangle + \langle \boldsymbol{x}, \boldsymbol{z} \rangle.$

(iii) $\langle a\boldsymbol{x}, \boldsymbol{y} \rangle = ax^1 y^1 + ax^2 y^2 = a(x^1 y^1 + x^2 y^2) = a\langle \boldsymbol{x}, \boldsymbol{y} \rangle.$

(iv) $\langle \boldsymbol{x}, \boldsymbol{x} \rangle = (x^1)^2 + (x^2)^2 > 0$ if $(x^1, x^2) \neq (0,0).$

The definition of the inner product in R^2 in the preceding example stems from the interpretation of R^2 as a rectangular cartesian coordinate plane and the definition of the inner product for geometric vectors. If we represent the vectors $\boldsymbol{x}$, $\boldsymbol{y}$, and $\boldsymbol{x} - \boldsymbol{y}$ as arrows in R^2 (Fig. 10-4) and use the Law of Cosines,

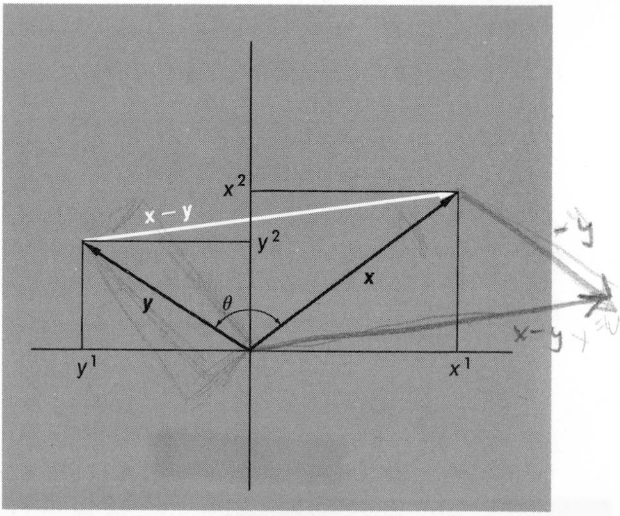

Figure 10-4

we get

$$|x - y|^2 = |x|^2 + |y|^2 - 2|x||y| \cos \phi = |x|^2 + |y|^2 - 2\langle x, y \rangle.$$

The distance formula in a rectangular cartesian coordinate plane tells us that

$$|x - y|^2 = (x^1 - y^1)^2 + (x^2 - y^2)^2$$
$$|x|^2 = (x^1)^2 + (x^2)^2$$
$$|y|^2 = (y^1)^2 + (y^2)^2.$$

Using these equations, the preceding equation reduces to

$$\langle x, y \rangle = x^1 y^1 + x^2 y^2.$$

Thus, the introduction of a rectangular cartesian coordinate system into the geometric plane not only establishes an isomorphism between the plane and R^2, but also identifies the geometric inner product space with R^2 as an inner product space as defined in Example 10-1. This inner product in R^2 is called the standard or usual inner product in R^2, and it is plain to see how it is generalized to R^n.

The ***standard inner product** in R^n* is defined as

$$\langle x, y \rangle = x^1 y^1 + x^2 y^2 + \cdots + x^n y^n.$$

Notice that with the standard inner product in R^n

$$|x| = \sqrt{(x^1)^2 + \cdots + (x^n)^2}.$$

There are other ways of making R^n an inner product space, as the following example shows.

Example 10-2 Show that the following definition makes R^2 an inner product space:

$$\langle x, y \rangle = 2x^1 y^1 + x^2 y^2 - x^1 y^2 - x^2 y^1.$$

Solution: It is plain to see that the right side of the defining equation is unchanged if the "x's" and "y's" are interchanged so that $\langle y, x \rangle = \langle x, y \rangle$. To verify the other properties, let us write the defining equation as

$$\langle x, y \rangle = x^1 y^1 + (x^2 - x^1)(y^2 - y^1).$$

Then

$\langle x, y\rangle = x^1y^1 + (x^2 - x^1)(y^2 - y^1)$

$$x^1(y^1 + z^1) + (x^2 - x^1)(y^2 + z^2 - y^1 - z^1) =$$
$$x^1y^1 + (x^2 - x^1)(y^2 - y^1) + x^1z^1 + (x^2 - x^1)(z^2 - z^1),$$

so

$$\langle \boldsymbol{x}, \boldsymbol{y} + \boldsymbol{z}\rangle = \langle \boldsymbol{x}, \boldsymbol{y}\rangle + \langle \boldsymbol{x}, \boldsymbol{z}\rangle.$$

Also,

$$\begin{aligned}\langle a\boldsymbol{x}, \boldsymbol{y}\rangle &= ax^1y^1 + (ax^2 - ax^1)(y^2 - y^1)\\ &= a[x^1y^1 + (x^2 - x^1)(y^2 - y^1)]\\ &= a\langle \boldsymbol{x}, \boldsymbol{y}\rangle\end{aligned}$$

and

$$\langle \boldsymbol{x}, \boldsymbol{x}\rangle = (x^1)^2 + (x^2 - x^1)^2 > 0 \quad \text{if} \quad (x^1, x^2) \neq (0,0).$$

Example 10-3 Let $a < b$ be any two numbers and let $I = [a,b]$. Show that $C(I)$ is an inner product space if we define

$$\langle \boldsymbol{g}, \boldsymbol{f}\rangle = \int_a^b g(t)f(t)dt.$$

Solution: The first three properties of Definition 10-1 are easy to verify, and we leave them for you as an exercise. Let us see what is involved in showing that

$$\langle f, f\rangle = \int_a^b [f(t)]^2 dt > 0 \quad \text{if} \quad f \neq \mathbf{0}.$$

First, $\mathbf{0}$ means the zero function; that is, $\mathbf{0}(t) = 0$ for all $t \in I$. Now if $f \neq \mathbf{0}$, then there is a number c in I such that $|f(c)| = p > 0$. It is a basic property of continuous functions that there is an interval J containing c in which $|f(t)| > p/2$. Thus, in J $[f(t)]^2 > 0$ and in the rest of $I, [f(t)]^2 \geq 0$. So the integral of $[f(t)]^2$ over I is positive if $f \neq \mathbf{0}$.

The inner product defined in the preceding example for $C(I)$ is called the ***usual integral inner product***. Notice that with the usual integral inner product

$$|f| = \left(\int_a^b [f(t)]^2 dt\right)^{1/2}.$$

For example, if $I = [0,1]$ and $\boldsymbol{e}_1(x) = x$, we see that

$$\langle e_1, e_1 \rangle = \int_0^1 e_1(x)\, e_1(x)\, dx =$$

$$|e_1|^2 = \int_0^1 x^2 dx = \tfrac{1}{3}.$$

It may seem strange to talk about the "length" of a function, but as we shall see in the next section, the norm of a vector in an "abstract" inner product space does have the usual properties of length. One of these properties is stated in part (c) of the following theorem. We will leave the proof of this theorem to you as an exercise.

THEOREM 10-1

Let V be an inner product space. Then
(a) $\langle \mathbf{0}, v \rangle = 0$ for any v. In particular $\langle \mathbf{0}, \mathbf{0} \rangle = 0$.
(b) If $\langle w, v \rangle = 0$ for every w in V, then $v = \mathbf{0}$.
(c) $|cv| = |c||v|$.

PROBLEMS 10

1. Write out the details required to show that Equations 10-11 are valid.

2. Find $|(1,1)|$ if the inner product in R^2 is
   (a) the standard inner product;
   (b) the one defined in Example 10-2.

3. Define $\langle (x^1, x^2), (y^1, y^2) \rangle = x^1 y^1 - x^1 y^2 + 2x^2 y^2 - x^2 y^1$. Does this equation define an inner product in R^2? If so, find $|(1,1)|$ with this inner product.

4. Show that the definition in Example 10-3 of $\langle f, g \rangle$ does satisfy Properties (i), (ii), and (iii) for an inner product.

5. Let $I = [0, 2\pi]$ and let s, c, and e_n denote the sine, cosine, and n^{th} power functions. Find the following if the usual integral inner product is used:
   (a) $\langle s, c \rangle$ (b) $|s|$ (c) $|c|$ (d) $|e_2|$
   (e) $\langle e_1, e_2 \rangle$ (f) $\langle s, e_0 \rangle$ (g) $\langle s, e_1 \rangle$ (h) $|s + e_1|$

6. Let $I_1 = [0,1]$ and $I_2 = [-1,1]$. Show that the polynomials $e_1(x) = x$ and $p(x) = 3x - 2$ are orthogonal functions in the space $C(I_1)$, but not in $C(I_2)$, with the usual integral inner product.

7. Find $P_u(v)$ if $u = OA$ and $v = OB$ where O is the origin of a cartesian coordinate system in the plane and A and B have the following coordinates:
   (a) $A = (0,2)$; $B = (1,1)$ (b) $A = (1,1)$; $B = (0,2)$
   (c) $A = (2,3)$; $B = (1,4)$ (d) $A = (-1,2)$; $B = (0,-1)$

8. Prove Theorem 10-1.

9. Justify the following equation involving summation notation:

$$\langle a^\alpha v_\alpha, w\rangle = a^\alpha\langle v_\alpha, w\rangle.$$

10. Let F be a linear operator such that $\langle F(x), y\rangle = 0$ for all x and y. Prove that F is the zero linear operator; that is, $F(z) = \mathbf{0}$ for every z.
11. In a rectangular cartesian coordinate plane the vector $(1,m)$ is parallel to a line of slope m. Use the inner product condition for orthogonality to derive the condition for perpendicularity of lines with slopes m_1 and m_2.

11 ORTHOGONAL PROJECTIONS. THE SCHWARZ AND TRIANGLE INEQUALITIES

In the preceding section we discussed the orthogonal projection of a geometric vector v on a non-zero vector u. Now that we have introduced the inner product into an abstract vector space we can talk about projections in an inner product space. We are guided by our geometric pictures (see Fig. 11-1) and Equation 10-6 to make a formal definition.

DEFINITION 11-1

If $u \neq \mathbf{0}$, the orthogonal projection of v on u, denoted by $P_u(v)$, is the vector defined by the equation

(11-1) $$P_u(v) = cu \quad \text{where} \quad c = \frac{\langle u, v\rangle}{\langle u, u\rangle}.$$

Example 11-1 With the usual integral inner product the space $C[0,1]$ is an inner product space. Find $P_{e_1}(e_2)$ if e_n is the nth power function.

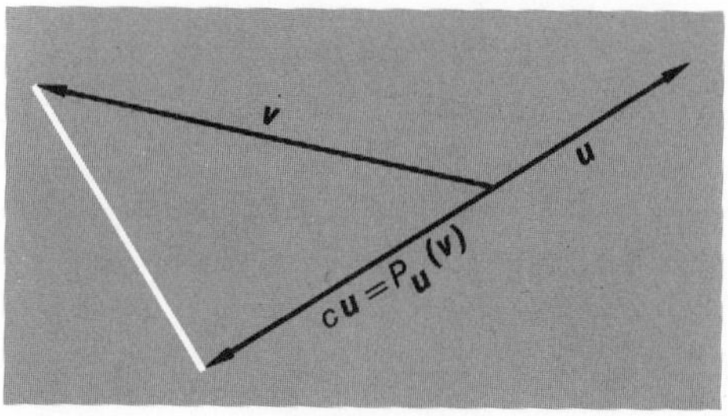

Figure 11-1

$P_{e_1}(e_2) = ce_1 = \frac{\langle e_1, e_2 \rangle}{\langle e_1, e_1 \rangle} e_1$

Solution: Because

$$\langle e_1, e_2 \rangle = \int_0^1 x^3 dx = \tfrac{1}{4}$$

and

$$\langle e_1, e_1 \rangle = \int_0^1 x^2 dx = \tfrac{1}{3},$$

then

$$c = \frac{\frac{1}{4}}{\frac{1}{3}} = \tfrac{3}{4}$$

and

$$P_{e_1}(e_2) = \tfrac{3}{4} e_1$$

If $u \neq 0$ and v are vectors in an inner product space, we can form the vector

$$v - P_u(v) = v - cu = z.$$

Our geometric picture suggests that $z \perp u$. To prove that z is orthogonal to u in any inner product space, we compute $\langle u, z \rangle$ using the definition of c in Equation 11-1:

$$\langle u, z \rangle = \langle u, v - cu \rangle = \langle u, v \rangle - c\langle u, u \rangle = 0.$$

We can write v as the sum $cu + z$; that is,

$$v = P_u(v) + z \quad \text{where} \quad z \perp u.$$

This decomposition of v into the sum of a vector along u and a vector orthogonal to u is unique. These facts are important enough to state as a theorem.

THEOREM 11-1

If $u \neq 0$ and v are any vectors in an inner product space, then there are unique vectors cu and z such that

$$v = cu + z \quad \text{and} \quad z \perp u.$$

Furthermore, the vector cu is equal to $P_u(v)$.

Proof: The only thing not proved in our discussion before the statement of this theorem is the uniqueness of c and z. So suppose that $\boldsymbol{v} = c\boldsymbol{u} + z$ and also that $\boldsymbol{v} = d\boldsymbol{u} + y$, where $z \perp \boldsymbol{u}$ and $y \perp \boldsymbol{u}$. Then from the equation

$$c\boldsymbol{u} + z = d\boldsymbol{u} + y$$

we have

$$\langle c\boldsymbol{u} + z, \boldsymbol{u}\rangle = \langle d\boldsymbol{u} + y, \boldsymbol{u}\rangle,$$

and hence,

$$c\langle \boldsymbol{u}, \boldsymbol{u}\rangle = d\langle \boldsymbol{u}, \boldsymbol{u}\rangle.$$

Because $\boldsymbol{u} \neq \mathbf{0}$, we conclude that $c = d$. It then follows that $y = z$. ∎

As Theorem 11-1 states, the vector $z = \boldsymbol{v} - P_{\boldsymbol{u}}(\boldsymbol{v})$ is orthogonal to $\boldsymbol{u}$. Of course, z may be the zero vector in which case $\langle \boldsymbol{u}, \mathbf{0}\rangle = 0$, so that we still write $z \perp \boldsymbol{u}$. In any case, of course, $|z| \geqq 0$. This simple observation leads us to a very important inequality that we will state as a theorem.

THEOREM 11-2

If $\boldsymbol{u}$ and $\boldsymbol{v}$ are vectors in an inner product space, then

(11-2) $$|\langle \boldsymbol{u}, \boldsymbol{v}\rangle| \leqq |\boldsymbol{u}||\boldsymbol{v}| \quad (\textit{Schwarz's Inequality}).$$

Proof: If $\boldsymbol{u} = \mathbf{0}$, then $|\langle \boldsymbol{u}, \boldsymbol{v}\rangle| = |\boldsymbol{u}||\boldsymbol{v}|$ because both sides of the equation are zero (Theorem 10-1). So suppose that $\boldsymbol{u} \neq \mathbf{0}$, and define $z = \boldsymbol{v} - P_{\boldsymbol{u}}(\boldsymbol{v}) = \boldsymbol{v} - c\boldsymbol{u}$. Then $|z|^2 = \langle z, z\rangle \geqq 0$, and so

$$\langle \boldsymbol{v} - c\boldsymbol{u}, \boldsymbol{v} - c\boldsymbol{u}\rangle \geqq 0$$

$$\langle \boldsymbol{v}, \boldsymbol{v}\rangle - 2c\langle \boldsymbol{u}, \boldsymbol{v}\rangle + c^2\langle \boldsymbol{u}, \boldsymbol{u}\rangle \geqq 0.$$

Using Equation 11-1 to replace c,

$$\langle \boldsymbol{v}, \boldsymbol{v}\rangle - \frac{2\langle \boldsymbol{u}, \boldsymbol{v}\rangle^2}{\langle \boldsymbol{u}, \boldsymbol{u}\rangle} + \frac{\langle \boldsymbol{u}, \boldsymbol{v}\rangle^2 \cdot \langle \boldsymbol{u}, \boldsymbol{u}\rangle}{\langle \boldsymbol{u}, \boldsymbol{u}\rangle^2} \geqq 0.$$

That is,

$$\langle \boldsymbol{v}, \boldsymbol{v}\rangle \geqq \frac{\langle \boldsymbol{u}, \boldsymbol{v}\rangle^2}{\langle \boldsymbol{u}, \boldsymbol{u}\rangle},$$

or

$$\langle \boldsymbol{v}, \boldsymbol{v} \rangle \cdot \langle \boldsymbol{u}, \boldsymbol{u} \rangle \geqq \langle \boldsymbol{u}, \boldsymbol{v} \rangle^2.$$

Taking positive square roots yields Equation 11-2. ∎

Example 11-2 Show that if f and g are in $C[a,b]$, then

$$\left(\int_a^b f(x)g(x)dx\right)^2 \leqq \int_a^b [f(x)]^2 dx \cdot \int_a^b [g(x)]^2 dx.$$

Solution: This inequality follows directly from Schwarz's Inequality (Equation 11-2) for the inner product space $C[a,b]$ with the usual integral inner product.

We have defined the length (or norm) of a vector by the equation $|\boldsymbol{v}|^2 = \langle \boldsymbol{v}, \boldsymbol{v} \rangle$. Now we will use the inner product to define the angle between two vectors. The obvious thing to do is to use Equation 10-4 as the definition of $\cos \theta$, for there is a unique angle θ with $0 \leqq \theta \leqq \pi$ whose cosine is a given number. Before we can proceed in that direction we need to know that the number on the right side of Equation 10-4 is between -1 and 1; that is, is it true that

$$-1 \leqq \frac{\langle \boldsymbol{u}, \boldsymbol{v} \rangle}{|\boldsymbol{u}||\boldsymbol{v}|} \leqq 1?$$

These inequalities are valid because of Schwarz's Inequality. Thus, we can *define* the angle θ between two non-zero vectors $\boldsymbol{u}$ and $\boldsymbol{v}$ to be that unique angle θ with $0 \leqq \theta \leqq \pi$ such that

$$\cos \theta = \frac{\langle \boldsymbol{u}, \boldsymbol{v} \rangle}{|\boldsymbol{u}||\boldsymbol{v}|}.$$

Example 11-3 Find the angle between the vectors $\boldsymbol{u} = (1,1)$ and $\boldsymbol{v} = (-1 - \sqrt{3}, -1 + \sqrt{3})$ in R^2 with the standard inner product.

Solution: We have

$$\begin{aligned}
\langle \boldsymbol{u}, \boldsymbol{v} \rangle &= -1 - \sqrt{3} - 1 + \sqrt{3} = -2 \\
\langle \boldsymbol{u}, \boldsymbol{u} \rangle &= 1 + 1 = 2 \\
\langle \boldsymbol{v}, \boldsymbol{v} \rangle &= 1 + 2\sqrt{3} + 3 + 1 - 2\sqrt{3} + 3 = 8.
\end{aligned}$$

Thus,

$$\cos \theta = \frac{-2}{\sqrt{2}\,\sqrt{8}} = -\tfrac{1}{2},$$

and so $\theta = \dfrac{2\pi}{3}$.

Example 11-4 Find the cosine of the angle between the power functions $\boldsymbol{e}_1$ and $\boldsymbol{e}_2$ in $C[0,1]$ with the usual integral inner product.

Solution: From Example 11-1 we know that $\langle \boldsymbol{e}_1, \boldsymbol{e}_2 \rangle = \frac{1}{4}$ and that $\langle \boldsymbol{e}_1, \boldsymbol{e}_1 \rangle = \frac{1}{3}$. Also,

$$\langle \boldsymbol{e}_2, \boldsymbol{e}_2 \rangle = \int_0^1 x^4\, dx = \tfrac{1}{5}.$$

Hence,

$$\cos \theta = \frac{\frac{1}{4}}{\dfrac{1}{\sqrt{3}}\,\dfrac{1}{\sqrt{5}}} = \frac{\sqrt{15}}{4}.$$

Thus, the angle between $\boldsymbol{e}_1$ and $\boldsymbol{e}_2$ in $C[0,1]$ is nearly zero!

One of the basic properties of length in ordinary geometry is that the length of one side of a triangle is not more than the sum of the lengths of the other two sides. If the line segments forming the sides of a triangle are directed so as to represent the vectors $\boldsymbol{u}$, $\boldsymbol{v}$, and $\boldsymbol{u} + \boldsymbol{v}$ (see Fig. 11-2), then this property of length can be expressed by the inequality:

$$|\boldsymbol{u} + \boldsymbol{v}| \leqq |\boldsymbol{u}| + |\boldsymbol{v}|.$$

It turns out that the norm of a vector in an inner product space also has this property.

THEOREM 11-3

If $\boldsymbol{u}$ and $\boldsymbol{v}$ are vectors in an inner product space, then

(11-3) $\qquad |\boldsymbol{u} + \boldsymbol{v}| \leqq |\boldsymbol{u}| + |\boldsymbol{v}|$ (Triangle Inequality).

Proof: Since both sides of Inequality 11-3 are non-negative, it is equivalent to the inequality we get by squaring both sides; namely,

$$\langle \boldsymbol{u} + \boldsymbol{v}, \boldsymbol{u} + \boldsymbol{v} \rangle \leqq \langle \boldsymbol{u}, \boldsymbol{u} \rangle + 2|\boldsymbol{u}||\boldsymbol{v}| + \langle \boldsymbol{v}, \boldsymbol{v} \rangle.$$

$\langle u, u+v \rangle + \langle v, u+v \rangle \leq \langle u, u \rangle + 2|u||v| + \langle v, v \rangle$

$\langle u, u \rangle + \langle u, v \rangle + \langle v, u \rangle + \langle v, v \rangle \leq \langle u, u \rangle + 2|u||v| + \langle v, v \rangle$

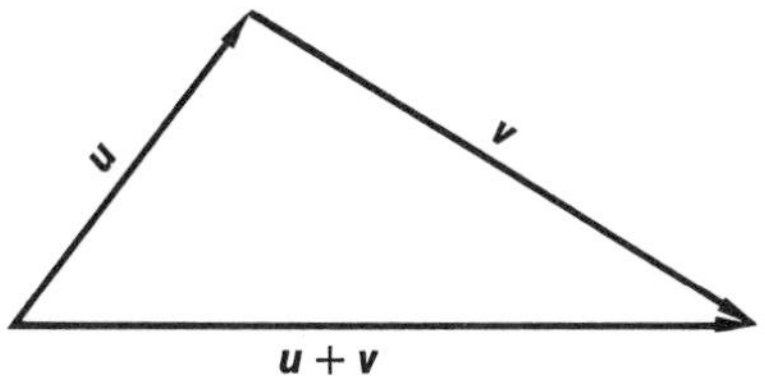

Figure 11-2

Expanding and simplifying, we get

$$2\langle u, v\rangle \leqq 2|u||v|$$

This inequality follows from Schwarz's Inequality, because $\langle u, v\rangle \leqq |\langle u, v\rangle|$. ∎

We have said that two vectors u_1 and u_2 are orthogonal if $\langle u_1, u_2\rangle = 0$. We also say that $\{u_1, u_2\}$ is an orthogonal set in that case. Now we extend this idea of an orthogonal set consisting of any number of vectors.

DEFINITION 11-2

A set S of vectors in an inner product space is called an ***orthogonal set*** if any two different vectors in S are orthogonal.

Example 11-5 Show that the natural basis in R^3 with the standard inner product is an orthogonal set.

Solution:

$$\langle(1,0,0), (0,1,0)\rangle = 0;$$
$$\langle(1,0,0), (0,0,1)\rangle = 0; \quad \text{and}$$
$$\langle(0,1,0), (0,0,1)\rangle = 0.$$

Thus, $\{(1,0,0), (0,1,0), (0,0,1)\}$ is an orthogonal set with the standard inner product.

The next theorem tells us that in a Euclidean space (finite dimensional inner product space) the number of vectors in an orthogonal set cannot exceed the dimension of the space.

THEOREM 11-4

An orthogonal set S of non-zero vectors in an inner product space is an independent set.

Proof: We will use our summation notation. Let $\boldsymbol{v}_1, \ldots, \boldsymbol{v}_n$ be vectors in S. Then, if $c^\alpha \boldsymbol{v}_\alpha = 0$,

$$\langle c^\alpha \boldsymbol{v}_\alpha, \boldsymbol{v}_k \rangle = 0,$$

and thus,

$$c^\alpha \langle \boldsymbol{v}_\alpha, \boldsymbol{v}_k \rangle = 0 \text{ for each } k = 1, \ldots, n. \tag{11-4}$$

Each $\boldsymbol{v}_j$ is in an orthogonal set, so $\langle \boldsymbol{v}_j, \boldsymbol{v}_k \rangle = 0$ unless $j = k$. Thus, each term in the sum in Equation 11-4 is zero except one (when $j = k$), and that equation reduces to

$$c^k \langle \boldsymbol{v}_k, \boldsymbol{v}_k \rangle = 0 \quad \text{(no Greek index, no sum).}$$

This equation is true for each k, and because $\boldsymbol{v}_k \neq 0$, then $c^k = 0$ for each k. Thus, the only linear combination of vectors in S equal to the zero vector is the zero linear combination, so S is an independent set. ∎

Example 11-6 Show that $\{(1,1,2), (-1,-1,1), (1,-1,0)\}$ is an independent set, and hence, a basis for R^3.

Solution: Make R^3 into a Euclidean space by introducing the standard inner product. Then the above set of vectors is an orthogonal set, and hence, independent according to the preceding theorem.

PROBLEMS 11

1. Find $P_{\boldsymbol{u}}(\boldsymbol{v})$ if the standard inner product in R^3 is used and if $\boldsymbol{u} = (1,1,1)$ when (a) $\boldsymbol{v} = (1,0,0)$ (b) $\boldsymbol{v} = (-1,-1,0)$ (c) $\boldsymbol{v} = (2,3,-4)$
2. Show that $\langle P_{\boldsymbol{u}}(\boldsymbol{v}), \boldsymbol{u} \rangle = \langle \boldsymbol{v}, \boldsymbol{u} \rangle$.
3. Show that if $\boldsymbol{w} \perp \boldsymbol{u}$, then $\langle P_{\boldsymbol{u}}(\boldsymbol{v}), \boldsymbol{w} \rangle = 0$ for any $\boldsymbol{v}$.
4. What is $P_{\boldsymbol{u}}(\boldsymbol{u})$? What can you conclude if $P_{\boldsymbol{u}}(\boldsymbol{v}) = \boldsymbol{v}$?
5. Show that $P_{\boldsymbol{u}}(\boldsymbol{v} + \boldsymbol{w}) = P_{\boldsymbol{u}}(\boldsymbol{v}) + P_{\boldsymbol{u}}(\boldsymbol{w})$.
6. Let $\boldsymbol{v}$ be a non-zero vector in an inner product space. Show that the set of all vectors orthogonal to $\boldsymbol{v}$ is a subspace. Interpret this fact in a three-dimensional geometric space.
7. Prove that $|P_{\boldsymbol{u}}(\boldsymbol{v})| \leq |\boldsymbol{v}|$.
8. Let $s_k(x) = \sin kx$. Show that $\{s_1, s_2, s_3\}$ is an independent set of vectors in $C[-\pi,\pi]$. (Hint: $2 \sin mx \cdot \sin nx = \cos(m - n)x - \cos(m + n)x$.)
9. Let $\boldsymbol{u} \neq \boldsymbol{0}$ and $\boldsymbol{v}$ be vectors in an inner product space and let $f(t) = \boldsymbol{v} - t\boldsymbol{u}$. Use simple calculus to show that f takes a minimum value when $t\boldsymbol{u} = P_{\boldsymbol{u}}(\boldsymbol{v})$. In other

words, show that $|v - P_u(v)| \leq |v - tu|$ for any number t. Interpret your result geometrically.

10. Define the distance between x and y by the formula

$$d(x, y) = |x - y|.$$

Prove that this distance has the following properties:
(i) $d(x, y) = d(y, x)$
(ii) $d(x, z) \leq d(x, y) + d(y, z)$
(iii) $d(x, y) = 0$ if, and only if $x = y$.

11. (This question makes use of the preceding two questions.) Suppose that $x^1, \ldots, x^n$ are n numbers that result from n measurements of a quantity. Consider these numbers as a vector $v = (x^1, \ldots, x^n)$ in R^n, which is an approximation to the "true" value vector $(y, y, \ldots, y) = yu$ where $u = (1, 1, \ldots, 1)$. To estimate y we agree to determine t such that $d(v, tu)$ is a minimum. Show that this procedure leads to taking the arithmetic mean (average) of the n measurements as our estimate.

12 ORTHONORMAL BASES

Theorem 11-4 states that in an n-dimensional Euclidean space an orthogonal set of non-zero vectors cannot contain more than n vectors. It is easy to verify (see Example 11-4) that the natural basis in R^n is an orthogonal set with the standard inner product. Thus, in at least one case, there is a set of n orthogonal vectors in that n-dimensional Euclidean space. In other words, R^n with the standard inner product has an orthogonal basis. In addition, each basis vector is of length (norm) 1. We say that such a basis in an orthonormal basis.

DEFINITION 12-1

An orthogonal set of vectors, each of norm 1, is called an ***orthonormal set***.

Example 12-1 Let $s_n(x) = (1/\sqrt{\pi}) \sin nx$. Show that $\{s_1, s_2, \ldots\}$ is an orthonormal set of vectors in the space $C[-\pi,\pi]$ with the usual integral inner product.

Solution: We use the trigonometric identity

$$2 \sin mx \cdot \sin nx = \cos(m - n)x - \cos(m + n)x$$

to write

$$\langle s_m, s_n \rangle = \frac{1}{2\pi} \int_{-\pi}^{\pi} [\cos(m - n)x - \cos(m + n)x]dx.$$

We leave this integration to you (Problem 11-8) to see that if $m \neq n$, then $\langle s_m, s_n \rangle = 0$ and that $\langle s_n, s_n \rangle = 1$.

Our next task is to prove that every Euclidean space has an orthonormal basis. The method we will use is to start with *any* given basis and construct an orthonormal basis from it. The construction process we will use is called the ***Gram-Schmidt Process***, and it is explained in the proof of the following theorem.

THEOREM 12-1

Every Euclidean space V (finite dimensional inner product space) has an orthonormal basis.

Proof: Let $\{\boldsymbol{b}_1, \ldots, \boldsymbol{b}_n\}$ be a basis for V. We will construct an orthogonal set of n non-zero vectors in a "step by step" manner. This set will be a basis because any set of non-zero orthogonal vectors is independent, and any independent set of n vectors is a basis for V. Then we divide each vector by its length to get an orthonormal basis. The Gram-Schmidt Process is used to obtain an orthogonal set $\{\boldsymbol{c}_1, \ldots, \boldsymbol{c}_n\}$. Let $P_j(\boldsymbol{v})$ be the orthogonal projection of $\boldsymbol{v}$ on $\boldsymbol{c}_j$. For example,

$$P_1(\boldsymbol{b}_2) = \left(\frac{\langle \boldsymbol{c}_1, \boldsymbol{b}_2 \rangle}{\langle \boldsymbol{c}_1, \boldsymbol{c}_1 \rangle}\right)\boldsymbol{c}_1 = d\boldsymbol{c}_1.$$

You can easily verify (see Problem 11-2) that

(12-1) $$\langle P_j(\boldsymbol{v}), \boldsymbol{c}_j \rangle = \langle \boldsymbol{v}, \boldsymbol{c}_j \rangle.$$

The vectors $\boldsymbol{c}_1, \ldots, \boldsymbol{c}_n$ are defined as follows:

(12-2)
$$\begin{aligned}
\boldsymbol{c}_1 &= \boldsymbol{b}_1 \\
\boldsymbol{c}_2 &= \boldsymbol{b}_2 - P_1(\boldsymbol{b}_2) \\
\boldsymbol{c}_3 &= \boldsymbol{b}_3 - P_1(\boldsymbol{b}_3) - P_2(\boldsymbol{b}_3) \\
&\vdots \\
\boldsymbol{c}_n &= \boldsymbol{b}_n - P_1(\boldsymbol{b}_n) - P_2(\boldsymbol{b}_n) - \cdots - P_{n-1}(\boldsymbol{b}_n).
\end{aligned}$$

Figure 12-1 shows how the $\boldsymbol{c}$-vectors are obtained if $n = 3$. The algebraic proof is rather long and consists of three parts.

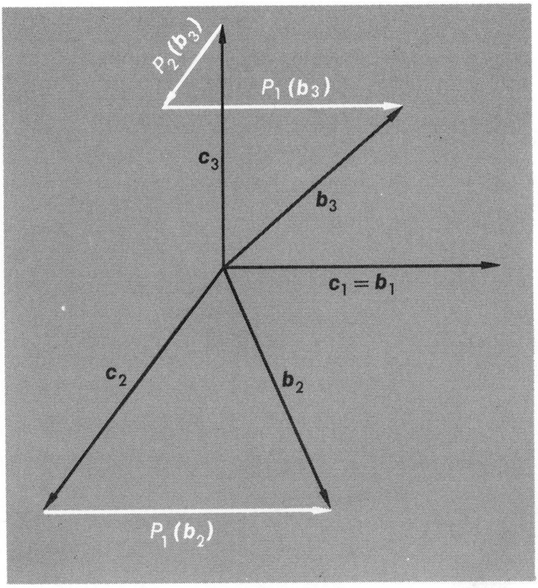

Figure 12-1

Part I. $\{c_1, \ldots, c_n\}$ is an orthogonal set.
Using Equations 12-1 and 12-2 with $j = 1$ and $v = b_2$,

$$\langle c_1, c_2 \rangle = \langle c_1, b_2 \rangle - \langle c_1, P_1(b_2) \rangle = 0.$$

Now $P_2(b_3)$ is a multiple of c_2, so $P_2(b_3) \perp c_1$. Utilizing this fact and Equation 12-1, with $j = 2$ and $v = b_3$,

$$\langle c_1, c_3 \rangle = \langle c_1, b_3 \rangle - \langle c_1, P_1(b_3) \rangle - \langle c_1, P_2(b_3) \rangle = 0.$$

Likewise, we can show that $\langle c_2, c_3 \rangle = 0$, so $\{c_1, c_2, c_3\}$ is an orthogonal set. We can continue in a step by step manner to show that $\{c_1, \ldots, c_n\}$ is an orthogonal set. To be rigorous, an induction argument should be employed to show that if $\{c_1, \ldots, c_k\}$ is an orthogonal set $(1 \leqq k < n)$, then so is $\{c_1, \ldots, c_k, c_{k+1}\}$.

Part II. $c_j \neq \mathbf{0}$ for $j = 1, \ldots, n$.

Again we proceed in a step by step manner. First, $c_1 \neq \mathbf{0}$ (Why?). If c_2 were $\mathbf{0}$, then from the equation defining c_2 we would conclude that b_2 is in Sp $\{b_1\}$. But it is not, because $\{b_1, b_2\}$ is an independent set. So $c_2 \neq \mathbf{0}$. Furthermore, since $c_1 = b_1$, and c_2 is a linear combination of b_1 and b_2 and because b_2 is a linear combination of c_1 and c_2, we have (according to Theorem 2-1) Sp $\{b_1, b_2\}$ = Sp $\{b_1, b_2, c_2\}$ = Sp $\{b_1, c_2\}$ =

Sp $\{c_1, c_2\}$. Now we use the same argument again. If $c_3 = \mathbf{0}$, then (according to the equation defining c_3) b_3 is in Sp $\{c_1, c_2\}$ = Sp $\{b_1, b_2\}$. But b_3 is not in the space generated by b_1 and b_2 because $\{b_1, b_2, b_3\}$ is an independent set. As before, it can be shown that Sp $\{b_1, b_2, b_3\}$ = Sp $\{c_1, c_2, c_3\}$. The procedure to show that $c_4 \neq \mathbf{0}$ is precisely the same. To complete a rigorous proof, an induction argument is required.

Part III. If $e_j = \dfrac{c_j}{|c_j|}$, then $E = \{e_1, \ldots, e_n\}$ is an orthonormal basis.

Because

$$|e_j| = \left|\frac{c_j}{|c_j|}\right| = \frac{|c_j|}{|c_j|} = 1$$

and

$$\langle e_j, e_k\rangle = \frac{1}{|c_j||c_k|}\cdot\langle c_j, c_k\rangle = 0 \quad \text{if} \quad j \neq k,$$

E is an orthonormal set of n vectors; that is, E is an orthonormal basis. ∎

Example 12-2 Carry out the Gram-Schmidt Process with the set $\{b_1, b_2\} = \{(1,1), (-1,2)\}$ to obtain an orthonormal basis for R^2, using the standard inner product.

Solution: $c_1 = (1,1)$ and $c_2 = (-1,2) - P_1(-1,2)$

where

$$P_1(-1,2) = \frac{\langle(-1,2), (1,1)\rangle}{\langle(1,1), (1,1)\rangle}(1,1)$$
$$= (\tfrac{1}{2})(1,1) = (\tfrac{1}{2}, \tfrac{1}{2}).$$

Thus (see Fig. 12-2),

$$c_2 = (-1,2) - (\tfrac{1}{2}, \tfrac{1}{2}) = (-\tfrac{3}{2}, \tfrac{3}{2}).$$

We see that $|c_1| = \sqrt{2}$ and $|c_2| = 3\sqrt{2}/2$. Thus, the vectors

$$e_1 = (1/\sqrt{2})(1,1) = (1/\sqrt{2}, 1/\sqrt{2})$$

and

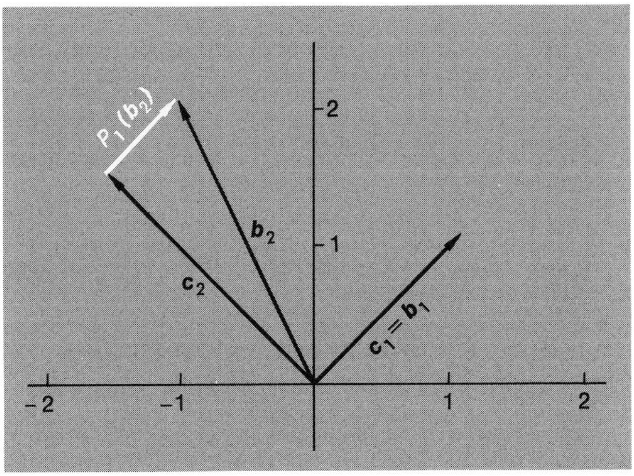

Figure 12-2

$$e_2 = (\tfrac{2}{3}\sqrt{2})(-\tfrac{3}{2}, \tfrac{3}{2}) = (-1/\sqrt{2}, 1/\sqrt{2})$$

form an orthonormal basis for R^2.

Although the Gram-Schmidt Process was introduced in a finite dimensional setting, it can be applied in some cases in an inner product space that is not of finite dimension. Let us consider just one important case as an example. The set of all polynomials (functions) on the interval $[-1,1]$ is an inner product space when we introduce the usual integral inner product. Then if $e_n(x) = x^n$ (n^{th} power),

$$\langle e_0, e_0 \rangle = \int_{-1}^{1} 1\, dx = 2,$$

$$\langle e_0, e_1 \rangle = \int_{-1}^{1} x\, dx = 0,$$

$$\langle e_1, e_1 \rangle = \langle e_0, e_2 \rangle = \int_{-1}^{1} x^2 dx = \tfrac{2}{3},$$

and so on. We see $e_0 \perp e_1$, but e_0 is not orthogonal to e_2. In general

$$\langle e_m, e_n \rangle = \int_{-1}^{1} x^{m+n} dx = \begin{cases} 0 & \text{if } m+n \text{ is odd} \\ \dfrac{2}{m+n+1} & \text{if } m+n \text{ is even.} \end{cases}$$

Thus, we could carry out the Gram-Schmidt Process on the sequence $\{e_0, e_1, \ldots\}$. The polynomials that are obtained are called the *normalized Legendre Polynomials.*

As we have seen, any n-dimensional vector space is isomorphic to R^n. An n-dimensional Euclidean space is isomorphic to R^n as a vector space, but even more is true. Since an orthonormal basis $E = \{e_1, \ldots, e_n\}$ exists in any Euclidean space V, we may choose it to define the standard isomorphism F from V to R^n. Thus, if $v = x^\alpha e_\alpha$, we set $F(v) = x = (x^1, \ldots, x^n)$. If $w = y^\beta e_\beta$, then

$$\langle v, w\rangle = \langle x^\alpha e_\alpha, y^\beta e_\beta\rangle = x^\alpha y^\beta \langle e_\alpha, e_\beta\rangle.$$

(This is a horrible double sum when you write it out!) Now E is an orthonormal basis, so $\langle e_j, e_k\rangle$ is equal to zero if $j \neq k$ and is equal to 1 if $j = k$. Thus,

$$\langle v, w\rangle = x^1y^1 + \cdots + x^ny^n.$$

If the standard inner product in R^n is used, we see that

$$\langle v, w\rangle = \langle x, y\rangle.$$

A linear map from one inner product space to another that "preserves" the inner product is called an ***isometry***. If there is an isomorphism from one inner product space to another that is an isometry, then we say the two inner product spaces are ***isometric***. Thus, if $F: V \to \hat{V}$ is an isomorphism and

$$\langle F(v), F(w)\rangle = \langle v, w\rangle,$$

then V and $\hat{V}$ are isometric. We can summarize the above discussion by stating that:

*Every Euclidean space of dimension **n** is isometric to the space **R**^{n} with the standard inner product.*

In particular, R^n with any inner product is a Euclidean space, and is isometric to R^n with the standard inner product. In this sense, there is no loss of generality in always choosing the standard inner product in R^n, and because it is the simplest inner product, that is usually what we do. In fact, we will use the "dot" notation to indicate that we are using the standard inner product because that is the inner product in R^n which we so often use. Thus, for x and y in R^n,

$$x \cdot y = x^1y^1 + \cdots + x^ny^n.$$

Since orthonormal bases play a special role, it is important to know how two orthonormal bases are related. Of course, if E and $\hat{E}$ are two bases in a

Euclidean space V, the coordinate transformation equations are (see Equation 7-8)

$$[v]_E = [I]_E^{\hat{E}}[v]_{\hat{E}}.$$

Suppose that E is an orthonormal basis. Under what conditions will $\hat{E}$ be an orthonormal basis? As we know (Equations 7-9), if $\hat{e}_j = a_j^\alpha e_\alpha$, then

$$[I]_E^{\hat{E}} = \begin{bmatrix} a_1^1 & \cdots & a_n^1 \\ \vdots & & \vdots \\ a_1^n & \cdots & a_n^n \end{bmatrix} = [\hat{e}_1 \ \ldots \ \hat{e}_n]_E.$$

In words, the columns of $[I]_E^{\hat{E}}$ are the E-coordinates of the $\hat{E}$ basis vectors. The columns can be considered as vectors in R^n. Using the fact that E is an orthonormal basis,

$$\begin{aligned} \langle \hat{e}_j, \hat{e}_k \rangle &= \langle a_j^\alpha e_\alpha, a_k^\beta e_\beta \rangle \\ &= a_j^\alpha a_k^\beta \langle e_\alpha, e_\beta \rangle \\ &= a_j^1 a_k^1 + \cdots + a_j^n a_k^n \\ &= \boldsymbol{a}_j \cdot \boldsymbol{a}_k. \end{aligned}$$

Thus $\hat{E}$ will be an orthonormal basis if, and only if, the columns of $[I]_E^{\hat{E}}$ are orthonormal vectors in R^n with the standard inner product. Let us form a matrix whose rows are the columns of $[I]_E^{\hat{E}}$. Such a matrix is called the transpose of $[I]_E^{\hat{E}}$.

DEFINITION 12-2

If $[M]$ is a matrix, the matrix $[M]^*$ whose rows are the columns of $[M]$ is called the ***transpose*** of $[M]$.

For example,

$$\begin{bmatrix} 1 & 2 \\ 3 & 4 \end{bmatrix}^* = \begin{bmatrix} 1 & 3 \\ 2 & 4 \end{bmatrix}.$$

If the columns of $[I]_E^{\hat{E}}$ are orthonormal vectors in R^n with the standard inner product, then the product of the transpose of $[I]_E^{\hat{E}}$ times $[I]_E^{\hat{E}}$ is $[I]$. To verify this statement, we write the multiplication of two matrices as the dot product of the "row vectors" of the first matrix times the "column vectors" of the second. Thus, if

$$[A] = \begin{bmatrix} \boldsymbol{a}^1 \\ \vdots \\ \boldsymbol{a}^n \end{bmatrix} \quad \text{and} \quad [B] = [\boldsymbol{b}_1 \ . \ . \ . \ \boldsymbol{b}_n],$$

where $\boldsymbol{a}^1, \ldots, \boldsymbol{a}^n, \boldsymbol{b}_1, \ldots, \boldsymbol{b}_n$ are vectors in R^n, then

(12-3)
$$[A][B] = \begin{bmatrix} \boldsymbol{a}^1 \cdot \boldsymbol{b}_1 & \ldots & \boldsymbol{a}^1 \cdot \boldsymbol{b}_n \\ \vdots & & \vdots \\ \boldsymbol{a}^n \cdot \boldsymbol{b}_1 & \ldots & \boldsymbol{a}^n \cdot \boldsymbol{b}_n \end{bmatrix}.$$

If we write the product of

$$[I]_E^{\hat{E}*} = \begin{bmatrix} \boldsymbol{a}_1 \\ \vdots \\ \boldsymbol{a}_n \end{bmatrix} \quad \text{and} \quad [I]_E^{\hat{E}} = [\boldsymbol{a}_1 \ . \ . \ . \ \boldsymbol{a}_n]$$

using the dot product notation, it is easy to see that

$$[I]_E^{\hat{E}*}[I]_E^{\hat{E}} = [I].$$

DEFINITION 12-3

A square matrix $[M]$ is said to be ***orthogonal*** if

$$[M]^* = [M]^{-1}.$$

An equivalent statement is that $[M]$ is orthogonal if its columns (or rows) form an orthonormal set of vectors in R^n with the standard inner product.

Now the results of our discussion can be stated in a concise form.

THEOREM 12-2

If E is an orthonormal basis in a Euclidean space, then the basis $\hat{E}$ is an orthonormal basis if, and only if, the matrix of the coordinate transformamation is an orthogonal matrix; that is, if, and only if, $[I]_E^{\hat{E}}$ is an orthogonal matrix.

We can use some geometric reasoning to obtain a description of the set of all 2 by 2 orthogonal matrices. Suppose that $E = \{\boldsymbol{e}_1, \boldsymbol{e}_2\}$ is an orthonormal basis in a geometric plane. Then $[M]$ is a 2 by 2 orthogonal matrix if, and only if, it is the matrix of the coordinate transformation to another orthonormal basis $\hat{E} = \{\hat{\boldsymbol{e}}_1, \hat{\boldsymbol{e}}_2\}$. Picture E and $\hat{E}$ as sets of perpendicular arrows in a plane with common initial points. It is perfectly clear that if you "rotate" the E arrows by an angle θ so as to make $\boldsymbol{e}_1$ coincide with $\hat{\boldsymbol{e}}_1$, then either $\boldsymbol{e}_2 = \hat{\boldsymbol{e}}_2$ or $\boldsymbol{e}_2 = -\hat{\boldsymbol{e}}_2$ (see Fig. 12-3). The matrix that represents the coordinate transformation $\hat{\boldsymbol{e}}_1 = \boldsymbol{e}_1$ and $\hat{\boldsymbol{e}}_2 = -\boldsymbol{e}_2$ is

$$\begin{bmatrix} 1 & 0 \\ 0 & -1 \end{bmatrix}.$$

Thus, $\hat{E}$ is obtained from E either by a rotation or by a rotation followed by a

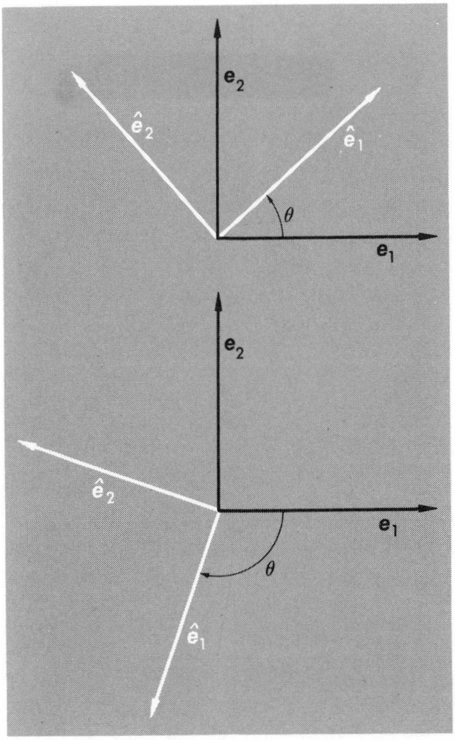

Figure 12-3

$[I]^{E}_{\hat{E}} = [e_1 \ldots e_n]_{\hat{E}}$

"flipping over" or reflection. In the first case the coordinate transformation matrix is given by Equation 7-10, and in the second case (since the operation is a composite operation) the matrix is

$$\begin{bmatrix} 1 & 0 \\ 0 & -1 \end{bmatrix} \begin{bmatrix} \cos\theta & \sin\theta \\ -\sin\theta & \cos\theta \end{bmatrix} = \begin{bmatrix} \cos\theta & \sin\theta \\ \sin\theta & -\cos\theta \end{bmatrix}.$$

Thus, every 2 by 2 orthogonal matrix is of the form

$$\begin{bmatrix} \cos\theta & \sin\theta \\ \mp\sin\theta & \pm\cos\theta \end{bmatrix}$$

for some angle θ.

We close this section by proving a theorem about products and transposes of matrices.

THEOREM 12-3

$$([A][B])^* = [B]^*[A]^*.$$

Proof: To show that this equation is valid, we will write the product on the right side of this equation as the dot product of "row vectors" times "column vectors" and compare our result with the matrix in Equation 12-3.

$$[B]^*[A]^* = \begin{bmatrix} b_1 \\ \vdots \\ b_n \end{bmatrix} [a^1 \cdots a^n] = \begin{bmatrix} b_1 \cdot a^1 & \ldots & b_1 \cdot a^n \\ \vdots & & \vdots \\ b_n \cdot a^1 & \ldots & b_n \cdot a^n \end{bmatrix}.$$

Because the dot product is symmetric, the matrix on the right side of this equation is the transpose of the matrix on the right side of Equation 12-3 and so our proof is complete. ∎

PROBLEMS 12

1. Let $E = \{e_1, e_2\}$ be a basis. Determine the condition that t must satisfy if $(e_1 + te_2) \perp (e_1 + 2e_2)$. What if E is an orthonormal basis?
2. Let $E = \{e_1, \ldots, e_n\}$ be an orthonormal basis. Show that the kth coordinate of any vector v in that basis is simply $\langle v, e_k \rangle$. Thus,

$$[v]_E = \begin{bmatrix} \langle v, e_1 \rangle \\ \vdots \\ \langle v, e_n \rangle \end{bmatrix}.$$

3. Let s and c be the sine and cosine functions in $C[-\pi,\pi]$ with the usual inner product. Apply the Gram-Schmidt Process to $\{s, c\}$ and find an orthonormal set.
4. Apply the Gram-Schmidt Process to find an orthonormal basis.
   (a) $\{(1,2), (-1,0)\}$ in R^2.
   (b) $\{(1,2,1), (2,-2,1), (1,0,3)\}$ in R^3.
5. Find the first three normalized Legendre Polynomials.
6. Consider the space of polynomials of degree less than 3 on the interval $[-1,1]$ with the usual integral inner product. We know that $\{e_0, e_1, e_2\}$ is a basis for the space P_3. Suppose that $p = a^\alpha e_\alpha$. Let $F(p) = (a^0, a^1, a^2)$. Is F an isometry of P_3 onto R^3 with the standard inner product? If not, can you define an inner product in R^3 so that F is an isometry? Can you define an isometry from P_3 onto R^3? (See the preceding problem!)
7. Prove that if $F(v) = v$ for every vector v, then the operator F is an isometry.
8. Prove that if F is an isometry in a finite dimensional space, then F is invertible.
9. Let F be a linear operator on a Euclidean space with an orthonormal basis E. Show that if $[F]_E^E = [A]$, then $a_j^i = \langle e_i, F(e_j) \rangle$.
10. Find $[M]^*$ if $[M]$ is the matrix

(a) $[I]$ (b) $\begin{bmatrix} 1 & 2 & 3 \\ 4 & 5 & 6 \\ 7 & 8 & 9 \end{bmatrix}$ (c) $\begin{bmatrix} 0 & 1 & 0 \\ 0 & 0 & 1 \\ 1 & 0 & 0 \end{bmatrix}$.

11. Show that $([A] + [B])^* = [A]^* + [B]^*$.
12. Show that $([A]^*)^{-1} = ([A]^{-1})^*$.
13. Show that if $[A]$ is orthogonal, then $[A]^*$ is orthogonal.
14. Show that if $[A]$ is orthogonal, then $[A]^{-1}$ is orthogonal.
15. Is the product of two orthogonal matrices orthogonal?
16. Determine t such that the matrix is orthogonal.

(a) $\frac{1}{3}\begin{bmatrix} 2 & 1 & -2 \\ 1 & 2 & 2 \\ 2 & -2 & t \end{bmatrix}$ (b) $\frac{1}{6}\begin{bmatrix} t & 2 & 0 \\ t & -1 & 3\sqrt{2} \\ t & -1 & -3\sqrt{2} \end{bmatrix}$.

17. Find numbers that make the following an orthogonal matrix:

$$\begin{bmatrix} u & v & w \\ 0 & x & y \\ 0 & 0 & z \end{bmatrix}$$

18. Let E and $\hat{E}$ be orthonormal bases. Define the linear operator F by the equations $F(\boldsymbol{e}_j) = \hat{\boldsymbol{e}}_j$.
(a) Find $[F]_E^E$.
(b) Show that $[F]_E^E$ is an orthogonal matrix.

13 ORTHOGONAL SUBSPACES. DIRECT SUMS

Let S be any set of vectors in an inner product space. The set of all vectors that are perpendicular to every vector in S is written $S^\perp$ and is called "S perp." Thus,

$$S^\perp = \{\boldsymbol{v} \text{ in } V : \boldsymbol{v} \perp \boldsymbol{s} \text{ for each } \boldsymbol{s} \text{ in } S \subset V\}.$$

In particular, it follows from Theorem 10-1 that if $O = \{\mathbf{0}\}$,

$$O^\perp = V \quad \text{and} \quad V^\perp = O.$$

Picturing a three-dimensional geometric space as a space of arrows from a point O, it is seen (Fig. 13-1) that if $S = \{\boldsymbol{v}\}$, then $S^\perp$ is a plane. Even though S is not a subspace in that case, $S^\perp$ is. Our next theorem states that $S^\perp$ is always a subspace.

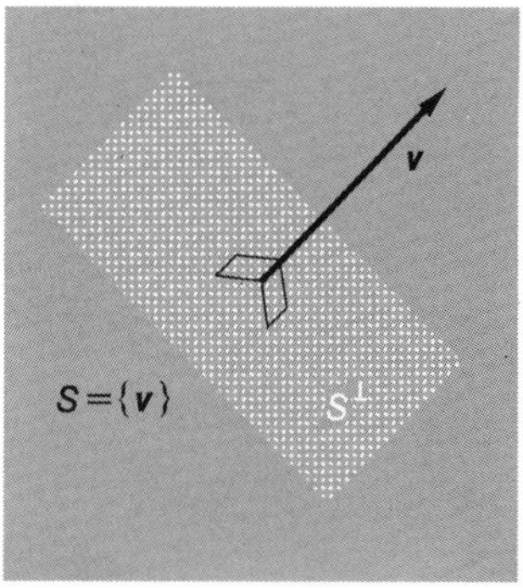

Figure 13-1

THEOREM 13-1

$S^{\perp}$ is a subspace.

Proof: If $\boldsymbol{v}$ and $\boldsymbol{w}$ are in $S^{\perp}$, then $\langle c\boldsymbol{v} + \boldsymbol{w}, \boldsymbol{s}\rangle = c\langle \boldsymbol{v}, \boldsymbol{s}\rangle + \langle \boldsymbol{w}, \boldsymbol{s}\rangle = 0$ for every $\boldsymbol{s}$ in S. Thus, $c\boldsymbol{v} + \boldsymbol{w}$ is in $S^{\perp}$, too. ∎

If W is a non-zero subspace of a Euclidean space V, then W has an orthonormal basis $\boldsymbol{e}_1, \ldots, \boldsymbol{e}_k$. This basis can be extended to a basis for V, and the Gram-Schmidt Process can be applied to get an orthonormal basis for V. Because the resulting orthonormal basis contains $\boldsymbol{e}_1, \ldots, \boldsymbol{e}_k$ (the Gram-Schmidt Process leaves these vectors unchanged), we can say that we can extend an orthonormal basis in W to an orthonormal basis in V, say $E = \{\boldsymbol{e}_1 \ldots, \boldsymbol{e}_k, \boldsymbol{e}_{k+1}, \ldots, \boldsymbol{e}_n\}$. Now we claim that $\boldsymbol{e}_{k+1}, \ldots, \boldsymbol{e}_n$ is a basis for $W^{\perp}$. First, if $\boldsymbol{v}$ is in Sp $\{\boldsymbol{e}_{k+1}, \ldots, \boldsymbol{e}_n\}$ and $\boldsymbol{w}$ is in W, then

$$\boldsymbol{v} = c^{k+1}\boldsymbol{e}_{k+1} + \cdots + c^n\boldsymbol{e}_n = c^{\alpha}\boldsymbol{e}_{\alpha} \quad (\alpha = k+1, \ldots, n)$$
$$\boldsymbol{w} = d^1\boldsymbol{e}_1 + \cdots + d^k\boldsymbol{e}_k = d^{\beta}\boldsymbol{e}_{\beta} \quad (\beta = 1, \ldots, k);$$

and so

$$\langle \boldsymbol{v}, \boldsymbol{w}\rangle = \langle c^{\alpha}\boldsymbol{e}_{\alpha}, d^{\beta}\boldsymbol{e}_{\beta}\rangle = c^{\alpha}d^{\beta}\langle \boldsymbol{e}_{\alpha}, \boldsymbol{e}_{\beta}\rangle = 0$$

because E is an orthonormal basis. Thus, every vector in Sp $\{\boldsymbol{e}_{k+1}, \ldots, \boldsymbol{e}_n\}$ is in $W^{\perp}$. Now suppose that $\boldsymbol{v}$ is in $W^{\perp}$. We show that $\boldsymbol{v}$ is in Sp $\{\boldsymbol{e}_{k+1}, \ldots, \boldsymbol{e}_n\}$. Let $\boldsymbol{v} = x^1\boldsymbol{e}_1 + \cdots + x^n\boldsymbol{e}_n$. Then $\langle \boldsymbol{v}, \boldsymbol{e}_1\rangle = 0$ because $\boldsymbol{v}$ is in $W^{\perp}$ and $\boldsymbol{e}_1$ is in W. But

$$0 = \langle \boldsymbol{v}, \boldsymbol{e}_1\rangle = \langle x^1\boldsymbol{e}_1 + \cdots + x^n\boldsymbol{e}_n, \boldsymbol{e}_1\rangle = x^1 \quad \text{(Why?)}.$$

So $\boldsymbol{v} = x^2\boldsymbol{e}_2 + \cdots + x^n\boldsymbol{e}_n$. Repeating our argument shows that $x^2 = \cdots = x^k = 0$, so that $\boldsymbol{v}$ is in Sp $\{\boldsymbol{e}_{k+1}, \ldots, \boldsymbol{e}_n\}$.

Summarizing, we showed that $W^{\perp} \subset$ Sp $\{\boldsymbol{e}_{k+1}, \ldots, \boldsymbol{e}_n\}$ and Sp $\{\boldsymbol{e}_{k+1}, \ldots, \boldsymbol{e}_n\} \subset W^{\perp}$, so $W^{\perp} =$ Sp $\{\boldsymbol{e}_{k+1}, \ldots, \boldsymbol{e}_n\}$. It follows that dim $W^{\perp} = n - k =$ dim $V -$ dim W. Furthermore, if $\boldsymbol{v}$ is any vector in V, then

$$\boldsymbol{v} = (x^1\boldsymbol{e}_1 + \cdots + x^k\boldsymbol{e}_k) + (x^{k+1}\boldsymbol{e}_{k+1} + \cdots + x^n\boldsymbol{e}_n),$$

or

(13-1) $\boldsymbol{v} = \boldsymbol{w} + \boldsymbol{w}^{\perp}$ where $\boldsymbol{w}$ is in W and $\boldsymbol{w}^{\perp}$ is in $W^{\perp}$.

The decomposition of v in Equation 13-1 is unique. For if $v = w_1 + w_1^\perp$ and $v = w_2 + w_2^\perp$, then $w_1 - w_2 = w_2^\perp - w_1^\perp$. But because W and $W^\perp$ are subspaces, the vector on the left of this equation is in W and the vector on the right is in $W^\perp$. The only vector in both W and $W^\perp$ is the zero vector (Why?). Thus, $w_1 = w_2$ and $w_1^\perp = w_2^\perp$. We have proved the following theorem:

THEOREM 13-2

If W is a subspace of a Euclidean space V, and v is any vector in V, then

(i) $\dim W + \dim W^\perp = \dim V$
(ii) there are unique vectors w and $w^\perp$ in W and $W^\perp$ such that $v = w + w^\perp$.

The first part of this theorem is a statement about dimensions of subspaces, and it reminds us of a similar kind of statement in Theorem 6-1. In the next section we will show how we can look at systems of equations in two different ways and make good use of these two theorems.

Property (ii) of Theorem 13-2 says that V can be split into two subspaces in such a way that each vector in V is the unique sum of a vector from each of the two parts. This idea is simply a generalization of the idea of splitting the plane into two subspaces (coordinate axes) and writing a vector as the unique sum of a vector in each coordinate axis. Just as we do not restrict ourselves to orthogonal coordinate systems, so too we remove the restriction that the two splitting subspaces be orthogonal.

DEFINITION 13-1

Let W and U be subspaces of V with the property that every vector v in V can be written as a unique sum:

$$v = w + u \text{ with } w \text{ in } W \text{ and } u \text{ in } U.$$

Then W and U are ***complementary subspaces***. We write

$$V = W \oplus U,$$

and say that V is the ***direct sum*** of W and U.

For example, we have seen that if W is a subspace of a Euclidean space, then W and $W^\perp$ are complementary subspaces and

$$V = W \oplus W^\perp. \tag{13-2}$$

If W and U are subspaces such that every vector $\boldsymbol{v} = \boldsymbol{w} + \boldsymbol{u}$, then W and U are complementary subspaces if, and only if, $\boldsymbol{w}$ and $\boldsymbol{u}$ are uniquely determined by $\boldsymbol{v}$. This situation occurs precisely when the only vector in both W and U is the zero vector. For if

$$\boldsymbol{v} = \boldsymbol{w}_1 + \boldsymbol{u}_1 = \boldsymbol{w}_2 + \boldsymbol{u}_2 \quad (\boldsymbol{w}_j \text{ in } W \text{ and } \boldsymbol{u}_j \text{ in } U),$$

then

$$(\boldsymbol{w}_1 - \boldsymbol{w}_2) = (\boldsymbol{u}_2 - \boldsymbol{u}_1).$$

Because $\boldsymbol{w}_1 - \boldsymbol{w}_2$ is in W and $\boldsymbol{u}_2 - \boldsymbol{u}_1$ is in U, we see that $\boldsymbol{w}_1 = \boldsymbol{w}_2$ and $\boldsymbol{u}_1 = \boldsymbol{u}_2$ precisely when we know that $W \cap U = \{\boldsymbol{0}\}$. We have shown that

THEOREM 13-3

$V = W \oplus U$ if, and only if, every $\boldsymbol{v}$ can be written as a sum $\boldsymbol{w} + \boldsymbol{u}$ and $W \cap U = \{\boldsymbol{0}\}$.

Let us look at R^3 as a coordinate 3-space to see that the statement of Theorem 13-3 is really quite natural. If W_1 is the XY-plane and W_2 is the YZ-plane, then every vector can be written as $\boldsymbol{w}_1 + \boldsymbol{w}_2$. Thus $(x, y, z) = (r, s, 0) + (0, t, u)$ for some numbers r, s, t, and u. But the same (x, y, z) may be represented in more than one way. For example, $(1,2,3) = (1,2,0) + (0,0,3) = (1,0,0) + (0,2,3)$. Notice that

$$\{XY\text{-plane}\} \cap \{YZ\text{-plane}\} = \{Y\text{-axis}\} \neq \{\boldsymbol{O}\}.$$

On the other hand, R^3 is the direct sum of the XY-plane and the Z-axis. In fact it seems reasonable to say that R^3 can be written as the direct sum of three subspaces; namely, the three coordinate axes. It is a simple matter to extend the idea of a direct sum to a sum of more than two terms.

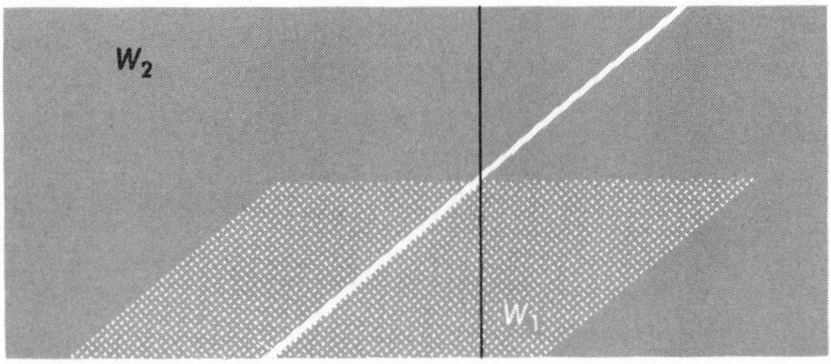

Figure 13-2

DEFINITION 13-2

If $W_1, \ldots, W_k$ are subspaces of V such that each $\boldsymbol{v}$ can be written in a unique way as a sum

$$\boldsymbol{v} = \boldsymbol{w}_1 + \cdots + \boldsymbol{w}_k \quad (\boldsymbol{w}_j \text{ in } \boldsymbol{w}_j),$$

then V is the direct sum of the subspaces, and we write

$$V = W_1 \oplus \cdots \oplus W_k.$$

Let V be finite dimensional and $V = W \oplus U$. Choose $\{\boldsymbol{w}_1, \ldots, \boldsymbol{w}_r\}$ and $\{\boldsymbol{u}_1, \ldots, \boldsymbol{u}_s\}$ as bases for W and U. Then every $\boldsymbol{v}$ is a unique linear combination

$$\boldsymbol{w} + \boldsymbol{u} = c^\alpha \boldsymbol{w}_\alpha + d^\beta \boldsymbol{u}_\beta.$$

Thus, every $\boldsymbol{v}$ is a unique linear combination of vectors in $\{\boldsymbol{w}_1, \ldots, \boldsymbol{w}_r, \boldsymbol{u}_1, \ldots, \boldsymbol{u}_s\}$, so this set is a basis for V. It follows that $\dim V = \dim W + \dim U$. This result can easily be extended to the case when V is the direct sum of more than two subspaces, and we state this extension as a theorem.

THEOREM 13-4

If V is a finite dimensional vector space and

$$V = W_1 \oplus \cdots \oplus W_k,$$

then

$$\dim V = \dim W_1 + \cdots + \dim W_k.$$

PROBLEMS 13

1. Find $W^\perp$ if $V = R^2$ and write $\boldsymbol{v} = \boldsymbol{w} + \boldsymbol{w}^\perp$ if $\boldsymbol{v} = (0,1)$ and W is the space generated by the given vectors.
(a) (1,1) (b) $(-3,2)$ (c) $(1,-1)$ and (2,2)
2. Find $W^\perp$ if $V = R^3$ and write $\boldsymbol{v} = \boldsymbol{w} + \boldsymbol{w}^\perp$ if $\boldsymbol{v} = (0,1,0)$ and W is the space generated by the given vectors.
(a) (1,1,1) (b) (1,1,1); (1,0,1) (c) (1,1,1); (1,0,1); (0,0,1)

3. Let $W = \text{Sp}\{(1,0)\}$. Find $U_1 \neq U_2$ such that $V = W \oplus U_1$ and $V = W \oplus U_2$. (This example shows that a "complement of W" is not unique.)
4. Let W_1 be generated by (1,1,0,0) and (1,0,1,0); W_2 by (1,–1,0,0) and (1,0,0,1); and W_3 by (0,1,0,1) and (0,0,1,1). Is $R^4 = W_1 \oplus W_2 \oplus W_3$?
5. Let O be the origin of a three-dimensional space. Let A, B, C be points with coordinates (1,2,0), (1,–2,0), and (1,1,1), respectively. Let $W_1 = \text{Sp}\{\boldsymbol{OA}, \boldsymbol{OB}\}$ and $W_2 = \text{Sp}\{\boldsymbol{OC}\}$. Show that the space is the direct sum $W_1 \oplus W_2$ and write the vector $\boldsymbol{OP}$ as a sum $\boldsymbol{w}_1 + \boldsymbol{w}_2$ if the coordinates of P are:
   (a) (1,0,0) (b) (0,0,1) (c) (1,2,3)
6. Show that if $\boldsymbol{v} \perp \boldsymbol{w}_j$ ($j = 1, \ldots, k$) and $W = \text{Sp}\{\boldsymbol{w}_1, \ldots, \boldsymbol{w}_k\}$, then $\boldsymbol{v}$ is in $W^{\perp}$.
7. Show that if W is a subspace of a Euclidean space, then $(W^{\perp})^{\perp} = W$.
8. Let W_1 and W_2 be subspaces of V. If $W_1 \cap W_2 = \{\boldsymbol{0}\}$, is $W_1^{\perp} \cap W_2^{\perp} = \{\boldsymbol{0}\}$?
9. Let W_1 and W_2 be subspaces of a finite dimensional space V. Show that if $W_1 \cap W_2 = \{\boldsymbol{0}\}$ and $\dim W_1 + \dim W_2 = \dim V$, then $V = W_1 \oplus W_2$.
10. Show that if V is a finite dimensional space and $V = W_1 \oplus W_2$, then $V = W_1^{\perp} \oplus W_2^{\perp}$. Illustrate this result with a sketch in a geometric plane.
11. State and prove an extension of Theorem 13-3 to the case in which three subspaces are involved.
12. Let $\{\boldsymbol{e}_1, \ldots, \boldsymbol{e}_k\}$ be any orthonormal set in a Euclidean space V. This set can be extended to an orthonormal basis $E = \{\boldsymbol{e}_1, \ldots, \boldsymbol{e}_n\}$.
   (a) Show that for any $\boldsymbol{v}$ in V
   $$|\boldsymbol{v}|^2 = \langle \boldsymbol{v}, \boldsymbol{e}_1 \rangle^2 + \cdots + \langle \boldsymbol{v}, \boldsymbol{e}_n \rangle^2.$$
   (b) Use part (a) to show that if $\{\boldsymbol{e}_1, \ldots, \boldsymbol{e}_k\}$ is any orthonormal set, then *Bessel's Inequality* holds:
   $$\langle \boldsymbol{v}, \boldsymbol{e}_1 \rangle^2 + \cdots + \langle \boldsymbol{v}, \boldsymbol{e}_k \rangle^2 \leqq |\boldsymbol{v}|^2.$$

Four

Linear Systems

Much of mathematics and its applications is concerned with the solution of equations of one type or another. In this chapter some of the problems associated with solving linear systems of equations will be considered. Nowadays the task of actually finding a solution of a large system of linear equations is carried out using the computer. Some work oriented toward using the computer for solving systems is given in Sections 16 and 17. The chapters following this one do not require these sections as prerequisite knowledge, so you may wish to omit reading them if you are not particularly interested in the mechanics of actually solving a linear system of equations. However, the first sections of this chapter are essential to later work in this book and they contain basic facts about linear systems and matrices that every student of mathematics should know.

14 SYSTEMS OF LINEAR EQUATIONS

The systems of equations

$$\text{(14-1)} \qquad \begin{aligned} 2x - y + z &= 3 \\ x + 3y - z &= 4 \end{aligned} \quad \text{and} \quad \begin{aligned} 2x - y + z &= 0 \\ x + 3y - z &= 0 \end{aligned}$$

are systems of two linear equations in three unknowns. The system on the right is the ***homogeneous system*** associated with the non-homogeneous system on the left. We will study systems of m equations in n unknowns:

$$\text{(14-2)} \qquad \begin{aligned} a_1^1 x^1 + \cdots + a_n^1 x^n &= b^1 \\ \vdots \qquad\qquad & \quad \vdots \\ a_1^m x^1 + \cdots + a_n^m x^n &= b^m. \end{aligned}$$

Using summation notation, such systems can be written compactly as

$$a_\beta^j x^\beta = b^j, \quad j = 1, \ldots, m; \beta = 1, \ldots, n.$$

A solution is a set of n numbers $x^1, \ldots, x^n$. Thus, *a solution is a vector* $\boldsymbol{x} = (x^1, \ldots, x^n)$ in R^n. The constant term is a vector $\boldsymbol{b} = (b^1, \ldots, b^m)$ in R^m. The matrix $[A]$ of the system is made up of the coefficients of the "x" terms. In matrix notation, Equation 14-2 is written

$$\text{(14-3)} \qquad [A][\boldsymbol{x}] = [\boldsymbol{b}],$$

and the associated homogeneous system is

$$\text{(14-4)} \qquad [A][\boldsymbol{x}] = [\boldsymbol{0}].$$

For example, the Systems 14-1 are written

$$\begin{bmatrix} 2 & -1 & 1 \\ 1 & 3 & -1 \end{bmatrix} \begin{bmatrix} x \\ y \\ z \end{bmatrix} = \begin{bmatrix} 3 \\ 4 \end{bmatrix} \quad \text{and} \quad \begin{bmatrix} 2 & -1 & 1 \\ 1 & 3 & -1 \end{bmatrix} \begin{bmatrix} x \\ y \\ z \end{bmatrix} = \begin{bmatrix} 0 \\ 0 \end{bmatrix}.$$

In order to apply some of our previous results, the rows and columns of $[A]$ will be considered as vectors in R^n and R^m. We will speak of these as the row vectors and column vectors of $[A]$. Let $\boldsymbol{a}_j$ be the vector in R^m that is in column j of $[A]$ and let $\boldsymbol{a}^k$ be the vector in R^n that is in row k of $[A]$. Thus,

$$a_j = (a_j^1, \ldots, a_j^m) \text{ and } a^k = (a_1^k, \ldots, a_n^k).$$

For example, if $[A]$ is the matrix of Systems 14-1,

$$[A] = \begin{bmatrix} 2 & -1 & 1 \\ 1 & 3 & -1 \end{bmatrix},$$

then

$$a_2 = (-1,3) \text{ and } a^1 = (2,-1,1).$$

Using the standard inner product in R^n (the dot product), we can write System 14-4 as n equations:

$$a^1 \cdot x = 0, \ldots, a^m \cdot x = 0.$$

For example, the homogeneous System 14-1 is

$$(2,-1,1) \cdot (x,y,z) = 0$$

$$(1,3,-1) \cdot (x,y,z) = 0.$$

the dot product = 0 for orthogonal vectors

Thus, x is a solution to System 14-4 if, and only if, x is a vector that is orthogonal to each of the row vectors of $[A]$. Hence (see Problem 13-6), x is a solution if, and only if, x is in $W^\perp$ where W is the subspace of R^n generated by the row vectors of $[A]$. The dimension of W is called the **row rank** of $[A]$. Roughly speaking, it is the number of independent row vectors of a matrix. Let us make use of Theorem 13-2, which states that dim W + dim $W^\perp$ = dim R^n = n. The set S_0 of all solutions is the subspace $W^\perp$. If r = row rank of $[A]$, then

(14-5) $$\dim S_0 = n - r.$$

Now let us write Equation 14-4 in the following form:

$$x^1 a_1 + \cdots + x^n a_n = 0.$$

For example, the homogeneous System 14-1 can be written in the form

$$x \begin{bmatrix} 2 \\ 1 \end{bmatrix} + y \begin{bmatrix} -1 \\ 3 \end{bmatrix} + z \begin{bmatrix} 1 \\ -1 \end{bmatrix} = \begin{bmatrix} 0 \\ 0 \end{bmatrix}.$$

If $F: R^n \to R^m$ is the linear map whose matrix (in the natural basis) is the coeffi-

$F: R^n \to R^m$

cient matrix $[A]$, then for any $\boldsymbol{y}$ in R^n, $F(\boldsymbol{y}) = y^1\boldsymbol{a}_1 + \cdots + y^n\boldsymbol{a}_n$. In other words, $F(\boldsymbol{y})$ is in Sp $\{\boldsymbol{a}_1, \ldots, \boldsymbol{a}_n\}$ for each $\boldsymbol{y}$ in R^n. In fact,

$$F(R^n) = \text{Sp}\ \{\boldsymbol{a}_1, \ldots, \boldsymbol{a}_n\}.$$

The ***column rank*** of $[A]$ is dim $F(R^n)$. Roughly speaking, it is the number of independent column vectors. The vector $\boldsymbol{x}$ is a solution to the homogeneous system (that is, belongs to the solution space S_0) if, and only if, $\boldsymbol{x}$ is in $K(F)$, the kernel of F. Now we apply Theorem 6-1, which states that dim $F(R^n)$ + dim $K(F)$ = dim $R^n = n$. If c is the column rank of $[A]$, then

$$\dim S_0 = n - c. \tag{14-6}$$

From Equations 14-5 and 14-6 we see that $r = c$; the *row rank of a matrix is equal to its column rank*. This number is called the ***rank*** of the matrix. Our results are summarized in the following theorem.

THEOREM 14-1

Let $[A]$ be an m by n matrix. Let r be the rank of $[A]$ and let S_0 be the space of solutions to the homogeneous system

$$[A][\boldsymbol{x}] = [\boldsymbol{0}].$$

Then

$$\dim S_0 = n - r.$$

In particular, the homogeneous system has only the trivial solution zero if, and only if, the rank of $[A]$ is n.

Let us apply Theorem 14-1 to the homogeneous System 14-1. The row rank of the matrix of the system cannot be more than 2, and the row vectors are independent. Thus, the rank of the matrix of the system is 2. It follows from Theorem 14-2 that the dimension of the solution space S_0 is equal to $3 - 2 = 1$. In order to specify S_0 we need only to find one vector $\boldsymbol{x}_0$ in R^3 that generates S_0. Every solution can then be written as $t\boldsymbol{x}_0$ for some number t. To solve the homogeneous System 14-1, let us rewrite it as

$$\begin{aligned} 2x - \ y &= -z \\ x + 3y &= \ \ z. \end{aligned}$$

Solving for x and y in terms of z:

$$x = -2z/7, \ y = 3z/7.$$

Let $z = 7t$ (an arbitrary, but convenient representation of z in view of our equations for x and y). Then $x = -2t$ and $y = 3t$. In other words,

$$(-2t, 3t, 7t)$$

is a solution, regardless of what number t is chosen. Stating it another way,

$$S_0 = \{t(-2,3,7)\} = \text{Sp}\,\{(-2,3,7)\}. \tag{14-7}$$

The method we used to find a solution in S_0 was not important. The fact is, if we could have guessed one solution, we would have known that we were finished because we knew that $\dim S_0 = 1$.

Let us interpret our results geometrically by picturing R^3 with the dot product as a coordinate 3-space. Then $2x - y + z = (2,-1,1) \cdot (x,y,z)$. Thus,

$$W_1 = \{(x,y,z): 2x - y + z = 0\} = \{\boldsymbol{x}: \boldsymbol{x} \perp (2,-1,1)\}$$

is a plane in coordinate 3-space that contains the origin (see Fig. 14-1). The vector $(2,-1,1)$ is called a *normal* vector to the plane W_1. Similarly, $W_2 = \{(x,y,z): x + 3y - z = 0\}$ is a plane containing the origin that has $(1,3,-1)$ as a normal vector. Solving the homogeneous System 14-1 amounts to finding the points in $W_1 \cap W_2$. It is not surprising that this set of points is a line. Parametric equations of that line are:

$$x = -2t, \quad y = 3t, \ z = 7t.$$

Figure 14-2 illustrates the situation.

Let S be the solution set of the non-homogeneous System 14-3. There are two important differences between S and S_0. The solution set of the associated homogeneous system S_0 is a subspace and is always non-empty because it contains $\boldsymbol{0}$. But S is *not* a subspace and *it may be empty*. However, if S does contain a a vector $\boldsymbol{x}$, and if $\boldsymbol{x}_0$ is any vector in S_0, then $\boldsymbol{x} + \boldsymbol{x}_0$ is in S because

$$[A][\boldsymbol{x} + \boldsymbol{x}_0] = [A][\boldsymbol{x}] + [A][\boldsymbol{x}_0] = [\boldsymbol{b}] + [\boldsymbol{0}] = [\boldsymbol{b}].$$

Similarly, if $\boldsymbol{x}_1$ and $\boldsymbol{x}_2$ are both solutions to the non-homogeneous system, then

$$[A][\boldsymbol{x}_1 - \boldsymbol{x}_2] = [A][\boldsymbol{x}_1] - [A][\boldsymbol{x}_2] = [\boldsymbol{b}] - [\boldsymbol{b}] = [\boldsymbol{0}].$$

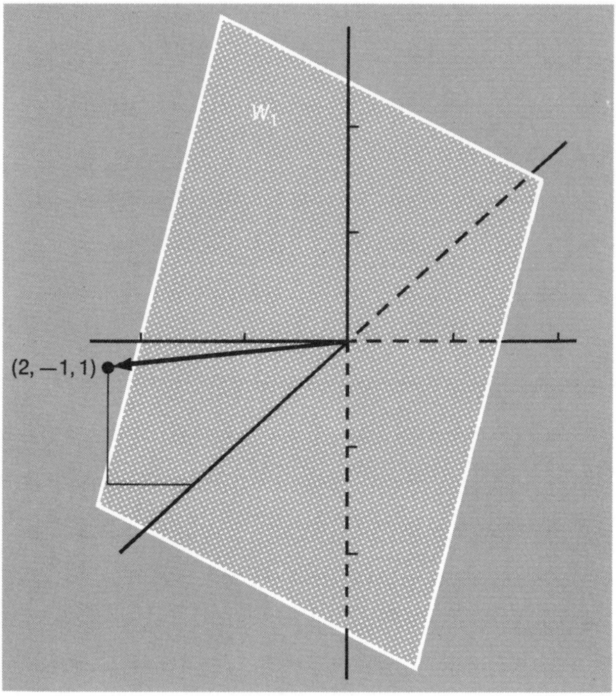

Figure 14-1

Thus, $\boldsymbol{x}_1 - \boldsymbol{x}_2$ is a vector $\boldsymbol{x}_0$ in S_0. It follows that *every* solution to the non-homogeneous System 14-3 can be found by finding *one* solution $\boldsymbol{x}_1$, because any other solution is of the form $\boldsymbol{x}_1 + \boldsymbol{x}_0$ for some $\boldsymbol{x}_0$ in S_0. This result is expressed by the equation

$$S = \boldsymbol{x}_1 + S_0 = \{\boldsymbol{x}\!:\boldsymbol{x} = \boldsymbol{x}_1 + \boldsymbol{x}_0;\ \boldsymbol{x}_0 \text{ in } S_0\}.$$

Let us find S for the non-homogeneous System 14-1. To do so we must find one solution to the system. We set $x = 1$ and solve the system

$$-y + z = 1$$
$$3y - z = 3$$

to find $y = 2$ and $z = 3$. Thus, (1,2,3) is one solution. You could set x (or y, or z) equal to some other number and find a different solution (for example, $(-1,5,10)$), but it will not change the final result. We use Equation 14-7 to write

$$S = (1,2,3) + S_0 = \{(1,2,3) + t(-2,3,7)\}.$$

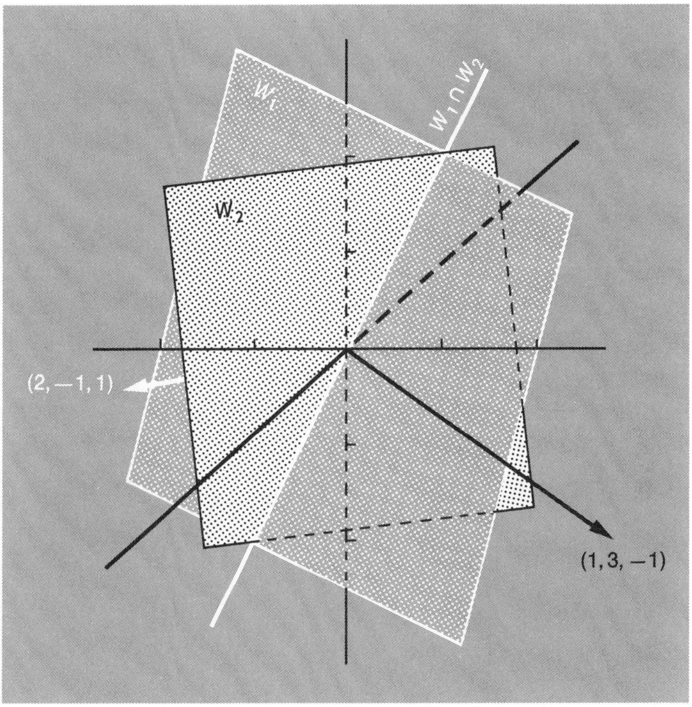

Figure 14-2

Let us now look at the situation geometrically. The point $P = (1,2,3)$ lies in both the sets

$$U_1 = \{(x, y, z): 2x - y + z = 3\},$$

and

$$U_2 = \{(x, y, z): x + 3y - z = 4\}.$$

Thus,

$$2(x - 1) - 1(y - 2) + 1(z - 3) = 0$$

for each point $X = (x, y, z)$ in U. In other words,

$$(2, -1, 1) \cdot \boldsymbol{PX} = 0$$

for each point X in U_1. Thus, U_1 is a plane containing P with $(2, -1, 1)$ as a normal vector. In the same way U_2 is a plane containing P with $(1,3,-1)$ as a normal vector. The planes U_1 and U_2 are thus parallel to the planes W_1 and W_2 defined by the two equations of the corresponding homogeneous system (see Fig. 14-3). It is not surprising to find that the solution set S is a line that is parallel to the line representing S_0. Parametric equations of the line representing S are

$$x = 1 - 2t, \quad y = 2 + 3t, \quad z = 3 + 7t.$$

Example 14-1 Discuss the non-homogeneous system and the associated homogeneous system:

$$\begin{aligned} r + s + t + u &= 4 \\ s + t &= 2 \\ r + u &= -2 \end{aligned}$$

Solution: If we replace $s + t$ with 2 and $r + u$ with -2 in the first equation, we get $0 = 4$, which is impossible. There is *no* solution to this system. The matrix of the system is

$$[A] = \begin{bmatrix} 1 & 1 & 1 & 1 \\ 0 & 1 & 1 & 0 \\ 1 & 0 & 0 & 1 \end{bmatrix}.$$

The rank of $[A]$ is $r \leqq 3$. In fact, since the first row is simply the sum of the second and third rows, the three rows do not form an independent set. Thus, $r \leqq 2$. Because the second and third rows do form an independent set, $r = 2$. Thus, if S_0 is the solution space of the homogeneous system $[A][\boldsymbol{x}] = [\mathbf{0}]$, we see that

$$\dim S_0 = 4 - 2 = 2.$$

This fact tells us to solve for two of the unknowns in terms of the other two. Because $t = -s$ and $u = -r$, $(r,s,-s,-r)$ is a solution for any number pair r, s. Because

$$(r,s,-s,-r) = (r,0,0,-r) + (0,s,-s,0)$$

we may write

$$\begin{aligned} S_0 &= \{r(1,0,0,-1) + s(0,1,-1,0)\} \\ &= \operatorname{Sp}\{(1,0,0,-1), (0,1,-1,0)\}. \end{aligned}$$

Notice that $\{(1,0,0,-1), (0,1,-1,0)\}$ is a basis for the solution space.

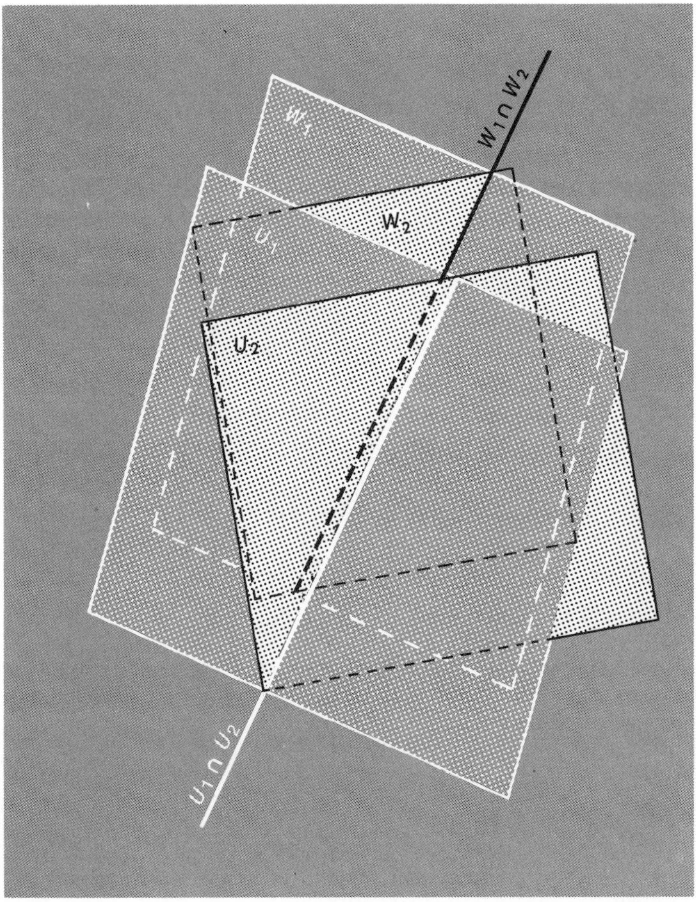

Figure 14-3

In the preceding example the non-homogeneous system $[A][x] = [b]$ did not have a solution. That is to say, in that example there was no vector $\boldsymbol{x}$ whose image was $\boldsymbol{b}$ under the linear map with matrix $[A]$. The non-homogeneous System 14-3 can be written as

$$x^1\boldsymbol{a}_1 + \cdots + x^n\boldsymbol{a}_n = \boldsymbol{b}.$$

From this form we can see that the vector $\boldsymbol{b}$ will be an image of some $\boldsymbol{x}$ precisely when $\boldsymbol{b}$ is a vector in the space spanned by the column vectors. In other words, a solution exists if $\boldsymbol{b}$ is in Sp $\{\boldsymbol{a}_1, \ldots, \boldsymbol{a}_n\}$, and only in that case. But to say that $\boldsymbol{b}$ is in Sp $\{\boldsymbol{a}_1, \ldots, \boldsymbol{a}_n\}$ is to say that Sp $\{\boldsymbol{a}_1, \ldots, \boldsymbol{a}_n, \boldsymbol{b}\}$ and Sp $\{\boldsymbol{a}_1, \ldots, \boldsymbol{a}_n\}$ have the same dimension. This dimension is the rank of $[A]$. The matrix obtained by adding the column vector $[b]$ to $[A]$ is written $[A|b]$, and is called the *augmented matrix* of the non-homogeneous system $[A][x] = [b]$. Our discussion above can now be summarized concisely.

THEOREM 14-2

The system $[A][x] = [b]$ has a solution if, and only if, the rank of the augmented matrix of the system is the same as the rank of the matrix of the system.

Example 14-2 Use Theorem 14-2 to confirm the results obtained in Example 14-1.

Solution: The rank of the augmented matrix

$$\left[\begin{array}{cccc|c} 1 & 1 & 1 & 1 & 4 \\ 0 & 1 & 1 & 0 & 2 \\ 1 & 0 & 0 & 1 & -2 \end{array}\right]$$

of the system in Example 14-1 is 3 (verify this fact). The rank of the matrix was found to be 2, so Theorem 14-2 predicts that no solution can be found to the non-homogeneous system.

PROBLEMS 14

1. Find solutions to the system, and to the associated homogeneous system. Describe the situation geometrically.

   (a) $\begin{aligned} x + y &= 1 \\ x - y &= 1 \\ 2x + y &= 2 \end{aligned}$ (b) $\begin{aligned} x + 2y &= 3 \\ 2x + 4y &= 6 \end{aligned}$

   (c) $\begin{aligned} x - 4y - z &= -3 \\ 2x - 3y + z &= -4 \end{aligned}$ (d) $\begin{aligned} x - 6y + 2z &= 1 \\ -2x + 12y - 4z &= -2 \end{aligned}$

2. Prove that a homogeneous system of m linear equations in n unknowns always has a non-trivial solution if $m < n$.
3. Prove that a non-homogeneous system of m linear equations in n unknowns either has no solution or infinitely many solutions if $m < n$.
4. Find a basis for the solution space of the system:

$$r + s + t + u + v + w = 0$$

$$r - s + t - u + v - w = 0.$$

5. Solve the system (see the preceding problem):

$$r + s + t + u + v + w = 2$$
$$r - s + t - u + v - w = 0.$$

6. Find the ranks of the following matrices:

(a) $\begin{bmatrix} 2 & -3 & 1 & -4 \\ 1 & -4 & -1 & -3 \\ 1 & -9 & -4 & -5 \end{bmatrix}$ (b) $\begin{bmatrix} 2 & -3 & 1 & 3 \\ 1 & -4 & -1 & 4 \\ 1 & -9 & -4 & 5 \end{bmatrix}$

(c) $\begin{bmatrix} 3 & 1 & 2 \\ 2 & 3 & 1 \\ 1 & 2 & 3 \\ 0 & 1 & 0 \end{bmatrix}$ (d) $\begin{bmatrix} 0 & 1 & 0 & 0 \\ 1 & 0 & 1 & 0 \\ 1 & 1 & 1 & 0 \\ 1 & 2 & 1 & 0 \end{bmatrix}$

7. Let $[A]$ be the 3 by 3 matrix that occurs as the first three columns in both 6(a) and 6(b). Does the system $[A][x] = [b]$ have a solution if
(a) $\boldsymbol{b} = (-4, -3, -5)$? (b) $\boldsymbol{b} = (3,4,5)$?

8. Let W be the plane containing the points (0,0,0), (1,1,1), and (−1,1,2). Find an equation for W.

9. Let U be the plane containing the origin with the vector (1,−1,1) as a normal vector. Find the intersection of the plane U and the plane W of the preceding problem.

10. Find the intersection of the plane U of Problem 9, the plane W of Problem 8, and
(a) The XY-plane.
(b) The plane containing the point (1,−1,1) such that the vector (1,−1,1) is a normal vector.
(c) The plane containing the points (1,1,1), (1,2,3), and (0,0,1).

15 SOLVING SYSTEMS. FINDING INVERSES

In the preceding section we proved (Theorem 14-2) that a system

$$[A][x] = [b]$$

of m equations in n unknowns has a solution if, and only if, the ranks of the augmented matrix and the coefficient matrix are the same. In order to use that theorem we must be able to find the rank of a matrix. In this section a technique that simplifies the task of determining the rank of a matrix will be described. This same technique is the basis for a practical method of solving systems of equations. It is not our aim to present you with problems to solve in order to help you become an efficient system-solver. Instead we want to give you some insight into the ideas that are the basis of efficient numerical methods for solving systems using computers.

Let $[A]$ be an m (row) by n (column) matrix. Using row vectors, we can write

$$[A] = \begin{bmatrix} \boldsymbol{a}^1 \\ \cdot \\ \cdot \\ \cdot \\ \boldsymbol{a}^m \end{bmatrix}.$$

Then rank $[A] = \dim \operatorname{Sp} \{\boldsymbol{a}^1, \ldots, \boldsymbol{a}^m\}$.

The order in which the row vectors are written if of no consequence in determining the space generated by them. Thus, two rows of a matrix can be interchanged, and the rank is unchanged.

If $c \neq 0$, then

$$\operatorname{Sp} \{\boldsymbol{a}^1, \ldots, c\boldsymbol{a}^k, \ldots, \boldsymbol{a}^m\} = \operatorname{Sp} \{\boldsymbol{a}^1, \ldots, \boldsymbol{a}^k, \ldots, \boldsymbol{a}^m\}.$$

Thus, the rank of a matrix is unaffected by multiplying a row by a non-zero number.

We can use Theorem 2-1 to show that

$$\operatorname{Sp} \{\boldsymbol{a}^1, \ldots, \boldsymbol{a}^j + \boldsymbol{a}^k, \ldots, \boldsymbol{a}^k, \ldots, \boldsymbol{a}^m\} = \operatorname{Sp} \{\boldsymbol{a}^1, \ldots, \boldsymbol{a}^j, \ldots, \boldsymbol{a}^k, \ldots, \boldsymbol{a}^m\}.$$

Thus, the rank of a matrix is unchanged if one row vector is replaced by the sum of that row vector and any other row vector. Summarizing:

THEOREM 15-1

The matrix obtained from $[A]$ by
(i) Interchanging any two row vectors;
(ii) Multiplying any row vector by a non-zero number;
(iii) Replacing a row vector by the sum of itself and another row;
has the same rank as $[A]$.

The use of this theorem will be illustrated by an example. In actual practice Operations (ii) and (iii) of Theorem 15-1 are often combined, as you will see. The basic idea is to use these operations to replace $[A]$ with a matrix in which the number of independent rows can be easily determined. Let

$$[A] = \begin{bmatrix} 2 & 1 & 2 \\ 2 & -4 & 1 \\ 1 & 1 & 1 \end{bmatrix}.$$

If we multiply the third row by -2, then add it to the first row, and subtract the third row from the second row, we get a new matrix whose rank is equal to the rank of $[A]$. The operations we have described will be denoted as follows:

$$\begin{bmatrix} 2 & 1 & 2 \\ 2 & -4 & 1 \\ 1 & 1 & 1 \end{bmatrix} \xrightarrow[\boxed{-III + II}]{\boxed{-2III + I}} \begin{bmatrix} 0 & -1 & 0 \\ 1 & -5 & 0 \\ 1 & 1 & 1 \end{bmatrix}.$$

Now we can carry out some more row vector manipulations on the resulting matrix. Each manipulation is one of the operations in Theorem 15-1, or a combination of them, so that each new matrix has the same rank as the old.

$$\begin{bmatrix} 0 & -1 & 0 \\ 1 & -5 & 0 \\ 1 & 1 & 1 \end{bmatrix} \xrightarrow{\boxed{5I - II}} \begin{bmatrix} -1 & 0 & 0 \\ 1 & -5 & 0 \\ 1 & 1 & 1 \end{bmatrix} \xrightarrow[\boxed{I + III}]{\boxed{I + II}} \begin{bmatrix} -1 & 0 & 0 \\ 0 & -5 & 0 \\ 0 & 1 & 1 \end{bmatrix} -$$

$$\xrightarrow{\boxed{III + II/5}} \begin{bmatrix} -1 & 0 & 0 \\ 0 & -5 & 0 \\ 0 & 0 & 1 \end{bmatrix} \xrightarrow[\boxed{II/-5}]{\boxed{I/-1}} \begin{bmatrix} 1 & 0 & 0 \\ 0 & 1 & 0 \\ 0 & 0 & 1 \end{bmatrix}.$$

The rows of the final matrix are independent, so the rank of that matrix is 3. Thus, rank $[A] = 3$.

Example 15-1 Determine the rank of the matrix

$$[A] = \begin{bmatrix} 2 & -1 & 1 \\ 1 & -2 & 3 \\ 3 & 0 & -1 \end{bmatrix}.$$

Solution:

$$\begin{bmatrix} 2 & -1 & 1 \\ 1 & -2 & 3 \\ 3 & 0 & -1 \end{bmatrix} \xrightarrow[\boxed{3III + II}]{\boxed{III + I}} \begin{bmatrix} 5 & -1 & 0 \\ 10 & -2 & 0 \\ 3 & 0 & -1 \end{bmatrix} -$$

$$\xrightarrow{\boxed{I - II/2}} \begin{bmatrix} 0 & 0 & 0 \\ 5 & -1 & 0 \\ 3 & 0 & -1 \end{bmatrix}$$
$$\xrightarrow{\boxed{II/2}}$$

It is easy to see that the rank of the final matrix is 2. Thus, rank $[A] = 2$.

Let us interpret the operations in Theorem 15-1 when the matrix to which they are applied is the augmented matrix $[A|\boldsymbol{b}]$ of a system of equations. You can easily verify that each operation yields the augmented matrix of a system equivalent to the original system. Let us illustrate this fact with an example. The matrix

$$[A|\boldsymbol{b}] = \left[\begin{array}{ccc|c} 1 & -6 & 2 & 0 \\ 2 & -3 & 1 & 1 \\ 3 & 4 & -1 & 0 \end{array}\right] \tag{15-1}$$

is the augmented matrix of the system

$$\begin{aligned} x - 6y + 2z &= 0 \\ 2x - 3y + z &= 1 \\ 3x + 4y - z &= 0. \end{aligned} \tag{15-2}$$

The matrix transition

$$\left[\begin{array}{ccc|c} 1 & -6 & 2 & 0 \\ 2 & -3 & 1 & 1 \\ 3 & 4 & -1 & 0 \end{array}\right] \begin{array}{c} \xrightarrow{\boxed{2III + I}} \\ \xrightarrow{\boxed{III + II}} \\ \end{array} \left[\begin{array}{ccc|c} 7 & 2 & 0 & 0 \\ 5 & 1 & 0 & 1 \\ 3 & 4 & -1 & 0 \end{array}\right]$$

is merely an abbreviated way of saying, "Replace the first equation by the sum of the first equation and twice the third; and replace the second equation by the sum of the second and third equations in order to get the system

$$\begin{aligned} 7x + 2y &= 0 \\ 5x + y &= 1 \\ 3x + 4y - z &= 0." \end{aligned}$$

This system has the same solution as the original System 15-2 and it is easier to solve. Let us construct another equivalent system that is even easier to solve by using some more row manipulations on the augmented matrix we obtained above.

$$\left[\begin{array}{ccc|c} 7 & 2 & 0 & 0 \\ 5 & 1 & 0 & 1 \\ 3 & 4 & -1 & 0 \end{array}\right] \xrightarrow{\boxed{I-2II}} \left[\begin{array}{ccc|c} -3 & 0 & 0 & -2 \\ 5 & 1 & 0 & 1 \\ 3 & 4 & -1 & 0 \end{array}\right] -$$

(15-3)
$$\begin{array}{l} \\ \xrightarrow{\boxed{5I+3II}} \\ \xrightarrow{\boxed{I+III}} \end{array} \left[\begin{array}{ccc|c} -3 & 0 & 0 & -2 \\ 0 & 3 & 0 & -7 \\ 0 & 4 & -1 & -2 \end{array}\right] \xrightarrow{\boxed{4II+3III}}$$

$$\rightarrow \left[\begin{array}{ccc|c} -3 & 0 & 0 & -2 \\ 0 & 3 & 0 & -7 \\ 0 & 0 & -3 & 22 \end{array}\right] \begin{array}{l} \xrightarrow{\boxed{I/-3}} \\ \xrightarrow{\boxed{II/3}} \\ \xrightarrow{\boxed{III/-3}} \end{array} \left[\begin{array}{ccc|c} 1 & 0 & 0 & \frac{2}{3} \\ 0 & 1 & 0 & -\frac{7}{3} \\ 0 & 0 & 1 & -\frac{22}{3} \end{array}\right].$$

The "reduced system" is

$$\begin{aligned} x \quad &= \tfrac{2}{3} \\ y &= -\tfrac{7}{3} \\ z &= -\tfrac{22}{3}, \end{aligned}$$

whose solution is $(\frac{2}{3}, -\frac{7}{3}, -\frac{22}{3})$.

Although the technique just described is useful for solving m equations in n unknowns when $m \neq n$, our main interest at the moment is when $m = n$; that is, the case of n equations in n unknowns. All the preceding statements are true if $[A]$ is a square matrix, but even more can be said in this case.

Recall that the non-homogeneous equation $[A][\boldsymbol{x}] = [\boldsymbol{b}]$ either had no solution, or if it had one solution $\boldsymbol{x}_1$, then the set S of all solutions was

$$S = \boldsymbol{x}_1 + S_0,$$

where S_0 is the solution space of the homogeneous equation

$$[A][\boldsymbol{x}] = [\boldsymbol{0}].$$

Furthermore,

(15-4) $$\dim S_0 = n - \operatorname{rank}[A].$$

If F is the linear operator on R^n whose matrix is $[A]$, then

$$\text{rank } [A] = \dim F(R^n) = n - \dim K(F), \tag{15-5}$$

where $K(F)$ is the kernel of F. These facts will be used to prove the following theorem.

THEOREM 15-2

Let $[A][x] = [b]$ be a system of n equations in n unknowns. Each of the following implies the other two.

(i) $[A][x] = [b]$ has a unique solution.
(ii) rank $[A] = n$.
(iii) $[A]$ is invertible.

Proof: Our method of proof is to show that (i) implies (ii); (ii) implies (iii); and (iii) implies (i).

(i) implies (ii). If the solution is unique, then $S_0 = \{\mathbf{0}\}$, so $\dim S_0 = 0$ and rank $[A] = n$ from Equation 15-4.

(ii) implies (iii). If rank $[A] = n$, then $\dim K(F) = 0$ from Equation 15-5, so $K(F) = \{\mathbf{0}\}$. Hence, F is invertible by Theorem 6-2. Thus, $[F] = [A]$ is invertible.

(iii) implies (i). If $[A]^{-1}$ exists, it is unique. If $[A][x] = [b]$, then $[A]^{-1}[A][x] = [A]^{-1}[b]$. So $[x] = [A]^{-1}[b]$ is uniquely determined by $[A]$ and $[b]$. ∎

In the proof of the preceding theorem we saw that if $[A]$ is invertible, then $[x] = [A]^{-1}[b]$ is the solution to the equation $[A][x] = [b]$. Thus, a solution of a system of equations can be found by finding the inverse of a matrix. Of course, as we pointed out in Section 9, to find $[A]^{-1}$ we must solve the matrix equation

$$[A][X] = [I] = [e_1 \ldots e_n], \tag{15-6}$$

where $\{e_1, \ldots, e_n\}$ is the natural basis for R^n. If x_j is the vector in R^n that is in column j of the matrix $[X]$, then the matrix Equation 15-6 can be written

$$[A][x_1 \ldots x_n] = [e_1 \ldots e_n].$$

Thus, Equation 15-6 is equivalent to n systems of n equations:

$$[A][x_j] = [e_j] \quad j = 1, \ldots, n.$$

To solve the first system we form the augmented matrix $[A|e_1]$ and use row manipulations to transform it to $[I|x_1]$. The vector x_1 is the vector in the first column of $[A]^{-1}$. In a similar way we find the other columns of $[A]^{-1}$. For example, if $[A]$ is the matrix of System 15-2, the augmented matrix $[A|e_2]$ is the matrix in Equation 15-1. The solution to System 15-2 is $x_2 = (\frac{2}{3}, -\frac{7}{3}, -\frac{22}{3})$, and x_2 is the last column vector in the final matrix of the transitions carried out in Equations 15-3. This column is the second column of $[A]^{-1}$:

$$[A]^{-1} = \begin{bmatrix} * & \frac{2}{3} & * \\ * & -\frac{7}{3} & * \\ * & -\frac{22}{3} & * \end{bmatrix}.$$

If we were to solve $[A|e_1]$ or $[A|e_3]$, we would carry out exactly the same sequence of row manipulations that we did to reduce $[A|e_2]$ to $[I|x_2]$. Thus, we can do the whole job at once. In a three by three case we start with $[A|e_1\ e_2\ e_3]$ and use row manipulations to reduce $[A]$ to $[I]$. The matrix that appears to the right of the vertical line is $[A]^{-1}$. Symbolically,

$$[A|I] \to [I|A^{-1}].$$

Example 15-2

$$\text{Find} \begin{bmatrix} 2 & 1 \\ 1 & 1 \end{bmatrix}^{-1}.$$

Solution:

$$\left[\begin{array}{cc|cc} 2 & 1 & 1 & 0 \\ 1 & 1 & 0 & 1 \end{array}\right] \xrightarrow{\boxed{I - III}} \left[\begin{array}{cc|cc} 1 & 0 & 1 & -1 \\ 1 & 1 & 0 & 1 \end{array}\right] \xrightarrow{\boxed{II - I}} \left[\begin{array}{cc|cc} 1 & 0 & 1 & -1 \\ 0 & 1 & -1 & 2 \end{array}\right].$$

Thus,

$$\begin{bmatrix} 2 & 1 \\ 1 & 1 \end{bmatrix}^{-1} = \begin{bmatrix} 1 & -1 \\ -1 & 2 \end{bmatrix}.$$

With an n by n matrix $[A]$, it is not always easy to tell at a glance whether or not it is invertible. We could find the rank of $[A]$ and then use Theorem 15-2, but the only practical way we have to find rank $[A]$ is to use row manipulations and reduce $[A]$ to a simpler form. So we might as well just write down $[A|I]$ and try to reduce the matrix on the left to $[I]$. If we can, $[A]^{-1}$ exists. The reduction process will work precisely when rank $[A] = n$. Thus, the process fails when the rows of $[A]$ form a dependent set of vectors in R^n. If $\boldsymbol{a}^1, \ldots, \boldsymbol{a}^n$ is a dependent set, then one of them is a linear combination of the others. By rearranging them, if necessary, we can write

$$\boldsymbol{a}^1 = c_2\boldsymbol{a}^2 + \cdots + c_n\boldsymbol{a}^n.$$

Replacing the first row of $[A]$ with

$$\boldsymbol{a}^1 - c_2\boldsymbol{a}^2 - \cdots - c_n\boldsymbol{a}^n$$

yields a matrix whose first row is the zero vector. Thus, the thing to do is to try to reduce $[A|I]$ to $[I|A^{-1}]$. If in the process you obtain a row of zeros, you can stop and conclude that $[A]^{-1}$ does not exist.

Example 15-3 Try to find the inverse of the matrix in Example 15-1 by using row manipulations.

Solution: The row manipulations used in Example 15-1 yield

$$\left[\begin{array}{rrr|rrr} 2 & -1 & 1 & 1 & 0 & 0 \\ 1 & -2 & 3 & 0 & 1 & 0 \\ 3 & 0 & -1 & 0 & 0 & 1 \end{array}\right] \rightarrow \left[\begin{array}{rrr|rrr} 0 & 0 & 0 & 1 & -\frac{1}{2} & -\frac{1}{2} \\ 5 & -1 & 0 & 0 & \frac{1}{2} & \frac{3}{2} \\ 3 & 0 & -1 & 0 & 0 & 1 \end{array}\right].$$

Now we can go no further. Of course, in this case we knew from Example 15-1 that the rank of our matrix was less than 3, so that the inverse did not exist. But this example illustrates the fact that we can try to find $[A]^{-1}$ without knowing whether it exists or not and find out if it exists in the process.

PROBLEMS 15

1. Determine the rank of the matrix

(a) $\begin{bmatrix} 1 & -1 & 1 & -1 \\ -1 & 1 & -1 & 1 \\ 1 & 1 & 1 & 1 \end{bmatrix}$ (b) $\begin{bmatrix} 1 & 0 & 1 & 1 & -1 \\ 1 & 1 & 0 & 0 & -1 \\ 0 & 1 & 0 & 1 & -1 \\ 0 & 0 & 1 & 0 & 1 \end{bmatrix}$

(c) $\begin{bmatrix} 1 & 0 & 1 & 0 & 2 & 1 \\ 0 & 0 & 0 & 1 & 1 & 1 \\ 1 & 0 & 1 & 0 & 1 & 0 \\ 1 & 1 & 0 & 3 & 3 & 3 \\ 2 & 1 & 1 & 3 & 4 & 3 \end{bmatrix}$ (d) $\begin{bmatrix} 2 & 1 & 1 & 1 \\ -2 & -3 & -3 & 1 \\ 6 & 3 & 3 & 3 \\ 6 & 5 & 5 & 1 \end{bmatrix}$

2. We found the second column of $[A]^{-1}$ if $[A]$ is the matrix of System 15-2. Find the other two columns.

3. Use row manipulations (of the augmented matrix) to solve, if possible,

(a) $\begin{aligned} x - y + 2z &= 4 \\ x + 2y + z &= 0 \\ 2x + 3y - z &= -2 \end{aligned}$ (b) $\begin{aligned} y &= x + z \\ y &= 3 + 2x \\ 4y &= 2z - x - 1 \end{aligned}$

(c) $\begin{aligned} x + y &= 2 \\ y + z &= -1 \\ z + w &= 0 \\ x + z &= y + w \end{aligned}$ (d) $\begin{aligned} 2x - y + z &= 1 \\ x + 2y - z &= 3 \\ x + 7y - 4z &= 8 \end{aligned}$

(e) $\begin{aligned} 3x + y + 2z &= 4 \\ 2x + 3y + z &= 5 \\ x + 2y + 3z &= 6 \\ -x - y + 4z &= 7 \end{aligned}$ (f) $\begin{aligned} 2x - 3y + z + 3w &= -1 \\ x - 4y - z + 4w &= 0 \\ x - 9y - 4z + 5w &= 1 \end{aligned}$

4. Find the inverse of the matrix, if it exists.

(a) $\begin{bmatrix} 0 & 1 & 0 & 0 \\ 1 & 0 & 0 & 0 \\ 0 & 0 & 0 & 1 \\ 0 & 0 & 1 & 0 \end{bmatrix}$ (b) $\begin{bmatrix} 2 & 1 & 2 \\ 1 & 1 & 1 \\ 2 & -4 & 1 \end{bmatrix}$

(c) $\begin{bmatrix} 2 & 1 \\ 5 & 3 \end{bmatrix}$ (d) $\begin{bmatrix} 1 & 0 & 0 \\ 2 & 1 & 0 \\ 3 & 2 & 1 \end{bmatrix}$

(e) $\begin{bmatrix} 2 & 2 & 1 \\ 1 & -4 & 1 \\ 2 & 1 & 1 \end{bmatrix}$ (f) $\begin{bmatrix} -3 & 1 & 0 & 0 \\ -8 & 3 & 0 & 0 \\ 0 & 0 & 4 & 9 \\ 0 & 0 & 1 & 2 \end{bmatrix}$

5. Use row manipulations to find a formula for $\begin{bmatrix} a & b \\ c & d \end{bmatrix}^{-1}$. State a necessary and sufficient condition in terms of the number $ad - bc$ for this inverse matrix to exist.

6. Let F be a linear operator in a space with a basis $\{e_1, e_2, e_3\}$. Determine whether or not F is an invertible operator, and if it is, find $F^{-1}(e_1)$, $F^{-1}(e_2)$, and $F^{-1}(e_3)$, if F is defined by the equations:
(a) $F(e_1) = e_1 + e_2$, $F(e_2) = e_2 + e_3$, $F(e_3) = e_3 + e_1$
(b) $F(x^1,x^2,x^3) = (2x^1 + x^2, x^2 + 2x^3, x^3 + 2x^1)$
(c) $F(x^1,x^2,x^3) = (x^1 + x^3, x^2 - x^1, x^2 + x^3)$
(d) $F(e_1) = F(e_2) = e_3$, $F(e_3) = e_1 + e_2$

16 TRIANGULAR DECOMPOSITION

A system of n linear equations in n unknowns can be described by an augmented matrix $[A|b]$ as in Equation 15-1. Such a system can be solved by using the row operations described in Theorem 15-1 to obtain an augmented matrix of an equivalent system that is simpler. In Section 15 the matrix $[A]$ was reduced to a diagonal matrix (whenever it was possible) to solve the system. It is just as easy to stop that process when the coefficient matrix is reduced to triangular form because a triangular system is easily solved by a substitution procedure. The process of reducing a system to a triangular system is called a *Gaussian Elimination* procedure.

A triangular system may be either a lower or an upper triangular system. The system

$$\begin{aligned} 2x \qquad &= 2 \\ x + 3y &= 7 \end{aligned}$$

is a lower triangular system, and the system

$$\begin{aligned} 5x + y + z &= 6 \\ 4y - z &= -2 \\ 3z &= 6 \end{aligned}$$

is an upper triangular system. The coefficient matrices of triangular systems are called triangular matrices.

DEFINITION 16-1

A matrix $[L]$ is a *lower triangular matrix* if each number above the main diagonal is zero; that is, if $l^i_j = 0$ for $j > i$. A matrix $[U]$ is an upper triangular matrix if $u^i_j = 0$ for $i > j$. The symbols $[L]$ and $[U]$ will always stand for lower and upper triangular matrices.

Let $[A|\boldsymbol{b}]$ be the augmented matrix of a system of n linear equations in n unknowns. Suppose that we could find triangular matrices such that $[A] = [L][U]$. Then the system

$$[A][\boldsymbol{x}] = [\boldsymbol{b}] \tag{16-1}$$

can be written

$$[L][U][\boldsymbol{x}] = [\boldsymbol{b}].$$

If we let

$$[U][\boldsymbol{x}] = [\boldsymbol{y}], \tag{16-2}$$

then

$$[L][\boldsymbol{y}] = [\boldsymbol{b}]. \tag{16-3}$$

Given $[L]$, $[U]$, and $[\boldsymbol{b}]$ we can solve first the triangular System 16-3 for $[\boldsymbol{y}]$ and then solve the triangular System 16-2 for $[\boldsymbol{x}]$ to obtain the solution to System 16-1. Solving Systems 16-2 and 16-3 is accomplished easily by using a substitution routine. The real work involved in this method of solving System 16-1 is the effort to find the matrices $[L]$ and $[U]$. It is not even obvious that such matrices exist for every matrix $[A]$. As a matter of fact they do exist, and we can even specify that the matrix $[L]$ have the number 1 in each main diagonal position. We will offer a "constructive proof" of this fact by giving rules for calculating $[L]$ and $[U]$ for a given $[A]$. To discover these rules, suppose that $[A] = [L][U]$ and that $[L]$ has 1's on its main diagonal. If the numbers in row i and column j in the matrices $[A]$, $[L]$, and $[U]$ are labeled a^i_j, l^i_j, and u^i_j respectively, then it follows from the rules for matrix multiplication that

$$a^i_j = l^i_\alpha u^\alpha_j = l^i_1 u^1_j + \cdots + l^i_n u^n_j \tag{16-4}$$

We can write out these equations in a step by step manner to solve for the numbers in [L] and [U]. Let us illustrate the procedure with an example.

Example 16-1 Write out and solve Equations 16-4 if

$$[A] = \begin{bmatrix} 2 & 1 & 0 \\ -8 & -5 & 1 \\ -4 & -2 & 3 \end{bmatrix}.$$

Solution: We want to find matrices [L] and [U] such that

$$\begin{bmatrix} 1 & 0 & 0 \\ l_1^2 & 1 & 0 \\ l_1^3 & l_2^3 & 1 \end{bmatrix} \begin{bmatrix} u_1^1 & u_2^1 & u_3^1 \\ 0 & u_2^2 & u_3^2 \\ 0 & 0 & u_3^3 \end{bmatrix} = \begin{bmatrix} 2 & 1 & 0 \\ -8 & -5 & 1 \\ -4 & -2 & 3 \end{bmatrix};$$

that is,

$$\begin{bmatrix} u_1^1 & u_2^1 & u_3^1 \\ l_1^2 u_1^1 & l_1^2 u_2^1 + u_2^2 & l_1^2 u_3^1 + u_3^2 \\ l_1^3 u_1^1 & l_1^3 u_2^1 + l_2^3 u_2^2 & l_1^3 u_3^1 + l_2^3 u_3^2 + u_3^3 \end{bmatrix} = [A].$$

Equating the first columns of these two matrices yields

$$u_1^1 = 2$$

$$2l_1^2 = -8, \text{ so } l_1^2 = -4$$

$$2l_1^3 = -4, \text{ so } l_1^3 = -2.$$

Equating the second columns gives us

$$u_2^1 = 1$$

$$l_1^2 + u_2^2 = -5, \text{ so } u_2^2 = -1$$

$$l_1^3 - l_2^3 = -2, \text{ so } l_2^3 = 0.$$

Setting the two third columns equal to each other tells us that

$$u_3^1 = 0$$

$$u_3^2 = 1$$

$$l_2^3 + u_3^3 = 3, \text{ so } u_3^3 = 3.$$

Thus we can write

$$\begin{bmatrix} 2 & 1 & 0 \\ -8 & -5 & 1 \\ -4 & -2 & 3 \end{bmatrix} = \begin{bmatrix} 1 & 0 & 0 \\ -4 & 1 & 0 \\ -2 & 0 & 1 \end{bmatrix} \begin{bmatrix} 2 & 1 & 0 \\ 0 & -1 & 1 \\ 0 & 0 & 3 \end{bmatrix}.$$

Now we return to the solution of Equations 16-4 in general. First we set $j = 1$. Since $u_j^k = 0$ if $k > j$, Equations 16-4 tell us that

$$a_1^i = l_1^i u_1^1, \quad i = 1, \ldots, n. \tag{16-5}$$

Thus $u_1^1 = a_1^1$, and for $i > 1$ we can solve these equations for l_1^i, provided that $u_1^1 \neq 0$. If $u_1^1 = 0$, but $a_1^i \neq 0$ for some number i, then an interchange of row i and row 1 in $[A]$ before we start solving Equations 16-5 will provide us with a "new" u_1^1 that is not zero. If $\boldsymbol{a}_1 = 0$; that is, if the first column of $[A]$ is zero, then we set

$$u_1^1 = l_1^2 = \cdots = l_1^n = 0,$$

and Equations 16-5 are satisfied.

Next, set $i = 1$ in Equations 16-4 to obtain

$$a_j^1 = u_j^1, \quad j = 2, \ldots, n. \tag{16-6}$$

Up to this point we have found the first column of $[L]$ and the first row of $[U]$ such that $[L][U] = [B]$, where either $[B] = [A]$ or $[B]$ is a matrix obtained from $[A]$ by interchanging the first row and some other row. Let b_j^i be the number in row i and column j of $[B]$. Then Equations 16-5 and 16-6 are $b_1^i = l_1^i u_1^1$ and $b_j^1 = u_j^1$.

Next we find the second column of $[L]$. Set $j = 2$ in Equations 16-4 (with $[A]$ replaced by $[B]$) to get

$$b_2^i = l_1^i u_2^1 + l_2^i u_2^2. \tag{16-7}$$

It follows that $u_2^2 = b_2^2 - l_1^2 u_2^1$, and for $i > 2$ we can solve for l_2^i unless $u_2^2 = 0$. If $u_2^2 = 0$, then we interchange row 2 with some row below it (in both the matrix $[B]$ and in the matrix $[L]$ to try and get a new $u_2^2 \neq 0$. If $b_2^i - l_2^i u_2^1 = 0$ for $i = 2, \ldots, n$, then we set

$$u_2^2 = l_2^3 = \cdots\cdots = l_2^n = 0$$

and Equations 16-7 are satisfied. Thus we have

$$l_2^i u_2^2 = c_2^i - l_1^i u_2^1$$

where c_j^i is a number in a matrix $[C]$ that is either the matrix $[B]$ or is obtained from that matrix by interchanging the second row with some row below it, and the corresponding rows in the $[L]$ matrix are also interchanged. Notice that $c_j^1 = b_j^1$ because the first row is kept fixed in this step. Example 16-2 illustrates how row interchanges are made.

Now set $i = 2$ in Equations 16-4 to get

$$u_j^2 = c_j^2 - l_1^2 u_j^1, \quad j = 3, \ldots, n. \tag{16-8}$$

And so it goes. Step by step we can compute a column of $[L]$ and a row of $[U]$. Except for giving a formal induction step we have completed the proof of the following basic decomposition theorem.

THEOREM 16-1

Let $[PA]$ denote a matrix obtained from a square matrix $[A]$ by a permutation of the n rows of $[A]$. For any given $[A]$ there is a lower triangular matrix $[L]$ with one's on the main diagonal, an upper triangular matrix $[U]$, and a matrix $[PA]$ such that

$$[PA] = [L][U].$$

Example 16-2 Find the triangular decomposition of the matrix

$$[A] = \begin{bmatrix} 1 & 2 & -3 & 4 \\ -1 & -2 & 3 & -1 \\ 3 & 6 & -9 & 10 \\ 2 & 4 & -4 & 7 \end{bmatrix}.$$

Solution: Equations 16-5 and 16-6 tell us that

$$u_1^1 = 1, l_1^2 = -1, l_1^3 = 3, l_1^4 = 2, u_2^1 = 2, u_3^1 = -3, \text{ and } u_4^1 = 4.$$

Since no interchange of rows was required, the numbers b_2^i in Equations 16-7 are the numbers a_2^i, and for $i = 2$ we have

$$u_2^2 = a_2^2 - l_1^2 u_2^1 = -2 - (-1)(2) = 0.$$

Our next step is to carry out the computations on the right sides of these equations with a_2^2 and l_1^2 replaced with a_2^3 and l_1^3, but we find that

$$a_2^3 - l_1^3 u_2^1 = 6 - (3)(2) = 0.$$

So we try again, using the fourth row.

$$a_2^4 - l_1^4 u_2^1 = 4 - (2)(2) = 0.$$

Thus, we cannot find a row interchange that leads to a non-zero u_2^2. Thus we set

$$u_2^2 = l_2^3 = l_2^4 = 0.$$

Since we have no row interchanges yet, Equations 16-8 tell us that

$$u_3^2 = 3 - (-1)(-3) = 0,$$

and

$$u_4^2 = -1 - (-1)(4) = 3.$$

Now we compute u_3^3 using Equations 16-4 with $i = j = 3$ to find that

$$u_3^3 = a_3^3 - l_1^3 u_3^1 - l_2^3 u_3^2 = -9 - (3)(-3) - (0)(0) = 0.$$

If we make the same computation with rows 3 and 4 interchanged in both $[A]$ and $[L]$ we get

$$a_3^4 - l_1^4 u_3^1 - l_2^4 u_3^2 = -4 - (2)(-3) - (0)(0) = 2,$$

so we will make this interchange and call our new matrix $[B]$. Thus $u_3^3 = 2$. Using Equations 16-4 with $i = 4$ and $j = 3$ we get

$$l_3^4 = (b_3^4 - l_1^4 u_3^1 - l_2^4 u_3^2)/u_3^3 = (-9 - (3)(-3) - (0)(0) = 0.$$

Notice that $b_3^4 = a_3^3$ and that l_1^4 and l_2^4 are the numbers previously computed for l_1^3 and l_2^3. Next, set $j = 4$ and $i = 3,4$ in Equations 16-4 to get

$$u_4^3 = b_4^3 - l_1^3 u_4^1 - l_2^3 u_4^2 = 7 - (2)(4) - (0)(3) = -1,$$

and

$$u_4^4 = b_4^4 - l_1^4 u_4^1 - l_2^4 u_4^2 - l_3^4 u_4^3 = 10 - (3)(4) - (0)(3) - (0)(-1) = -2.$$

Thus we have the decomposition

$$\begin{bmatrix} 1 & 2 & -3 & 4 \\ -1 & -2 & 3 & -1 \\ 2 & 4 & -4 & 7 \\ 3 & 6 & -9 & 10 \end{bmatrix} = \begin{bmatrix} 1 & 0 & 0 & 0 \\ -1 & 1 & 0 & 0 \\ 2 & 0 & 1 & 0 \\ 3 & 0 & 0 & 1 \end{bmatrix} \begin{bmatrix} 1 & 2 & -3 & 4 \\ 0 & 0 & 0 & 3 \\ 0 & 0 & 2 & -1 \\ 0 & 0 & 0 & -2 \end{bmatrix}.$$

This decomposition is not unique since we arbitrarily set $l_2^3 = l_2^4 = 0$ at one stage of our computations. We might have set, for example, $l_2^3 = 1$ and $l_2^4 = 0$ at that stage. Then (recall that we later interchanged the third and fourth rows of $[L]$) you can easily verify that the only changes in our final $[L]$ and $[U]$ matrices are that $l_2^4 = 1$ instead of 0, and $u_4^4 = -5$ instead of -2.

There are n^2 numbers that need to be specified in order to define $[L]$ and $[U]$. These numbers can be placed in an n by n matrix in a natural manner. If $[A] = [L][U]$, we define $[LU]$ to be the n by n matrix obtained by replacing the zeros below the main diagonal of $[U]$ with the corresponding numbers in $[L]$. Thus, for a given $[A]$, an $[LU]$ matrix associated with $[A]$ is obtained by finding the triangular decomposition and setting

$$[LU] = [L] - [I] + [U].$$

The numbers in $[LU]$ are supplied by the formula

(16-9)
$$lu_j^i = \begin{cases} u_j^i & \text{if} \quad i \leqq j \\ l_j^i & \text{if} \quad i > j \end{cases}$$

Example 16-3 Find an $[LU]$ matrix for the matrix

$$[A] = \begin{bmatrix} 1 & 2 & 3 \\ 4 & 13 & 18 \\ 7 & 54 & 78 \end{bmatrix}.$$

Solution: Use Equations 16-4 with $j = 1$ to get $u_1^1 = a_1^1 = 1$, $l_1^2 = a_1^2/u_1^1 = 4$, and $l_1^3 = a_1^3/u_1^1 = 7$. Next, use Equations 16-4 with $i = 1$ to get

$$u_2^1 = a_2^1 = 2 \quad \text{and} \quad u_3^1 = a_3^1 = 3.$$

Next use Equations 16-4 with $j = 2$ to obtain

$$u_2^2 = a_2^2 - l_1^2 u_2^1 = 13 - 8 = 5,$$

and

$$l_2^3 = (u_2^3 - l_1^3 u_2^1)/u_2^2 = (54 - 14)/5 = 8.$$

By setting $i = 2$ in Equation 16-4 we find that

$$u_3^2 = a_3^2 - l_1^2 u_3^1 = 18 - 12 = 6.$$

Finally, we can use Equation 16-4 with $i = 3$ to get

$$u_3^3 = a_3^3 - l_1^3 u_3^1 - l_2^3 u_3^2 = 78 - 21 - 48 = 9.$$

It follows that

$$[L] = \begin{bmatrix} 1 & 0 & 0 \\ 4 & 1 & 0 \\ 7 & 8 & 1 \end{bmatrix} \quad \text{and} \quad [U] = \begin{bmatrix} 1 & 2 & 3 \\ 0 & 5 & 6 \\ 0 & 0 & 9 \end{bmatrix}.$$

Thus

$$[LU] = \begin{bmatrix} 1 & 2 & 3 \\ 4 & 5 & 6 \\ 7 & 8 & 9 \end{bmatrix}.$$

Calculating an $[LU]$ matrix is a good job for a computer. The computation can be described by means of flow charts or programs. In Appendix A there are such flow charts and programs together with a brief explanation about how a flow chart is obtained for Equations 16-4.

PROBLEMS 16

1. Solve the following lower triangular systems.

   (a) $\begin{aligned} 2x \quad\quad\quad\; &= 6 \\ x - 3y \quad\; &= -3 \\ x - y + 2z &= 3 \end{aligned}$ (b) $\begin{aligned} x + 1 &= 0 \\ 2x + y &= 0 \\ 2z - 3x &= 0 \\ 3w + z &= 0 \end{aligned}$

2. Solve the following upper triangular systems.

   (a) $\begin{aligned} x + y + 3z &= 3 \\ y - 2z &= -2 \\ 5z &= 5 \end{aligned}$ (b) $\begin{aligned} x + y + w + z &= 2 \\ 2y + 2w - z &= 0 \\ z &= 0 \end{aligned}$

3. Write out Equations 16-4 and use them to find $[L]$ and $[U]$ matrices such that $[A] = [L][U]$ if $[A]$ is equal to:

   (a) $\begin{bmatrix} 1 & 1 \\ 2 & 2 \end{bmatrix}$ (b) $\begin{bmatrix} -1 & 1 \\ 0 & 5 \end{bmatrix}$

   (c) $\begin{bmatrix} 1 & 1 & 0 \\ 1 & 2 & 1 \\ 1 & 2 & 1 \end{bmatrix}$ (d) $\begin{bmatrix} -1 & 0 & 3 \\ 0 & -1 & -5 \\ -3 & -2 & 1 \end{bmatrix}.$

4. Write out the $[LU]$ matrix for each of the matrices in the preceding problem.
5. Find the $[LU]$ matrix for:

(a) $\begin{bmatrix} 0 & 0 & 0 & 1 \\ 0 & 0 & 1 & 1 \\ 0 & 1 & 1 & 1 \\ 1 & 0 & 0 & 0 \end{bmatrix}$ (b) $\begin{bmatrix} 1 & 0 & 1 & 0 \\ 0 & 1 & 0 & 1 \\ 1 & 0 & 1 & 0 \\ 0 & 1 & 0 & 1 \end{bmatrix}$.

17 GAUSSIAN ELIMINATION

Computing an $[LU]$ matrix for $[A]$ is essentially a Gaussian Elimination procedure. Let us first consider the operations of Theorem 15-1 in terms of matrix multiplications. If a matrix is obtained from $[A]$ by interchanging row i and row k, then it can be obtained by multiplying $[A]$ on the left by the matrix derived from $[I]$ by interchanging rows i and k. The following equation illustrates this fact by showing the interchanging of the second and third rows of a matrix as a matrix multiplication.

$$\begin{bmatrix} 1 & 0 & 0 \\ 0 & 0 & 1 \\ 0 & 1 & 0 \end{bmatrix} \begin{bmatrix} 1 & 2 & 3 \\ 4 & 5 & 6 \\ 7 & 8 & 9 \end{bmatrix} = \begin{bmatrix} 1 & 2 & 3 \\ 7 & 8 & 9 \\ 4 & 5 & 6 \end{bmatrix}.$$

Any reordering of the rows of a matrix can be accomplished by multiplying that matrix on the left by a matrix obtained from $[I]$ by the same reordering. A matrix obtained from $[I]$ by a row rearrangement is called a permutation matrix. The matrix $[PA]$ of Theorem 16-1 is equal to $[P][A]$ for some permutation matrix $[P]$.

Let $\boldsymbol{b}^1, \ldots, \boldsymbol{b}^n$ be the row vectors of a matrix $[B]$, and let $\boldsymbol{a}_1, \ldots, \boldsymbol{a}_n$ be the column vectors of a matrix $[A]$. Then

$$[C] = [B][A] = \begin{bmatrix} \boldsymbol{b}^1 \cdot \boldsymbol{a}_1 \ldots \boldsymbol{b}^1 \cdot \boldsymbol{a}_n \\ \\ \boldsymbol{b}^n \cdot \boldsymbol{a}_1 \ldots \boldsymbol{b}^n \cdot \boldsymbol{a}_n \end{bmatrix}$$

where, as before, $\boldsymbol{b}^i \cdot \boldsymbol{a}_j = b^i_\alpha a^\alpha_j$. Let $\boldsymbol{e}_1, \ldots, \boldsymbol{e}_n$ be the natural basis in R^n. If $\boldsymbol{b}^i = r\boldsymbol{e}_i$ for some number r, then

$$c^i_j = \boldsymbol{b}^i \cdot \boldsymbol{a}_j = r\boldsymbol{e}_i \cdot \boldsymbol{a}_j = ra^i_j, \quad j = 1, \ldots, n.$$

Thus, row i of the product is simply r times row i of $[A]$. For example, if $\boldsymbol{b}^1 = 2\boldsymbol{e}_1$ and $\boldsymbol{b}^2 = 3\boldsymbol{e}_2$, then

$$\begin{bmatrix} 2 & 0 \\ 0 & 3 \end{bmatrix} \begin{bmatrix} a_1^1 & a_2^1 \\ a_1^2 & a_2^2 \end{bmatrix} = \begin{bmatrix} 2a_1^1 & 2a_2^1 \\ 3a_1^2 & 3a_2^2 \end{bmatrix}$$

Thus, multiplication of a row of a matrix by a number (Operation (ii) of Theorem 15-1) can be carried out by matrix multiplication. If $\boldsymbol{b}^i = \boldsymbol{e}_i + s\boldsymbol{e}_k$ for some number s, then

$$c_j^i = \boldsymbol{b}^i \cdot \boldsymbol{a}_j = a_j^i + sa_j^k, \quad j = 1, \ldots, n.$$

In words, row i of the product is the sum of row i and s times row k of $[A]$. Thus, replacing row i by the sum of a multiple r of itself and s times row k (a combination of Operations (ii) and (iii) of Theorem 15-1) is achieved by multiplying $[A]$ on the left by a matrix obtained from $[I]$ by replacing row i (that is, $\boldsymbol{e}_i$) with $r\boldsymbol{e}_i + s\boldsymbol{e}_k$. To illustrate this procedure using the notation of Section 15, we write

$$[A] = \begin{bmatrix} 1 & 1 & 1 \\ 2 & -4 & 1 \\ 2 & 1 & 2 \end{bmatrix} \xrightarrow{\boxed{-2I + III}} \begin{bmatrix} 1 & 1 & 1 \\ 2 & -4 & 1 \\ 0 & -1 & 0 \end{bmatrix}.$$

Using matrix multiplication to make this transformation we have

$$\begin{bmatrix} 1 & 0 & 0 \\ 0 & 1 & 0 \\ -2 & 0 & 1 \end{bmatrix} \begin{bmatrix} 1 & 1 & 1 \\ 2 & -4 & 1 \\ 2 & 1 & 2 \end{bmatrix} = \begin{bmatrix} 1 & 1 & 1 \\ 2 & -4 & 1 \\ 0 & -1 & 0 \end{bmatrix}$$

Similarly,

$$\begin{bmatrix} 1 & 1 & 1 \\ 2 & -4 & 1 \\ 2 & 1 & 2 \end{bmatrix} \xrightarrow{\boxed{-2I + II}} \begin{bmatrix} 1 & 1 & 1 \\ 0 & -6 & -1 \\ 0 & -1 & 0 \end{bmatrix}$$

is represented as

$$\begin{bmatrix} 1 & 0 & 0 \\ -2 & 1 & 0 \\ 0 & 0 & 1 \end{bmatrix} \begin{bmatrix} 1 & 1 & 1 \\ 2 & -4 & 1 \\ 2 & 1 & 2 \end{bmatrix} = \begin{bmatrix} 1 & 1 & 1 \\ 1 & -6 & -1 \\ 0 & -1 & 0 \end{bmatrix}.$$

In fact, the changes in both the second and third rows can be represented by

$$\begin{bmatrix} 1 & 0 & 0 \\ -2 & 1 & 0 \\ -2 & 0 & 1 \end{bmatrix} \begin{bmatrix} 1 & 1 & 1 \\ 2 & -4 & 1 \\ 2 & 1 & 2 \end{bmatrix} = \begin{bmatrix} 1 & 1 & 1 \\ 0 & -6 & -1 \\ 0 & -1 & 0 \end{bmatrix}. \tag{17-1}$$

The third row of the matrix on the right can be replaced by $-\frac{1}{6}$ times the second row plus the third row by the multiplication

$$\begin{bmatrix} 1 & 0 & 0 \\ 0 & 1 & 0 \\ 0 & -\frac{1}{6} & 1 \end{bmatrix} \begin{bmatrix} 1 & 1 & 1 \\ 0 & -6 & -1 \\ 0 & -1 & 0 \end{bmatrix} = \begin{bmatrix} 1 & 1 & 1 \\ 0 & -6 & -1 \\ 0 & 0 & \frac{1}{6} \end{bmatrix}.$$

From this equation and Equation 17-1 it follows that

$$\begin{bmatrix} 1 & 0 & 0 \\ 0 & 1 & 0 \\ 0 & -\frac{1}{6} & 0 \end{bmatrix} \begin{bmatrix} 1 & 0 & 0 \\ -2 & 1 & 0 \\ -2 & 0 & 1 \end{bmatrix} \begin{bmatrix} 1 & 1 & 1 \\ 2 & -4 & 1 \\ 2 & 1 & 2 \end{bmatrix} = \begin{bmatrix} 1 & 1 & 1 \\ 0 & -6 & -1 \\ 0 & 0 & \frac{1}{6} \end{bmatrix}.$$

That is,

$$\begin{bmatrix} 1 & 0 & 0 \\ -2 & 1 & 0 \\ -\frac{5}{3} & -\frac{1}{6} & 1 \end{bmatrix} \begin{bmatrix} 1 & 1 & 1 \\ 2 & -4 & 1 \\ 2 & 1 & 2 \end{bmatrix} = \begin{bmatrix} 1 & 1 & 1 \\ 0 & -6 & -1 \\ 0 & 0 & \frac{1}{6} \end{bmatrix}. \tag{17-2}$$

This equation states that for the given matrix $[A]$ there is a lower triangular matrix $[M]$ such that $[M][A]$ is an upper triangular matrix $[U]$. To prove that that fact is valid for any square matrix we use Theorem 16-1 and the elementary facts stated in the next theorem.

THEOREM 17-1

Let $[L]$ and $[M]$ be lower triangular n by n matrices, and let $[U]$ and $[V]$ be upper triangular n by n matrices.

(i) $[U][V]$ and $[L][M]$ are upper and lower triangular matrices, respectively.

(ii) The inverse of a triangular matrix exists if, and only if, none of its main diagonal numbers are zero.

(iii) If the inverse of a triangular matrix exists, then it is a triangular matrix of the same type. For example, $[U]^{-1}$ is an upper triangular matrix, if it exists.

Proof: The proofs of parts (i) and (iii) of this theorem are straightforward tasks that we leave to you in the Problems.

To prove (ii) let us consider the case of a lower triangular matrix $[L]$. The first row vector forms an independent set of vectors if, and only if, $l_1^1 \neq 0$. Now consider the set consisting of the first two row vectors. The second row vector $\boldsymbol{l}^2$ is a linear combination of $\boldsymbol{l}^1$; that is, $\boldsymbol{l}^2 = b\boldsymbol{l}^1$ if, and only if, $l_2^2 = 0$. Thus, $\{\boldsymbol{l}^1, \boldsymbol{l}^2\}$ is an independent set if, and only if, $l_1^1 l_2^2 \neq 0$. Continuing with the same line of reasoning we see that $\boldsymbol{l}^3 = c_1\boldsymbol{l}^1 + c_2\boldsymbol{l}^2$ if, and only if, $l_3^3 = 0$, and hence $\{\boldsymbol{l}^1, \boldsymbol{l}^2, \boldsymbol{l}^3\}$ is an independent set if, and only if, $l_1^1 l_2^2 l_3^3 \neq 0$. And so it goes. It is now easy to see that the rank $[L] = n$ if, and only if, $l_1^1 l_2^2 \ldots l_n^n \neq 0$ since the rank of $[L]$ is the dimension of the space generated by the row vectors. It follows from Theorem 15-2 that $[L]^{-1}$ exists precisely when rank $[L] = n$, and this occurs precisely when no diagonal number of $[L]$ is zero. A similar argument can be used for a $[U]$ matrix. ∎

If $[A]$ is any square matrix, then according to Theorem 16-1 there are triangular matrices and a permutation matrix $[P]$ such that

$$[P][A] = [L][U].$$

Furthermore, the number 1 is in each main diagonal position in $[L]$ so according to Theorem 17-1 $[L]^{-1}$ exists, and it is a lower triangular matrix. We set $[M] = [L]^{-1}$ so that

$$[M][P][A] = [U]. \tag{17-3}$$

Multiplying $[A]$ by $[M][P]$ carries out the row operations of the Gaussian Elimination process in which $[A]$ is reduced to upper triangular form.

If $[A]$ is invertible then it follows from Equation 17-3 and the fact that both $[M]$ and $[P]$ are invertible that $[U]$ is invertible. In this case no diagonal number in $[U]$ is zero so we may write

$$[U] = \begin{bmatrix} 1 & u_2^1/u_2^2 & \ldots & u_n^1/u_n^n \\ 0 & 1 & \ldots & u_n^2/u_n^n \\ \vdots & \vdots & & \vdots \\ 0 & 0 & \ldots & 1 \end{bmatrix} \begin{bmatrix} u_1^1 & 0 & \ldots & 0 \\ 0 & u_2^2 & \ldots & 0 \\ \vdots & \vdots & & \vdots \\ 0 & 0 & \ldots & u_n^n \end{bmatrix} = [U_1][D].$$

If we let $[V] = [U]^{-1}$ and use Equation 17-3, we can write

$$[V][M][P][A] = [D].$$

In this case, multiplying $[A]$ on the left by the matrix $[V][M][P]$ carries out the row operations that reduce $[A]$ to diagonal form.

Example 17-1 Find an $[LU]$ decomposition of the matrix

$$\begin{bmatrix} 1 & 1 & 1 \\ 2 & -4 & 1 \\ 2 & 1 & 2 \end{bmatrix}.$$

Solution: It follows from Equation 17-3 and our discussion above that $[U]$ is the matrix on the right of Equation 17-2 and $[L]^{-1}$ is the matrix on the left. You can easily calculate that

$$\begin{bmatrix} 1 & 0 & 0 \\ -2 & 1 & 0 \\ -\frac{5}{3} & -\frac{1}{6} & 1 \end{bmatrix}^{-1} = \begin{bmatrix} 1 & 0 & 0 \\ 2 & 1 & 0 \\ 2 & \frac{1}{6} & 1 \end{bmatrix}$$

so that an $[LU]$ decomposition of our matrix is

$$\begin{bmatrix} 1 & 1 & 1 \\ 2 & -6 & -1 \\ 2 & \frac{1}{6} & \frac{1}{6} \end{bmatrix}.$$

PROBLEMS 17

1. Find the 3 by 3 matrix $[M]$ such that if a 3 by 3 matrix is multiplied on the left by $[M]$ the following row operations are carried out. (See Example 15-1 to check your results.)
   (a) The first row is replaced by the sum of the first and third rows.
   (b) The second row is replaced by the sum of the second row and three times the third row.
   (c) The operations in both (a) and (b) are carried out.
   (d) The first row is replaced by the sum of the first row and one-half of the second row.
   (e) The second row is replaced by one-half the second row.
   (f) Operations (c), (d), and (e) are carried out in the order indicated.
2. Find the matrices that produce each step of the operations indicated in Equations 15-3.

3. Find the two matrices that produce the two operations indicated in Example 15-2, and find the inverse in that example by multiplying your two matrices.

4. Use the method employed in the preceding problem to find the inverse of the matrix

$$\begin{bmatrix} 2 & 2 & 1 \\ 1 & -4 & 1 \\ 2 & 1 & 1 \end{bmatrix}.$$

5. Use the results of Problem 16-3 to find a lower triangular matrix $[M]$ such that $[M][A]$ is an upper triangular matrix if $[A]$ is:
   (a) The matrix in Problem 16-3a.
   (b) The matrix in Problem 16-3b.
   (c) The matrix in Problem 16-3c.
   (d) The matrix in Problem 16-3d.

6. Find a matrix $[M]$ such that $[M][A]$ is a diagonal matrix if $[A]$ is:
   (a) The matrix in Problem 16-5a.
   (b) The matrix in Example 17-1.

Five

Determinants

Associated with a square matrix is a number called the determinant of the matrix. That number can be defined by giving a rule to calculate it. You are probably familiar with the rule for calculating the determinant of a 2 by 2 matrix, and perhaps you know how to calculate determinants of larger matrices also. In this chapter we will see that the determinant of a 2 by 2 matrix can be interpreted geometrically as the area of a certain parallelogram with an algebraic sign attached (a "signed" area). Then, once again, we will generalize a geometric idea by abstracting some basic properties and then using those basic properties as axioms. Thus, we are led to define a signed volume in Euclidean spaces of any dimension.

In this chapter we will discuss the calculation of the determinant of a matrix by the method of Expansion by Cofactors and derive the basic properties of determinants. And, because a square matrix and a linear operator are intimately related, it is not surprising that we will encounter the idea of the determinant of an operator. We will see that there is a simple geometric interpretation of the determinant of a linear operator as a "distortion factor." Furthermore, some of the basic properties of determinants are most easily proved by exploiting the idea of the determinant of an operator.

It used to be that determinants were studied because they can be used to solve systems of linear equations. This method (called Cramer's Rule) is presented as a problem at the end of Section 19. Actually it has little practical value as far as solving systems is concerned, but it is useful to know in certain situations.

18 SIGNED AREA AND VOLUME

A direction can be assigned to a geometric line by an arrow of unit length that lies in the line and specifies the positive direction as the direction in which the arrow points. Let $\boldsymbol{e}_1$ be the unit vector represented by that arrow. A line can be considered as a one-dimensional Euclidean space with $\{\boldsymbol{e}_1\}$ as a basis. The signed distance from P to Q, denoted by $D(\boldsymbol{PQ})$, is the length of the segment PQ with a plus or minus sign depending on whether the arrow $\boldsymbol{PQ}$ is in the same or opposite direction as $\boldsymbol{e}_1$. If $\boldsymbol{u} = \boldsymbol{PQ}$, then the signed length of $\boldsymbol{u}$, denoted by $D(\boldsymbol{u})$, is equal to $D(\boldsymbol{PQ})$. If $\boldsymbol{u} = u^1\boldsymbol{e}_1$, then (see Fig. 18-1)

$$D(\boldsymbol{u}) = \langle \boldsymbol{u}, \boldsymbol{e}_1 \rangle = u^1.$$

Now consider a two-dimensional Euclidean space and choose an orthonormal basis $E = \{\boldsymbol{e}_1, \boldsymbol{e}_2\}$ in it. An arrow representing $\boldsymbol{e}_1$ can be mapped onto an arrow representing $\boldsymbol{e}_2$ by a rotation of $\pi/2$. A rotation will be called a positive rotation (with respect to E) if it is in the same direction as the rotation of $\boldsymbol{e}_1$ onto $\boldsymbol{e}_2$, and will be called a negative rotation if it is in the opposite direction. Thus, $\boldsymbol{e}_2$ is mapped onto $\boldsymbol{e}_1$ by a negative rotation of $\pi/2$, or as we shall say, by a rotation of $-\pi/2$. Suppose $\{\boldsymbol{u}_1, \boldsymbol{u}_2\}$ is an independent set of vectors. The arrows representing $\boldsymbol{u}_1$ and $\boldsymbol{u}_2$ are non-parallel, non-zero arrows, and there is a unique angle θ $(0 \leq \theta \leq \pi)$ between them. The arrow representing $\boldsymbol{u}_1$ can be mapped onto the arrow representing $\boldsymbol{u}_2$ by a rotation. This rotation will be a rotation of either θ or $-\theta$. The signed area associated with $\boldsymbol{u}_1$ and $\boldsymbol{u}_2$, denoted by $D(\boldsymbol{u}_1, \boldsymbol{u}_2)$,

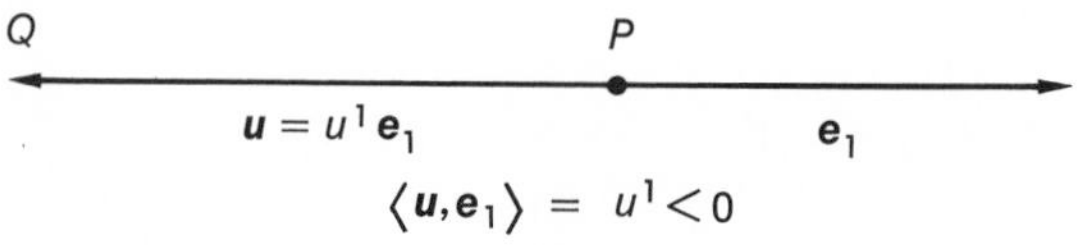

Figure 18-1

7-11 $[I]^{E}_{\hat{E}} = \begin{bmatrix} \cos\theta & \sin\theta \\ -\sin\theta & \cos\theta \end{bmatrix}$

is the area of the parallelogram whose sides are arrows representing $\boldsymbol{u}_1$ and $\boldsymbol{u}_2$ with a plus or minus sign depending on whether the rotation of $\boldsymbol{u}_1$ onto $\boldsymbol{u}_2$ is plus or minus (see Fig. 18-2). If either $\boldsymbol{u}_1$ or $\boldsymbol{u}_2$ is the zero vector, or if the arrows representing $\boldsymbol{u}_1$ and $\boldsymbol{u}_2$ are parallel, then the area of the "parallelogram" determined by $\boldsymbol{u}_1$ and $\boldsymbol{u}_2$ is zero. Thus, if $\{\boldsymbol{u}_1, \boldsymbol{u}_2\}$ is a dependent set, we say that $D(\boldsymbol{u}_1, \boldsymbol{u}_2) = 0$. Notice that

$$D(\boldsymbol{e}_1, \boldsymbol{e}_2) = 1 \quad \text{and} \quad D(\boldsymbol{e}_2, \boldsymbol{e}_1) = -1.$$

In order to compute a formula for the $D(\boldsymbol{u}_1, \boldsymbol{u}_2)$ when $\boldsymbol{u}_1$ and $\boldsymbol{u}_2$ are nonzero vectors, we will make use of Equation 7-11. From that equation we see that if the vector $\boldsymbol{u}_1 = u_1^1\boldsymbol{e}_1 + u_1^2\boldsymbol{e}_2$ is rotated by $\pi/2$, we get the vector $-u_1^2\boldsymbol{e}_1 + u_1^1\boldsymbol{e}_2$ (see Fig. 18-3). It is clear that the length of this vector is $|\boldsymbol{u}_1|$, and so

(18-1)
$$\boldsymbol{v}_1 = \frac{(-u_1^2\boldsymbol{e}_1 + u_1^1\boldsymbol{e}_2)}{|\boldsymbol{u}_1|}$$

is a unit vector. Furthermore, $\boldsymbol{v}_1$ is obtained from $\boldsymbol{u}_1$ by a positive rotation and

$$D(\boldsymbol{u}_1, \boldsymbol{v}_1) = |\boldsymbol{u}_1| > 0.$$

Now consider the parallelogram determined by $\boldsymbol{u}_1$ and $\boldsymbol{u}_2$ (see Fig. 18-4). The "base" of the parallelogram is $|\boldsymbol{u}_1|$ and its "height" is $|c|$, where

$$P_{\boldsymbol{v}_1}(\boldsymbol{u}_2) = c\boldsymbol{v}_1$$

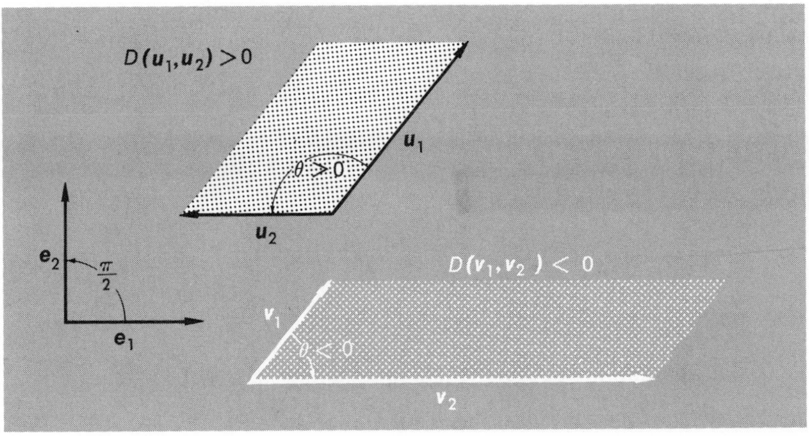

Figure 18-2

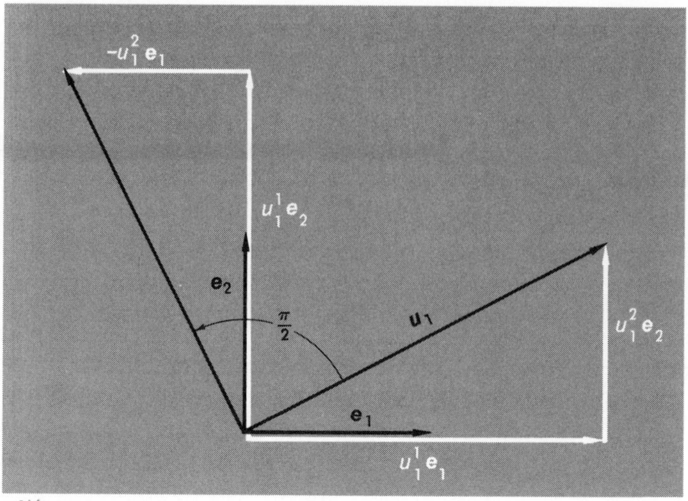

Figure 18-3

and (see Equation 10-6) $c = \langle \boldsymbol{u}_2, \boldsymbol{v}_1 \rangle$. Furthermore, c has the same sign as the rotation of $\boldsymbol{u}_1$ onto $\boldsymbol{u}_2$. Thus,

$$\begin{aligned} D(\boldsymbol{u}_1, \boldsymbol{u}_2) &= c|\boldsymbol{u}_1| \\ &= \langle \boldsymbol{u}_2, \boldsymbol{v}_1 \rangle |\boldsymbol{u}_1| \\ &= \langle \boldsymbol{u}_2, |\boldsymbol{u}_1| \boldsymbol{v}_1 \rangle \\ &= \langle u_2^1 \boldsymbol{e}_1 + u_2^2 \boldsymbol{e}_2, -u_1^2 \boldsymbol{e}_1 + u_1^1 \boldsymbol{e}_2 \rangle. \end{aligned}$$

Expanding, we get

$$D(\boldsymbol{u}_1, \boldsymbol{u}_2) = u_1^1 u_2^2 - u_1^2 u_2^1.$$

The *number* $u_1^1 u_2^2 - u_1^2 u_2^1$ is the *determinant* of the matrix whose column vectors are the coordinates of $\boldsymbol{u}_1$ and $\boldsymbol{u}_2$. We use vertical bars to denote the determinant of a matrix. Thus,

$$(18\text{-}2) \qquad D(\boldsymbol{u}_1, \boldsymbol{u}_2) = \begin{vmatrix} u_1^1 & u_2^1 \\ u_1^2 & u_2^2 \end{vmatrix} = u_1^1 u_2^2 - u_2^1 u_1^2.$$

Example 18-1 Suppose that E is the natural basis in R^2 with the standard inner product. Find $D((2,3), (4,5))$.

Solution: Using Equation 18-2

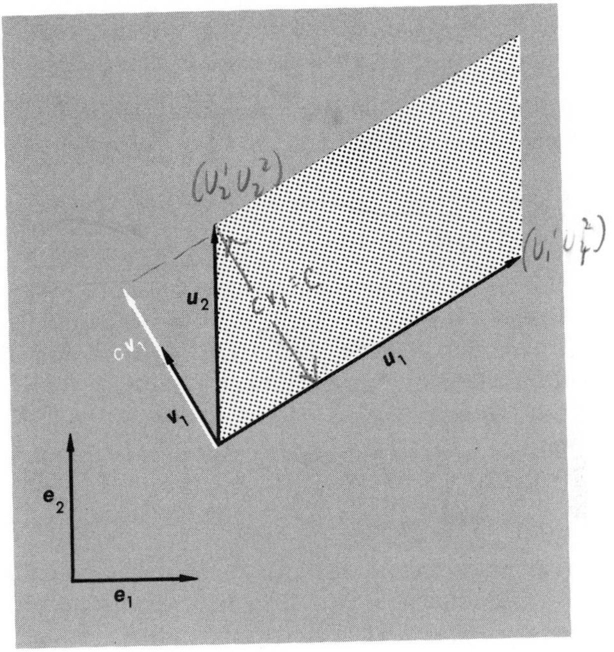

Figure 18-4

$$D\big((2,3),(4,5)\big) = \begin{vmatrix} 2 & 4 \\ 3 & 5 \end{vmatrix} = 10 - 12 = -2.$$

You should sketch a picture to illustrate this result.

Using Equation 18-2, it is easy to verify that the signed area associated with two vectors has the following four properties:

$$\begin{aligned} &D(\boldsymbol{u}_2, \boldsymbol{u}_1) = -D(\boldsymbol{u}_1, \boldsymbol{u}_2) \\ &D(\boldsymbol{u}_1 + \boldsymbol{v}, \boldsymbol{u}_2) = D(\boldsymbol{u}_1, \boldsymbol{u}_2) + D(\boldsymbol{v}, \boldsymbol{u}_2) \\ &D(c\boldsymbol{u}_1, \boldsymbol{u}_2) = c\, D(\boldsymbol{u}_1, \boldsymbol{u}_2) \\ &D(\boldsymbol{e}_1, \boldsymbol{e}_2) = 1. \end{aligned} \tag{18-3}$$

For example, the first property follows from the fact that

$$u_2^1 u_1^2 - u_1^1 u_2^2 = -(u_1^1 u_2^2 - u_2^1 u_1^2).$$

To extend our idea of signed area to that of signed volume in a three-dimensional Euclidean space and, in fact, to n-dimensional Euclidean spaces, we will use the same "abstraction" procedure that we used to develop the idea of an "abstract" vector space (Section 1) and an "abstract" inner product space (Section 10). We make use of the four properties listed in Equation 18-3 as a guide to make the following definition.

DEFINITION 18-1

Let $E = \{e_1, \ldots, e_n\}$ be an orthonormal basis in a Euclidean space. The signed volume associated with an ordered set of n vectors $\{u_1, \ldots, u_n\} = U$ with respect to E is a number, written $D(u_1, \ldots, u_n)$ or $D(U)$, such that for each j and k ($1 \leq j \leq n; 1 \leq k \leq n$):
1) $D(u_1, \ldots, u_j, \ldots, u_k, \ldots, u_n) = -D(u_1, \ldots, u_k, \ldots, u_j, \ldots, u_n)$
2) $D(u_1, \ldots, cu_j + v, \ldots, u_n) = c\,D(U) + D(u_1, \ldots, v, \ldots, u_n)$
3) $D(E) = 1$.

Remarks. Property (1) states that D is an *alternating* function. Property (2) states that D is a linear function if $n - 1$ of the n vectors are kept fixed. In this case D is said to be *multilinear*. The volume function depends on E, so we should write $D_E(U)$ instead of just $D(U)$. It turns out, however, that our simplified notation is sufficient for our purposes.

In our informal discussion preceding Definition 18-1 we saw that a unique signed volume function D exists if $n = 2$. We will assume that signed volume functions exist if $n > 2$ and state some further properties that such functions must have. The first theorem can be proved by a straightforward use of the defining properties of a signed volume function, and we leave its proof for the problems.

THEOREM 18-1

(i) If $\mathbf{0}$ is in U, then $D(U) = 0$.
(ii) If $u_j = u_k$ for $j \neq k$, then $D(U) = 0$.
(iii) If U is a dependent set, then $D(U) = 0$.

Suppose that $U = \{u_1, \ldots, u_n\}$ is an independent set of vectors in an n-dimensional Euclidean space in which an orthonormal basis E has been chosen. Then U is also a basis and each vector e_j is a linear combination of vectors in U; that is, for each $j = 1, \ldots, n$

$$e_j = e_j^1 u_1 + \cdots + e_j^n u_n = e_j^\alpha u_\alpha.$$

Thus, we can write

$$D(\boldsymbol{e}_1, \ldots, \boldsymbol{e}_n) = D(e_1^\alpha \boldsymbol{u}_\alpha, \ldots, e_n^\beta \boldsymbol{u}_\beta).$$

Using the properties in Definition 18-1,

$$1 = e_1^\alpha \ldots e_n^\beta D(\boldsymbol{u}_\alpha, \ldots, \boldsymbol{u}_\beta). \tag{18-4}$$

The right side of this equation that is written so compactly using summation notation becomes a horrible mess if we write it all out for a large n, but we will not need to do that. To see why, let us look at the case in which $n = 3$. According to Theorem 18-1, any term in the sum in which two of the indices of $\boldsymbol{u}_i, \boldsymbol{u}_j, \boldsymbol{u}_k$ are equal is zero. Thus, the only terms that need to be written are those in which $\{i, j, k\}$ is some permutation of $\{1, 2, 3\}$. Furthermore, in this case it follows from Property 1) of Definition 18-1 that $D(\boldsymbol{u}_i, \boldsymbol{u}_j, \boldsymbol{u}_k) = \pm D(\boldsymbol{u}_1, \boldsymbol{u}_2, \boldsymbol{u}_3)$. In general

$$D(\boldsymbol{u}_i, \ldots, \boldsymbol{u}_j) = \pm D(\boldsymbol{u}_1, \ldots, \boldsymbol{u}_n).$$

Now if $D(\boldsymbol{u}_1, \ldots, \boldsymbol{u}_n)$ were equal to zero, then it would follow that the right side of Equation 18-4 is zero, which is a contradiction. Thus, if U is an independent set, $D(U) \neq 0$. Combining this fact with Theorem 18-1 (iii) we can state the following useful theorem.

THEOREM 18-2

An ordered set U of n vectors is independent if, and only if, $D(U) \neq 0$.

Suppose that U is any ordered set of n vectors in a Euclidean space in which an orthonormal basis $E = \{\boldsymbol{e}_1, \ldots, \boldsymbol{e}_n\}$ has been chosen. Is it possible that there are two (or more) volume functions associated with E? In other words, assuming volume functions do exist, do the properties listed in Definition 18-1 define a unique volume function? The answer is yes, because if we write each vector in U as

$$\boldsymbol{u}_j = u_j^\alpha \boldsymbol{e}_\alpha \quad (j = 1, \ldots, n),$$

then the properties used to define signed volume require us to compute $D(U)$ as follows:

$$D(U) = u_1^\alpha \ldots u_n^\beta D(\boldsymbol{e}_\alpha, \ldots, \boldsymbol{e}_\beta). \tag{18-5}$$

Because the coordinates of a vector in a given basis are uniquely determined, $D(U)$ is uniquely determined and can be computed using Equation 18-5. In using this equation notice that

$$D(e_i, \ldots, e_j) = \pm D(e_1, \ldots, e_n) = \pm 1,$$

if $\{i, \ldots, j\}$ is a permutation of $\{1, \ldots, n\}$, and zero otherwise. Furthermore, there is a sign change each time a pair of vectors is interchanged in the expression on the left of this equation so that

(18-6) $$D(e_i, \ldots, e_j) = (-1)^N$$

where N is the number of interchanges required to transform the ordered set $\{i, \ldots, j\}$ into the ordered set $\{1, \ldots, n\}$. For example,

$$\begin{aligned} D(e_2, e_3, e_1) &= -D(e_1, e_3, e_2) \\ &= -(-D(e_1, e_2, e_3)) \\ &= 1. \end{aligned}$$

The formula for computing $D(U)$ could be written as an indicated sum

(18-7) $$D(U) = \sum (-1)^N u_1^i \ldots u_n^j$$

where $\{i, \ldots, j\}$ is derived from $\{1, \ldots, n\}$ by N interchanges, and the sum is taken over all permutations of $\{1, \ldots, n\}$. We will learn other methods for computing $D(U)$, but to illustrate Equation 18-7 let us write the sum out if $n = 3$.

(18-8) $$\begin{aligned} D(u_1, u_2, u_3) = u_1^1u_2^2u_3^3 - u_1^1u_2^3u_3^2 - u_1^2u_2^1u_3^3 \\ + u_1^2u_2^3u_3^1 + u_1^3u_2^1u_3^2 - u_1^3u_2^2u_3^1. \end{aligned}$$

The number $D(u_1, \ldots, u_n)$ is called the determinant of the matrix whose columns are the coordinates of $u_1, \ldots, u_n$, and we write

$$D(u_1, \ldots, u_n) = \begin{vmatrix} u^1 & \ldots & u_n^1 \\ \cdot & & \cdot \\ \cdot & & \cdot \\ \cdot & & \cdot \\ u_1^n & \ldots & u_n^n \end{vmatrix}.$$

Example 18-2 Find $D(U)$ if E is the natural basis in R^3 with the standard inner product and $U = \{e_2, e_3, (1,0,1)\}$.

Solution:

$$D((0,1,0), (0,0,1), (1,0,1)) = \begin{vmatrix} 0 & 0 & 1 \\ 1 & 0 & 0 \\ 0 & 1 & 1 \end{vmatrix} = 1.$$

PROBLEMS 18

1. Prove Theorem 18-1 (i).
2. Prove Theorem 18-1 (ii).
3. Prove Theorem 18-1 (iii).
4. Suppose that U is a dependent set of n vectors and F is a linear operator in V. Prove that $D(F(U)) = 0$.
5. Find $D(U)$ in each case.
   (a) $\boldsymbol{u}_1 = \boldsymbol{e}_1 + 4\boldsymbol{e}_2, \boldsymbol{u}_2 = 3\boldsymbol{e}_1 + 5\boldsymbol{e}_2$
   (b) $\boldsymbol{u}_1 = 2\boldsymbol{e}_1 + 4\boldsymbol{e}_2, \boldsymbol{u}_2 = 3\boldsymbol{e}_1 + 6\boldsymbol{e}_2$
   (c) $\boldsymbol{u}_1 = \boldsymbol{e}_1 + \boldsymbol{e}_2 + \boldsymbol{e}_3, \boldsymbol{u}_2 = \boldsymbol{e}_1 + 2\boldsymbol{e}_2 + 3\boldsymbol{e}_3, \boldsymbol{u}_3 = \boldsymbol{e}_1 + 3\boldsymbol{e}_2 + 6\boldsymbol{e}_3$
   (d) $\boldsymbol{u}_1 = \boldsymbol{e}_1 + \boldsymbol{e}_2 + \boldsymbol{e}_3, \boldsymbol{u}_2 = 3\boldsymbol{u}_3 - \boldsymbol{u}_1, \boldsymbol{u}_3 = \boldsymbol{u}_1 + \boldsymbol{u}_2$
   (e) $\boldsymbol{u}_1 = 3\boldsymbol{e}_1 + 8\boldsymbol{e}_2 + 2\boldsymbol{e}_3, \boldsymbol{u}_2 = 4\boldsymbol{e}_1 + 7\boldsymbol{e}_2 - \boldsymbol{e}_3, \boldsymbol{u}_3 = -5\boldsymbol{e}_1 - 2\boldsymbol{e}_2 + 8\boldsymbol{e}_3$
6. Suppose that $\boldsymbol{w} = x^\alpha \boldsymbol{u}_\alpha$ and let W be the set U with $\boldsymbol{u}_2$ replaced with $\boldsymbol{w}$. Express $D(W)$ in terms of $D(U)$.
7. Determine whether the vectors are independent if the coordinates in a chosen orthonormal basis E are:

   (a) $\begin{bmatrix} 3 \\ 4 \end{bmatrix}$ and $\begin{bmatrix} 5 \\ 6 \end{bmatrix}$ (b) $\begin{bmatrix} 3 \\ 4 \\ 1 \end{bmatrix}, \begin{bmatrix} 0 \\ 1 \\ 2 \end{bmatrix}, \begin{bmatrix} 1 \\ 0 \\ 2 \end{bmatrix}$

   (c) $\begin{bmatrix} 3 \\ 4 \\ 5 \end{bmatrix}, \begin{bmatrix} 4 \\ 5 \\ 6 \end{bmatrix}, \begin{bmatrix} 5 \\ 6 \\ 7 \end{bmatrix}$ (d) $\begin{bmatrix} 1 \\ 0 \\ -1 \\ 0 \end{bmatrix}, \begin{bmatrix} 0 \\ 1 \\ 0 \\ 1 \end{bmatrix}, \begin{bmatrix} 1 \\ 0 \\ 1 \\ 0 \end{bmatrix}, \begin{bmatrix} 3 \\ 0 \\ 1 \\ 0 \end{bmatrix}$.
8. Use the formulas in Section 7 for rotation of axes in a plane to show that if $\hat{E}$ is obtained from the chosen orthonormal basis E by a rotation, then $D(\hat{E}) = 1$.

19 DETERMINANTS OF MATRICES

Let $U = \{\boldsymbol{u}_1, \ldots, \boldsymbol{u}_n\}$ be an ordered set of n vectors in an n-dimensional Euclidean space. Each vector in U has a unique set of coordinates with respect to a fixed orthonormal basis E. The signed volume $D(\boldsymbol{u}_1, \ldots, \boldsymbol{u}_n)$ with respect to E is the determinant of the square matrix $[\boldsymbol{u}_1 \ldots \boldsymbol{u}_n]_E$ whose columns are the coordinates of $\boldsymbol{u}_1, \ldots, \boldsymbol{u}_n$ with respect to E. Given any square matrix $[A]$ its columns can be considered as coordinate column matrices of vectors in R^n with respect to the natural basis. With this understanding we say its columns "are" vectors in R^n. If D is the signed volume function associated with the natural basis in R^n, then the determinant of $[A]$ is $D(\boldsymbol{a}_1, \ldots, \boldsymbol{a}_n)$ where $\boldsymbol{a}_j$ is the jth column vector of $[A]$. We could write $D(A)$ for this determinant with the understanding that $A = \{\boldsymbol{a}_1, \ldots, \boldsymbol{a}_n\}$. But to emphasize that it is the determinant of a matrix $[A]$ we write $det[A]$ instead of $D(A)$. Thus,

$$det[A] = \begin{vmatrix} a^1 & \cdots & a^1_n \\ \vdots & & \vdots \\ a^n_1 & \cdots & a^n_n \end{vmatrix}.$$

Using the indicated sum notation of Equation 18-7,

$$det[A] = \sum (-1)^N a^i_1 \ldots a^j_n.$$

There are $n!$ products in this sum so it is not easy to find the determinant of an n by n matrix if n is large. For example, the determinant of a 10 by 10 matrix involves more than $3\frac{1}{2}$ million products. Thus, there is a major computing problem involved in finding such a determinant. To simplify the task of computing the determinant of a matrix that is not too large sometimes we can make use of some of the basic properties of signed volumes. Let us begin by examining the case in which $n = 3$ and write the sum indicated in Equation 18-8 in factored form.

$$det[A] = a^1_1(a^2_2 a^3_3 - a^3_2 a^2_3) - a^2_1(a^1_2 a^3_3 - a^3_2 a^1_3) + a^3_1(a^1_2 a^2_3 - a^2_2 a^1_3).$$

Thus, we can write

(19-1) $$det[A] = a^1_1 \begin{vmatrix} a^2_2 & a^2_3 \\ a^3_2 & a^3_3 \end{vmatrix} - a^2_1 \begin{vmatrix} a^1_2 & a^1_3 \\ a^3_2 & a^3_3 \end{vmatrix} + a^3_1 \begin{vmatrix} a^1_2 & a^1_3 \\ a^2_2 & a^2_3 \end{vmatrix}.$$

The determinants in this sum are determinants of matrices derived from $[A]$ by deleting certain rows and columns. For example, the second term in the sum is the determinant of the matrix obtained from $[A]$ by deleting row 2 and column 1 of $[A]$.

DEFINITION 19-1

Let $\Delta^i_j(A)$ be the determinant (a number) of the matrix derived from $[A]$ by deleting row i and column j. The ***cofactor of*** $\boldsymbol{a}^i_j$ is the number $(-1)^{i+j}\,\Delta^i_j(A)$. It is denoted by A^j_i. (Notice the interchange of indices!) Thus,

$$A^j_i = (-1)^{i+j}\,\Delta^i_j(A).$$

The indices are reversed in the cofactor notation because later we will form a matrix with the number A_i^j in row j and column i. It also makes it possible for us to use our summation notation to write Equation 19-1 as

$$det[A] = a_1^\alpha A_\alpha^1. \tag{19-2}$$

Any column can be used to evaluate $det[A]$ by first interchanging it with the first column and then using Equation 19-2 to evaluate the new determinant. For example, let us evaluate $det[A]$ by using the second column. If $[B]$ is the matrix obtained by interchanging the first and second columns of $[A]$, then for each $i = 1,2,3$;

$$b_1^i = a_2^i,\ b_2^i = a_1^i, \quad \text{and} \quad b_3^i = a_3^i.$$

Furthermore, the same determinant is involved in computing the cofactors B_i^1 and A_i^2; that is,

$$\Delta_2^j(A) = \Delta_1^j(B).$$

But in one case we multiply the determinant by $(-1)^{1+i}$ and in the other case we multiply by $(-1)^{i+2}$. Thus,

$$B_j^1 = (-1)^{1+j}\,\Delta_1^j(B) = (-1)^{1+j}\,\Delta_2^j(A) = -A_j^2. \tag{19-3}$$

Using the first property of Definition 18-1,

$$det[A] = -det[B] = -b_1^\alpha B_\alpha^1 = a_2^\alpha A_\alpha^2. \tag{19-4}$$

We can repeat our argument with "2" replaced by "3" to obtain the formula

$$det[A] = a_k^\alpha A_\alpha^k, \quad (k \text{ a fixed number, } 1 \leqq k \leqq 3). \tag{19-5}$$

If the twenty-four products involved in the sum for the determinant of a 4 by 4 matrix are written out, you can derive equations similar to those in Equation 19-5. In fact, an induction argument can be supplied to show that the determinant of any matrix can be written as a sum involving the cofactors of a matrix:

$$det[A] = a_k^\alpha A_\alpha^k, \quad (k \text{ a fixed number, } 1 \leqq k \leqq n). \tag{19-6}$$

The method of evaluating the determinant of a matrix by using Equation 19-6 is called the method of ***Expansion by Cofactors***, or simply, expansion by the kth column.

Example 19-1 Evaluate $\begin{vmatrix} 0 & 1 & 0 & 0 \\ 1 & 0 & 3 & 0 \\ 1 & -1 & 0 & 0 \\ 1 & 0 & 1 & 2 \end{vmatrix}$.

Solution: Since there are more zeros in the fourth column than in any other, we will expand by the fourth column. Using $k = 4$ in Equation 19-6, our determinant is equal to

$$2(-1)^8 A_4^4 = 2\begin{vmatrix} 0 & 1 & 0 \\ 1 & 0 & 3 \\ 1 & -1 & 0 \end{vmatrix}.$$

Now we expand by the third column to get

$$2 \cdot 3 \cdot (-1)^5 \begin{vmatrix} 0 & 1 \\ 1 & -1 \end{vmatrix} = -6(0 - 1) = 6$$

as the value of our determinant.

Using the basic properties in Definition 18-1 can sometimes reduce the amount of calculation necessary to evaluate a determinant. Using Property (2), for example,

$$\begin{aligned} det[c\boldsymbol{a}_1\ \boldsymbol{a}_2\ \boldsymbol{a}_3] &= D(c\boldsymbol{a}_1, \boldsymbol{a}_2, \boldsymbol{a}_3) \\ &= c\ D(\boldsymbol{a}_1, \boldsymbol{a}_2, \boldsymbol{a}_3) \\ &= c\ det[\boldsymbol{a}_1\ \boldsymbol{a}_2\ \boldsymbol{a}_3]. \end{aligned}$$

Thus,

$$\begin{vmatrix} 2 & 1 & 3 \\ 4 & 2 & 6 \\ 6 & 0 & 9 \end{vmatrix} = 2\begin{vmatrix} 1 & 1 & 3 \\ 2 & 2 & 6 \\ 3 & 0 & 9 \end{vmatrix} = 6\begin{vmatrix} 1 & 1 & 1 \\ 2 & 2 & 2 \\ 3 & 0 & 3 \end{vmatrix} = 0,$$

where we used Theorem 18-1 to conclude that our last determinant is zero. Also, because

$$D(\boldsymbol{a}_1, \boldsymbol{a}_2, \boldsymbol{a}_3) = D(\boldsymbol{a}_1 + \boldsymbol{a}_2, \boldsymbol{a}_2, \boldsymbol{a}_3),$$

then

$$\begin{vmatrix} 1 & 2 & 4 \\ 1 & -1 & 0 \\ 2 & -2 & 2 \end{vmatrix} = \begin{vmatrix} 3 & 2 & 4 \\ 0 & -1 & 0 \\ 0 & -2 & 2 \end{vmatrix} = 3\begin{vmatrix} -1 & 0 \\ -2 & 2 \end{vmatrix} = -6.$$

With a little practice these methods of simplifying the computation of a determinant can become useful.

The sum on the right side of the equation used to evaluate a determinant using expansion by the kth row; namely,

$$det[A] = a_k^1 A_1^k + \cdots + a_k^n A_n^k,$$

looks like a sum involved in the multiplication of two matrices. To capitalize on that fact, we define the matrix known as the classical adjoint of $[A]$ and denoted by $[A]^\dagger$ by the following equation:

$$[A]^\dagger = \begin{bmatrix} A_1^1 & \cdots & A_n^1 \\ \vdots & & \vdots \\ A_1^n & \cdots & A_n^n \end{bmatrix}$$

where A_j^i is the cofactor of a_i^j (again notice the interchange of indices). Equation 19-5 states that each number on the main diagonal of $[A]^\dagger[A]$ is equal to $det[A]$. For example,

$$\begin{bmatrix} A_1^1 & \cdots & A_3^1 \\ \vdots & \ddots & \vdots \\ A_1^3 & \cdots & A_3^3 \end{bmatrix} \cdot \begin{bmatrix} a_1^1 & \cdots & a_3^1 \\ \vdots & & \vdots \\ a_1^3 & \cdots & a_3^3 \end{bmatrix}$$

is equal to

$$\begin{bmatrix} A_1^1 a_1^1 + \cdots + A_3^1 a_1^3 & * & * \\ * & A_1^2 a_2^1 + \cdots + A_3^2 a_2^3 & * \\ * & * & A_1^3 a_3^1 + \cdots + A_3^3 a_3^3 \end{bmatrix}.$$

Now let us look at the terms that lie off the main diagonal in this product. For example, let us find the value of

$$A_\alpha^1 a_2^\alpha = A_1^1 a_2^1 + A_2^1 a_2^2 + A_3^1 a_2^3.$$

Consider the matrix $[B]$ whose first and second columns are the second column of $[A]$ and whose third column is the third column of $[A]$. In short, let $[B] = [\boldsymbol{a}_2\ \boldsymbol{a}_2\ \boldsymbol{a}_3]$. Because

$$\Delta^j_2(B) = \Delta^j_1(B) = \Delta^j_1(A)$$

we have

$$B^2_j = (-1)^{2+j}\,\Delta^j_2(B) = (-1)^{2+j}\,\Delta^j_1(A) = -A^1_j.$$

Because $[B]$ has two identical columns it follows from Theorem 18-1 that $det[B] = 0$. Thus we see that

$$A^1_\alpha a^\alpha_2 = 0.$$

In a completely analogous manner it can be shown that for a square matrix $[A]$ of any size, the sum

$$A^j_\alpha a^\alpha_k = 0 \quad \text{if} \quad j \neq k.$$

Thus, $[A]^\dagger[A]$ is a diagonal matrix, and the diagonal numbers are $det[A]$. In short,

(19-7) $$[A]^\dagger[A] = (det[A])\,[I].$$

It follows from our earlier work (see Theorem 9-3) that if $det[A] \neq 0$, then the matrix obtained by multiplying $[A]^\dagger$ by the reciprocal of $det[A]$ is the inverse of $[A]$. Thus, if $det[A] \neq 0$, then

(19-8) $$[A][A]^\dagger = (det[A])\,[I].$$

We can also state the following theorem that gives us an alternate method of computing $[A]^{-1}$ if $[A]$ is invertible.

THEOREM 19-1

If $[A]$ is a square matrix and $det[A] \neq 0$, then $[A]$ is invertible, and furthermore

$$[A]^{-1} = \frac{1}{det[A]}\,[A]^\dagger.$$

Example 19-2 Compute $[A]^{-1}$ using Theorem 19-1 if

$$[A] = \begin{bmatrix} 3 & 1 \\ 4 & 2 \end{bmatrix}.$$

Solution: In computing cofactors in this example we utilize the fact that the determinant of a 1 by 1 matrix is the number itself. Thus, $A_1^1 = 2$, $A_1^2 = -4$, $A_2^1 = -1$, $A_2^2 = 3$, and

$$[A]^{\dagger} = \begin{bmatrix} 2 & -1 \\ -4 & 3 \end{bmatrix}.$$

Utilizing the fact that $det[A] = 2$, we find that

$$[A]^{-1} = \begin{bmatrix} 1 & -\frac{1}{2} \\ -2 & \frac{3}{2} \end{bmatrix}.$$

Notice that

$$[A][A]^{\dagger} = [A]^{\dagger}[A] = \begin{bmatrix} 2 & 0 \\ 0 & 2 \end{bmatrix}.$$

Let $[A] = [\boldsymbol{a}_1 \ldots \boldsymbol{a}_n]$ be a square matrix. The columns of the transpose $[A]^*$ are the rows of $[A]$. To avoid confusion, for the moment let us write

$$[A]^* = [B] = [\boldsymbol{b}_1 \ldots \boldsymbol{b}_n],$$

so that $b_j^i = a_i^j$. It is easy to see that the cofactors also are related by this same type of equation; namely, $B_j^i = A_i^j$. Using Equation 19-6,

$$det[B] = b_k^{\alpha} B_{\alpha}^k = a_{\alpha}^k A_k^{\alpha}.$$

The sum on the right is the number that appears in row k and column k of $[A][A]^{\dagger}$. By Equation 19-8, if $det[A] \neq 0$, this number is $det[A]$, so that $det[B] = det[A]$. If, however, $det[A] = 0$, then the columns of $[A]$ form a dependent set of vectors. From our earlier work with the rank of a matrix we can conclude that the rows of $[A]$ also form a dependent set of vectors. Hence, the columns of $[A]^* = [B]$ are dependent. Thus, $det[A]^* = det[A]$ in this case also. We have shown that

$$det[A]^* = det[A]. \tag{19-9}$$

As a result of Equation 19-9 we can restate a number of our earlier results about determinants in terms of rows instead of columns. We leave it to you to do so.

PROBLEMS 19

1. Evaluate the determinant of the matrix

(a) $\begin{bmatrix} 2 & 0 & 3 \\ 0 & 1 & 0 \\ 4 & 0 & 5 \end{bmatrix}$ (b) $\begin{bmatrix} 1 & 0 & 0 & 1 \\ 0 & 1 & 0 & 0 \\ 1 & 0 & 0 & 0 \\ 0 & 0 & 1 & 0 \end{bmatrix}$

(c) $\begin{bmatrix} 1 & 0 & 1 & 0 \\ 0 & 1 & 0 & 1 \\ 2 & 0 & 1 & 0 \\ 0 & 2 & 0 & 1 \end{bmatrix}$ (d) $\begin{bmatrix} 4 & 1 & 0 & 2 \\ 6 & 0 & 0 & -1 \\ 3 & -1 & 1 & 0 \\ -5 & 3 & 0 & 1 \end{bmatrix}$

2. Find $[A]^\dagger$ if $[A]$ is the matrix in
   (a) Problem 1(a) (b) Problem 1(b) (c) Problem 1(c) (d) Problem 1(d)
3. Find $[A]^{-1}$ using the results of Problems 1 and 2 if $[A]$ is the matrix in
   (a) Problem 1(a) (b) Problem 1(b) (c) Problem 1(c) (d) Problem 1(d)
4. Let $[A]$ be a square matrix. Show that:
   (a) If $[B]$ is derived by interchanging two rows of $[A]$ then $det[B] = -det[A]$.
   (b) If $[B]$ is derived by replacing the first row of $[A]$ by the sum of the first and second rows of $[A]$, then $det[B] = det[A]$.
   (c) If $[B]$ is derived by multiplying a row of $[A]$ by c then $det[B] = c\, det[A]$.
5. Use operations of the type indicated in the preceding problem to help you evaluate $det[A]$ if $[A]$ is the matrix

(a) $\begin{bmatrix} 0 & 1 & 2 \\ 1 & -1 & -2 \\ 3 & -2 & -3 \end{bmatrix}$ (b) $\begin{bmatrix} 1 & -1 & 1 & -1 \\ 1 & 1 & 1 & 1 \\ -1 & 1 & 1 & 1 \\ 1 & 1 & -1 & 1 \end{bmatrix}$

6. Let $[A] = [\boldsymbol{a}_1 \ldots \boldsymbol{a}_n]$, and suppose that

$$\boldsymbol{b} = x^1\boldsymbol{a}_1 + \cdots + x^n\boldsymbol{a}_n = x^\alpha\boldsymbol{a}_\alpha.$$

Show that

$$det[\boldsymbol{a}_1 \ldots \boldsymbol{a}_{j-1}\, \boldsymbol{b}\, \boldsymbol{a}_{j+1} \ldots \boldsymbol{a}_n] = x^j\, det[A].$$

7. The linear system

$$\begin{array}{ccccc} a_1^1 x^1 & + \cdots + & a_n^1 x^n & = & b^1 \\ \vdots & & \vdots & \vdots & \vdots \\ a_1^n x^1 & + \cdots + & a_n^n x^n & = & b^n \end{array}$$

can be written as $[A][\boldsymbol{x}] = [\boldsymbol{b}]$, or as

$$x^1\boldsymbol{a}_1 + \cdots + x^n\boldsymbol{a}_n = \boldsymbol{b},$$

where $[A] = [\boldsymbol{a}_1 \ldots \boldsymbol{a}_n]$. The preceding problem gives us a method for solving for $\boldsymbol{x}$ if $det[A] \neq 0$. It is called ***Cramer's Rule***. Write out this rule as it applies to the system

$$\begin{aligned} ax + by &= c \\ dx + ey &= f. \end{aligned}$$

20 THE DETERMINANT OF AN OPERATOR

Let V be an n-dimensional Euclidean space in which a signed volume function has been introduced. A linear operator F in V can be represented by a matrix $[F]$ if a basis is chosen in V. Thus, we can associate with F the determinant $det[F]$ and a number is then associated with F for each basis. In this section we will see that different matrix representations (corresponding to different bases in V) have the same determinant. Thus, this number can be called the determinant of F, and it has a geometric interpretation. It is a "distortion" factor that tells us the ratio of the signed volume of $F(U)$ to the signed volume of U for each set U of n vectors.

Let E and $\hat{E}$ be any two bases in V. We will review the method used in the proof of Theorem 3-1 by which E is replaced by $\hat{E}$ in a step-by-step fashion. There are numbers $c^1, \ldots, c^n$, not all zero, such that

(20-1) $$\hat{\boldsymbol{e}}_1 = c_1^\alpha \boldsymbol{e}_\alpha.$$

Relabeling, if necessary, we can assume that $c_1^1 \neq 0$, so we can solve for $\boldsymbol{e}_1$ to get

$$\boldsymbol{e}_1 = \frac{1}{c_1^1}(\hat{\boldsymbol{e}}_1 - c_1^2\boldsymbol{e}_2 - \cdots - c_1^n\boldsymbol{e}_n).$$

It follows from Theorems 2-1 and 4-2 that

$$E_1 = \{\hat{e}_1, e_2, \ldots, e_n\}$$

is a basis for V. Now a similar argument can be used (see the proof of Theorem 3-1) to show that

$$E_2 = \{\hat{e}_1, \hat{e}_2, e_3, \ldots, e_n\}$$

is a basis for V. Thus, in a step by step fashion we obtain a sequence of basis sets $E, E_1, \ldots, E_{n-1}, \hat{E}$. If D is the signed volume function associated with some fixed basis (not necessarily E), then it follows from Equation 20-1 and the basic properties of a signed volume that

$$D(E_1) = c_1^1 D(E). \tag{20-2}$$

Now suppose that F is a linear operator in V. Then

$$F(\hat{e}_1) = F(c_1^\alpha e_\alpha) = c_1^\alpha F(e_\alpha).$$

In the same way that Equation 20-1 leads to Equation 20-2, the preceding equation leads to the equation

$$D(F(E_1)) = c_1^1 D(F(E)). \tag{20-3}$$

Because neither $D(E_1)$ nor $D(E)$ is zero (Why?), we can solve Equation 20-2 for c_1^1, and then Equation 20-3 can be written as

$$\frac{D(F(E_1))}{D(E_1)} = \frac{D(F(E))}{D(E)}.$$

The method of deriving E_2 from E_1 is precisely the same as the way in which E_1 is derived from E. So we can write an analogous equation in which E_1 and E are replaced with E_2 and E_1. Thus,

$$\frac{D(F(E_2))}{D(E_2)} = \frac{D(F(E_1))}{D(E_1)} = \frac{D(F(E))}{D(E)}.$$

The point is that in each step of our method of obtaining $\hat{E}$ from E the ratio of the signed volume of the image of the basis set to the signed volume of the basis set is the same. Thus,

$$\frac{D(F(\hat{E}))}{D(\hat{E})} = \frac{D(F(E))}{D(E)} \tag{20-4}$$

for any two basis sets E and $\hat{E}$. We have completed the difficult part of the proof of the following theorem that will be used to define the determinant of an operator.

THEOREM 20-1

Let F be a linear operator in an n-dimensional Euclidean space with a signed volume function D. Then there is a number k such that for any set U of n vectors

$$D(F(U)) = kD(U).$$

The number k does *not* depend on U.

Proof: If U is a dependent set, then both sides of our equation are equal to zero according to Theorem 18-1 and Problem 18-4. If U_1 and U_2 are two independent sets, then they can be chosen as bases, and the number k is the common ratio expressed in Equation 20-4. ∎

Theorem 20-1 is used to define the determinant of an operator. We simply call the number k of that theorem the determinant of the operator F and write $|F| = k$. Thus, the equation in Theorem 20-1 becomes

$$D(F(U)) = |F|D(U). \tag{20-5}$$

For example, if I is the identity operator, then $I(U) = U$ for any set U, and so $D(U) = |I|D(U)$. It follows, as we might expect, that $|I| = 1$.

Once a signed volume is chosen in V, then $|F|$ is defined without referring to any particular basis. In particular, we could choose to represent F in the orthonormal basis E that is used to define a signed volume. In that case $D(E) = 1$, and

$$D(F(E)) = |F|.$$

Now, if $F(e_j) = a_j^\alpha e_\alpha$ ($j = 1, \ldots, n$), then the matrix representation of F in the basis E is $[A]$. In short, $[F] = [A]$. If $A = \{\boldsymbol{a}_1, \ldots, \boldsymbol{a}_n\}$, then $F(E) = A$, and so $D(F(E)) = det[A] = det[F]$. Thus, we see that

$$|F| = det[F].$$

It is implicit in our definition of $|F|$ that it is possible to compute the determinant of the operator F by finding the matrix of F with respect to any basis we wish, and then finding the determinant of that matrix. We will get the same answer no matter what basis is chosen. This fact will be more evident after we have established a few more results about determinants.

THEOREM 20-2

Let $[A]$ and $[B]$ be n by n matrices. Then

$$det([A][B]) = det[A]\, det[B].$$

In words, the determinant of a product is the product of the determinants.

Proof: Let E be the natural basis in R^n with the standard inner product. There is a unique signed volume function D in R^n associated with E. If $A = \{\boldsymbol{a}_1, \ldots, \boldsymbol{a}_n\}$ is the set of column vectors of $[A]$, then $det[A] = D(A)$. If F is the linear operator in R^n whose matrix in the natural basis is $[A]$ (that is, if $[F] = [A]$), then, as we saw above,

$$|F| = det[F] = det[A].$$

In a similar way, if G is the linear operator such that $[G] = [B]$, then

$$|G| = det[G] = det[B],$$

and

$$|F \circ G| = det([F \circ G]).$$

Because $[F \circ G] = [F][G]$, it follows from this last equation that

$$det([F][G]) = |F \circ G|. \tag{20-6}$$

Using the definition of the determinant of an operator, and the fact that $D(E) = 1$,

$$|F \circ G| = D(F(G(E))) = |F|D(G(E)) = |F||G| = det[F]\, det[G].$$

Our result follows from this equation and Equation 20-6. ∎

THEOREM 20-3

A linear operator F in a Euclidean space V is invertible if, and only if, $|F| \neq 0$.

20-5 $\Delta(F(u)) = |F|\Delta(u)$

Proof: Let E be any basis for V. From Equation 20-5 $D(F(E)) \neq 0$ if, and only if, $|F| \neq 0$. From Theorem 18-2 $D(F(E)) \neq 0$ if, and only if, $F(E)$ is a basis. But $F(E)$ is a basis if, and only if, F is invertible (Why?).   ■

If F is an invertible operator, then $F \circ F^{-1} = I$, and hence, $|F \circ F^{-1}| = |I|$. Using Theorem 20-2, we see that $|F\|F^{-1}| = 1$, from which we conclude that

(20-7) $$|F^{-1}| = |F|^{-1}.$$

Any square matrix $[A]$ is the matrix of some linear operator F in a Euclidean space with a fixed basis. Then $[F^{-1}] = [A]^{-1}$, and $det[A] = |F|$, so that Equation 20-7 can be interpreted as a statement about determinants of matrices; namely,

(20-8) $$det([A]^{-1}) = (det[A])^{-1}.$$

Example 20-1   Show that if E is a basis and if $F(e_1) = 3e_1 + 8e_2 + 2e_3$, $F(e_2) = 4e_1 + 7e_2 - e_3$, and $F(e_3) = -5e_1 - 2e_2 + 8e_3$; then F is not invertible.

Solution:

$$|F| = det[F] = \begin{vmatrix} 3 & 4 & 5 \\ 8 & 7 & -2 \\ 2 & -1 & 8 \end{vmatrix} = 0.$$

Now we can see explicitly that to compute $|F|$ we may choose any basis we want and compute $det[F]$. For if E and $\hat{E}$ are any two bases, Theorem 9-4 tells us that there is a matrix $[M]$ such that

$[F]_{\hat{E}}^{\hat{E}} = [I]_{E}^{\hat{E}} {}^{-1} [F]_{E}^{E} [I]_{\hat{E}}^{E}$

$$[F]_{\hat{E}}^{\hat{E}} = [M]^{-1}[F]_{E}^{E}[M].$$

It follows from Theorem 20-2 and Equation 20-8 that

$$\begin{aligned} det[F]_{\hat{E}}^{\hat{E}} &= (det[M]^{-1}) \, det[F]_{E}^{E} \, det[M] \\ &= (det[M])^{-1} \, det[F]_{E}^{E} \, det[M] \\ &= det[F]_{E}^{E}. \end{aligned}$$

THEOREM 20-4

If $[A]$ is an orthogonal matrix, then $det[A] = \pm 1$.

See Def. 12-3 p. 98

Proof: From the definition of an orthogonal matrix we know that $[A]^{-1} = [A]^*$, and so

$$det[A]^{-1} = det[A]^* = det[A].$$

But

$$det([A][A]^{-1}) = det[I],$$

and hence,

$$det[A]\, det[A]^{-1} = 1.$$

Thus,

$$(det[A])^2 = 1,$$

and the result follows. ∎

We are now in a position to answer an important question about volumes. When we informally discussed volume in spaces of dimension 1 and 2, we assigned the volume of *all* orthonormal sets to be ± 1. Since the volume concept has now been put on a firm logical basis, we should ask whether or not the volume of any orthonormal set is ± 1, because we did not assume this fact in our axiomatic development. Our definition of a volume function assigned the volume 1 to some fixed orthonormal set of n vectors. Then the volume of every basis is determined, so the following question needs to be answered: Suppose we choose one orthonormal basis E so that $D(E) = 1$. Is it true that $D(\hat{E}) = \pm 1$ for every other orthonormal basis $\hat{E}$? The answer to that question is the following theorem.

THEOREM 20-5

Let D be a volume function in a Euclidean space with respect to an orthonormal basis E. If $\hat{E}$ is any orthonormal basis, then $D(\hat{E}) = \pm 1$.

Proof: The formal part of the proof is one line:

$$D(\hat{E}) = det[\hat{e}_1 \ldots \hat{e}_n]_E = det[I]_E^{\hat{E}} = \pm 1.$$

We leave it to you as an exercise to supply the reason for each step. ∎

PROBLEMS 20

1. Let V be a Euclidean space with a volume function with respect to an orthonormal basis E. Let F be a linear operator in V.
   (a) Find $|F|$ if $F(\boldsymbol{e}_1) = \boldsymbol{e}_1 + \boldsymbol{e}_2$; $F(\boldsymbol{e}_2) = \boldsymbol{e}_2 + \boldsymbol{e}_3$; and $F(\boldsymbol{e}_3) = \boldsymbol{e}_3 + \boldsymbol{e}_1$.
   (b) If $|F| = 1$, $F(\boldsymbol{e}_1) = \boldsymbol{e}_1$, and $F(\boldsymbol{e}_2) = \boldsymbol{e}_2$, what can you conclude about $F(\boldsymbol{e}_3)$?
   (c) Suppose that F is defined by the equations $F(\boldsymbol{e}_j) = \boldsymbol{u}_j$ $(j = 1,2,3)$ where each $\boldsymbol{u}_j$ is given by Problem 18-5c. Is F invertible? If so, define F^{-1} by giving its values for $\boldsymbol{e}_1$, $\boldsymbol{e}_2$, and $\boldsymbol{e}_3$ and verify Equation 20-7.
   (d) Same as (c) except replace 18-5c with 18-5d.
   (e) Same as (c) except replace 18-5c with 18-5e.
2. Verify that $det([A][B]) = det[A]\,det[B]$ directly by computation if

   (a)
$$[A] = \begin{bmatrix} 1 & 2 \\ 2 & 3 \end{bmatrix} \qquad [B] = \begin{bmatrix} 1 & -1 \\ 2 & 3 \end{bmatrix}$$

   (b)
$$[A] = \begin{bmatrix} 1 & 0 & 1 \\ 0 & 1 & 1 \\ 1 & 1 & 0 \end{bmatrix} \qquad [B] = \begin{bmatrix} 0 & 0 & 1 \\ 1 & 0 & 1 \\ 0 & 1 & 1 \end{bmatrix}$$

3. Suppose that E is the natural basis in R^3 and that F is the operator defined by the equations in Problem 1(a). Compute $D(U)$ and $D(F(U))$ if
   (a) $U = \{(1,1,0), (0,1,1), (1,0,1)\}$
   (b) $U = \{(1,1,0), (1,0,1), (0,1,1)\}$
   (c) $U = \{(1,2,3), (2,3,1), (3,1,2)\}$
4. Explain the proof of Theorem 20-5.

Six

The Geometric Characterization of a Linear Operator

In Chapter Two we learned that a linear operator in a finite dimensional vector space could be thought of as a square matrix. This interpretation is an algebraic or numeric interpretation of a linear operator. Our goal in this chapter is to show that, in geometric terms, every linear operator can be constructed from two simple geometric operators; namely, projection and reflection operators. We have already encountered the idea of an orthogonal projection (Definition 11-1), and the notion of a reflection also has a simple geometric interpretation. Some of the details of the proofs in this chapter are rather burdensome, and at times we have left them for you to work out, not to shift the burden of the work to you, but rather to try to keep the main ideas in plain sight. Some of the more difficult details have been worked out for you in Appendix B, but our advice is not to bother with Appendix B the first time you read this chapter.

21 THE TRANSPOSE OF A LINEAR OPERATOR

Suppose that $[A]$ is a 2 by 2 matrix. The transpose of $[A]$ is the matrix $[A]^*$ whose columns are the rows of $[A]$. Let F be the linear operator in R^2 whose matrix representation in the natural basis is $[A]$. Using the standard inner product (the dot product),

$$F(\mathbf{x}) \cdot \mathbf{y} = (a_1^1 x^1 + a_2^1 x^2) y^1 + (a_1^2 x^1 + a_2^2 x^2) y^2.$$

Regrouping, we can write this equation as

(21-1) $$F(\mathbf{x}) \cdot \mathbf{y} = x^1(a_1^1 y^1 + a_1^2 y^2) + x^2(a_2^1 y^1 + a_2^2 y^2).$$

If G is the operator in R^2 defined by the equation

$$G(y^1, y^2) = (a_1^1 y^1 + a_1^2 y^2, a_2^1 y^1 + a_2^2 y^2),$$

then Equation 21-1 may be written

$$F(\mathbf{x}) \cdot \mathbf{y} = \mathbf{x} \cdot G(\mathbf{y}).$$

The matrix of G in the natural basis is $[A]^*$. Thus, $[G] = [F]^*$ and G will be called the transpose of F. We write $G = F^*$.

Let E be any orthonormal basis in a Euclidean space V. If F is a linear operator in V whose matrix representation in the basis E is $[A]$, then

$$\langle F(\mathbf{e}_k), \mathbf{e}_j \rangle = \langle a_k^\alpha \mathbf{e}_\alpha, \mathbf{e}_j \rangle = a_k^\alpha \langle \mathbf{e}_\alpha, \mathbf{e}_j \rangle.$$

Because E is an orthonormal basis, every term in this last sum is zero except for the term in which $\alpha = j$, and then $\langle \mathbf{e}_j, \mathbf{e}_j \rangle = 1$. Thus,

(21-2) $$\langle F(\mathbf{e}_k), \mathbf{e}_j \rangle = a_k^j.$$

If F^* is the operator whose matrix representation in the orthonormal basis E is $[A]^*$, then

(21-3) $$\langle \mathbf{e}_k, F^*(\mathbf{e}_j) \rangle = \langle \mathbf{e}_k, a^{*\alpha}_{\ j} \mathbf{e}_\alpha \rangle = a^{*k}_{\ j} = a_k^j.$$

From Equations 21-2 and 21-3 we can conclude that

$$\langle \mathbf{e}_k, F^*(\mathbf{e}_j) \rangle = \langle F(\mathbf{e}_k), \mathbf{e}_j \rangle.$$

It is then an easy matter to show that for any two vectors $\boldsymbol{x}$ and $\boldsymbol{y}$ in V,

$$\langle F(\boldsymbol{x}), \boldsymbol{y}\rangle = \langle \boldsymbol{x}, F^*(\boldsymbol{y})\rangle. \tag{21-4}$$

Once again it would be helpful to have a "coordinate free" definition of F^*. Equation 21-4 suggests a definition, but in order to use that equation for a definition we must show that given F, there is only one operator F^* that makes Equation 21-4 valid.

THEOREM 21-1

Let F be a linear operator in a Euclidean space V. Then there exists a unique operator F^* such that

$$\langle F(\boldsymbol{x}), \boldsymbol{y}\rangle = \langle \boldsymbol{x}, F^*(\boldsymbol{y})\rangle \text{ for all } \boldsymbol{x}, \boldsymbol{y} \text{ in } V.$$

Proof: If we choose an orthonormal basis E for V and define F^* by saying that in the basis E we have $[F^*] = [F]^*$, then F^* exists such that Equation 21-4 is valid. Suppose that a second operator F_1^* exists such that Equation 21-4 is valid. Then

$$\langle \boldsymbol{x}, F^*(\boldsymbol{y})\rangle = \langle \boldsymbol{x}, F_1^*(\boldsymbol{y})\rangle \text{ for all } \boldsymbol{x}, \boldsymbol{y}.$$

It follows that

$$\langle \boldsymbol{x}, (F^* - F_1^*)(\boldsymbol{y})\rangle = 0 \text{ for all } \boldsymbol{x}, \boldsymbol{y};$$

and hence

$$(F^* - F_1^*)(\boldsymbol{y}) = \boldsymbol{0} \text{ for all } \boldsymbol{y} \text{ (Why?)}.$$

Thus,

$$F^* - F_1^* = 0.$$

■

DEFINITION 21-1

Let F be a linear operator on a Euclidean space V. The operator F^* defined by Equation 21-4 is called the ***transpose*** of F.

The relationship between the matrices of F and F^* *in an orthonormal basis* is what we would like it to be; namely, $[F^*] = [F]^*$. The relationship of the matrices is more complicated if a non-orthonormal basis is used.

Example 21-1 If E is the natural basis in R^3 and $F(e_1) = e_2 + e_3$, $F(e_2) = e_3 + e_1$, and $F(e_3) = e_1 + e_2$, find F^*.

Solution:

$$[F] = \begin{bmatrix} 0 & 1 & 1 \\ 1 & 0 & 1 \\ 1 & 1 & 0 \end{bmatrix}.$$

Because $[F]^* = [F]$, in this case $F^* = F$.

THEOREM 21-2

$$(F + G)^* = F^* + G^* \quad \text{and} \quad F^{**} = F.$$

Proof:

$$\begin{aligned} \langle (F + G)(x), y \rangle &= \langle F(x), y \rangle + \langle G(x), y \rangle \\ &= \langle x, F^*(y) \rangle + \langle x, G^*(y) \rangle \\ &= \langle x, (F^* + G^*)(y) \rangle. \end{aligned}$$

But $\langle (F + G)(x), y \rangle = \langle x, (F + G)^*(y) \rangle$ by definition, so our first result follows.

The equations

$$\begin{aligned} \langle F(x), y \rangle &= \langle x, F^*(y) \rangle = \langle F^*(y), x \rangle \\ &= \langle y, F^{**}(x) \rangle = \langle F^{**}(x), y \rangle \end{aligned}$$

show that $F^{**} = F$. ∎

The properties of transposes of operators that we just proved, along with the property

(21-5) $$(F \circ G)^* = G^* \circ F^*$$

that we ask you to prove in Problem 21-2, were proved for matrices in Problems 12. Thus, we could choose a fixed orthonormal basis, and the operator properties then follow from the matrix properties. The proof that we gave for Theorem 21-2 has the advantage that it was independent of the choice of basis and it is valid in the infinite dimensional case, too. Our proof for the existence of F^* did depend on the fact that we were talking about a finite dimensional space, and we cannot conclude in the infinite dimensional case in general that a linear operator has a transpose.

THEOREM 21-3

If F is a linear operator in a Euclidean space, then $|F^*| = |F|$.

Proof: To compute $|F^*|$, choose an orthonormal basis E. Let $[F]$ be the matrix of F in the basis E. Then

$$|F^*| = det[F^*] = det[F]^* = det[F] = |F|. \qquad \blacksquare$$

In Section 12 an isometry was defined as a linear map that preserved the inner product. Thus, a linear operator $F: V \to V$ is an isometry if

$$\langle F(v), F(w) \rangle = \langle v, w \rangle \text{ for all } v \text{ and } w \text{ in } V.$$

Our next theorem tells us that isometries are precisely those operators whose inverse and transpose are the same.

THEOREM 21-4

A linear operator $F: V \to V$ is an isometry if, and only if, $F^{-1} = F^*$.

$$\text{from } \langle F(x), y \rangle = \langle x, F^*(y) \rangle$$

Proof: If F is an isometry, then

$$\langle v, w \rangle = \langle F(v), F(w) \rangle = \langle v, (F^* \circ F)(w) \rangle$$

$$\langle v, F^*(F(w)) \rangle$$

for all v and w. Thus,

$$F^* \circ F = I$$

and so F^{-1} does exist. Furthermore, $F^{-1} = F^*$.
Conversely, if $F^* = F^{-1}$, then

$$\langle F(v), F(w) \rangle = \langle v, (F^* \circ F)(w) \rangle = \langle v, w \rangle,$$

and so F is an isometry. $\qquad \blacksquare$

In any basis $[F^{-1}] = [F]^{-1}$, and in an orthonormal basis $[F^*] = [F]^*$. Thus, the matrix representing an isometry in an orthonormal basis is an orthogonal matrix. This statement is not true if the restriction to an orthonormal basis is removed.

If $[A]^* = [A]$, the matrix is said to be *symmetric*. In this case it is "symmetric" with respect to the main diagonal (see Example 21-1). If the matrix $[F]$ of an operator with respect to an orthonormal basis is a symmetric matrix, then $F^* = F$ and $\langle F(u), v \rangle = \langle u, F(v) \rangle$ for all u, v.

DEFINITION 21-2

If $F = F^*$; that is, if $\langle F(\boldsymbol{u}), \boldsymbol{v}\rangle = \langle \boldsymbol{u}, F(\boldsymbol{v})\rangle$ for all $\boldsymbol{u}$, $\boldsymbol{v}$ in V, then F is called a ***symmetric operator***.

Example 21-2 Let F be a symmetric operator. Show that cF is a symmetric operator.

Solution: For all $\boldsymbol{u}$ and $\boldsymbol{v}$

$$\langle (cF)(\boldsymbol{u}), \boldsymbol{v}\rangle = c\langle F(\boldsymbol{u}), \boldsymbol{v}\rangle = c\langle \boldsymbol{u}, F(\boldsymbol{v})\rangle = \langle \boldsymbol{u}, (cF)(\boldsymbol{v})\rangle.$$

Example 21-3 Let F and G be symmetric operators. Show that $F + G$ is a symmetric operator.

Solution: Using Theorem 21-2,

$$(F + G)^* = F^* + G^* = F + G.$$

The preceding two examples say that *a linear combination of symmetric operators is a symmetric operator*. Just as every vector in a Euclidean space can be written as a linear combination of certain basic (basis) vectors, so every symmetric operator can be written as a linear combination of certain basic symmetric operators. These basic symmetric operators are the projection operators, which we will study in the next section.

PROBLEMS 21

1. Let F be an operator in R^2 and let $\hat{\boldsymbol{e}}_1 = (1,0)$ and $\hat{\boldsymbol{e}}_2 = (1,1)$. Find $[F^*]$, $[F]^{\hat{E}}_{\hat{E}}$, and $[F^*]^{\hat{E}}_{\hat{E}}$ if $[F]$ is the matrix

(a) $\begin{bmatrix} 1 & 2 \\ 3 & 4 \end{bmatrix}$ (b) $\begin{bmatrix} -1 & 1 \\ -1 & 2 \end{bmatrix}$ ← IN ORTHONORMAL BASIS

(c) $\begin{bmatrix} 1 & 2 \\ 2 & 3 \end{bmatrix}$ (d) $\begin{bmatrix} 0 & 1 \\ -1 & 0 \end{bmatrix}$

2. Prove that $(F \circ G)^* = G^* \circ F^*$. Write a similar equation for $(F \circ G \circ H)^*$.
3. Prove that $(F^{-1})^* = (F^*)^{-1}$.
4. Prove that if F is a symmetric operator and G is an isometry, then $G^{-1} \circ F \circ G$ is symmetric.

5. Suppose that F and G are symmetric operators. Under what conditions is $F \circ G$ a symmetric operator?
6. Let $\{e_1, e_2, e_3\} = E$ be a basis for V. Define the operator F by the equation

$$F(v) = \langle v, e_1 \rangle e_1.$$

Show that F is a symmetric operator. Find the matrix of F if $V = R^3$ and E is the natural basis. What is the rank of F?

7. Let F be a linear operator in an inner product space V and let $s(u, v) = \langle F(u), v \rangle$. Show that $s(u, v)$ is an inner product (different from the one indicated by $\langle u, v \rangle$ if $F \neq I$) if, and only if, F is a symmetric operator with the property that $\langle F(v), v \rangle$ is positive if $v \neq 0$.
8. Let $V = \{f : f \text{ in } C^\infty[0,1], f(0) = f(1) = 0\}$ with the usual integral inner product. Let D be the derivative operator.
   (a) Use integration by parts to show that $\langle f', g \rangle = -\langle f, g' \rangle$.
   (b) Is D symmetric?
   (c) Is D^2 symmetric?

22 PROJECTIONS AND REFLECTIONS

The orthogonal projection of v on a non-zero vector w in a Euclidean space V (see Definition 11-1) is the vector

$$P_w(v) = cw,$$

where

$$c = \frac{\langle w, v \rangle}{\langle w, w \rangle}. \tag{22-1}$$

Let $W = \text{Sp}\,\{w\}$ and suppose that w_1 is any non-zero vector in W. Then $w_1 = kw$ for some non-zero number k, and

$$P_{w_1}(v) = c_1 w_1,$$

where

$$c_1 = \frac{\langle kw, v \rangle}{\langle kw, kw \rangle}. \tag{22-2}$$

From Equations 22-1 and 22-2 it follows that $kc_1 = c$, so that

$$P_{w_1}(v) = c_1 k w = cw = P_w(v).$$

Since the projections of a vector $\boldsymbol{v}$ on any two non-zero vectors in W are the same, we can consider the projection of $\boldsymbol{v}$ onto the subspace W to be the projection of $\boldsymbol{v}$ onto any non-zero vector in W. We will now generalize this idea of the projection of a vector onto a one-dimensional subspace to the notion of projections onto subspaces of dimensions other than 1.

First, if W is a one-dimensional subspace, it follows from Theorem 11-1 and our discussion above that

$$\boldsymbol{v} = P_W(\boldsymbol{v}) + \boldsymbol{z}$$

where $\boldsymbol{z}$ is in $W^{\perp}$, and we have written P_W for the projection operator defined in the preceding paragraph. Now using Equation 13-2 we can write $V = W \oplus W^{\perp}$, and there are unique vectors $\boldsymbol{w}$ in W and $\boldsymbol{w}^{\perp}$ in $W^{\perp}$ such that $\boldsymbol{v} = \boldsymbol{w} + \boldsymbol{w}^{\perp}$. Thus, if W is one dimensional, $P_W(\boldsymbol{v})$ is the "part of $\boldsymbol{v}$" that is in W when V is expressed as the direct sum of W and $W^{\perp}$. This fact suggests the way in which we can generalize our idea of projection to the case when W is any subspace of V, not just a one-dimensional subspace. Our formal definition of the projection operator is the following.

DEFINITION 22-1

Let V be any Euclidean space and W be a subspace of V. Every $\boldsymbol{v}$ in V can be written in a unique way as $\boldsymbol{v} = \boldsymbol{w} + \boldsymbol{w}^{\perp}$ where $\boldsymbol{w} \in W$ and $\boldsymbol{w}^{\perp} \in W^{\perp}$. The ***projection on W***, written P_W, is the operator defined by the equation

$$P_W(\boldsymbol{v}) = \boldsymbol{w}.$$

We have defined an *orthogonal projection.* A more general projection could be defined by using any pair of complementary subspaces, but we will not use such projections. If W is a one-dimensional subspace, the projection just defined coincides with the idea of the orthogonal projection we talked about before. If $W = V$, then $P_W = I$; and if $W = \{\boldsymbol{0}\}$, then P_W is the zero operator.

If $V = W \oplus W^{\perp}$ and $\boldsymbol{v}_1$ and $\boldsymbol{v}_2$ are two vectors in V, then we can write

$$\boldsymbol{v}_1 = \boldsymbol{w}_1 + \boldsymbol{w}_1^{\perp} \text{ and } \boldsymbol{v}_2 = \boldsymbol{w}_2 + \boldsymbol{w}_2^{\perp}$$

where $\boldsymbol{w}_1$ and $\boldsymbol{w}_2$ are in W and $\boldsymbol{w}_1^{\perp}$ and $\boldsymbol{w}_2^{\perp}$ are in $W^{\perp}$. Then

$$\begin{aligned} P_W(c\boldsymbol{v}_1 + \boldsymbol{v}_2) &= P_W(c\boldsymbol{w}_1 + \boldsymbol{w}_2 + c\boldsymbol{w}_1^{\perp} + \boldsymbol{w}_2^{\perp}) \\ &= c\boldsymbol{w}_1 + \boldsymbol{w}_2 = cP_W(\boldsymbol{v}_1) + P_W(\boldsymbol{v}_2). \end{aligned}$$

Thus, P_W is a linear operator. As you can easily verify,

$$P_W(V) = W \quad \text{and} \quad K(P_W) = W^\perp.$$

The operator $P_{W^\perp}$ is the projection on $W^\perp$; and you can also easily verify that

$$P_W \circ P_{W^\perp} = P_{W^\perp} \circ P_W = 0, \text{ the zero operator.}$$

SINCE $W \circ W^\perp = 0$

If

$$v = w + w^\perp,$$

then for every v

$$P_W \circ P_W(v) = P_W(w) = w = P_W(v).$$

Thus,

$$P_W^2 = P_W.$$

Next, we show that P_W is a symmetric operator.

THEOREM 22-1

A projection is a symmetric operator.

Proof: Using the notation above,

$= \langle w_1, w_2 \rangle + \langle w, w_2^\perp \rangle = \langle w, w_2 \rangle$

$$\langle P_W(v_1), v_2 \rangle = \langle w_1, w_2 + w_2^\perp \rangle = \langle w_1, w_2 \rangle \quad \text{(Why?)}$$
$$\langle v_1, P_W(v_2) \rangle = \langle w_1 + w_1^\perp, w_2 \rangle = \langle w_1, w_2 \rangle.$$

Because $\langle v_1, P_W(v_2) \rangle = \langle P_W(v_1), v_2 \rangle$, we know that $P_W^* = P_W$. ∎

Suppose that $W_1, \ldots, W_k$ are mutually orthogonal subspaces and

$$V = W_1 \oplus \cdots \oplus W_k.$$

Let P_j be the projection on W_j. Then P_j is a symmetric operator, and from Examples 21-2 and 21-3 we know that $c^1 P_1 + \cdots + c^k P_k$ is a symmetric operator for any set of numbers $c^1, \ldots, c^k$. In short, if $F = c^\alpha P_\alpha$, then F is a symmetric operator. The converse of this fact, namely, that there are numbers and projection operators such that any symmetric operator S can be written as a sum $c^\alpha P_\alpha$, is an important theorem that we will prove later.

If W is a line (subspace) in a two-dimensional geometric space, then the image of a point P under an orthogonal reflection about W is the point Q such that W is the perpendicular bisector of the segment PQ. Thus, if

$$\boldsymbol{v} = \boldsymbol{OP} = \boldsymbol{w} + \boldsymbol{w}^{\perp}$$

(see Fig. 22-1), then the image of $\boldsymbol{v}$ under a reflection R_W about W is

$$R_W(\boldsymbol{v}) = \boldsymbol{w} - \boldsymbol{w}^{\perp}.$$

Just as we generalized the notion of an (orthogonal) projection, so too we generalize the idea of an (orthogonal) reflection by the following definition.

DEFINITION 22-2

Let W be a subspace of a Euclidean space V. If $\boldsymbol{v}$ is any vector in V, there are unique vectors $\boldsymbol{w}$ and $\boldsymbol{w}^{\perp}$ such that $\boldsymbol{v} = \boldsymbol{w} + \boldsymbol{w}^{\perp}$ where $\boldsymbol{w}$ is in W and $\boldsymbol{w}^{\perp}$ is in $W^{\perp}$. The ***reflection about*** W, written R_W, is the operator defined by the equation

$$R_W(\boldsymbol{v}) = \boldsymbol{w} - \boldsymbol{w}^{\perp}.$$

We have defined an *orthogonal reflection*, but because these are the only kind of reflections we will use, we will omit the word "orthogonal" in our description of a reflection. If $W = V$, then $R_W = I$; and if $W = \{\boldsymbol{0}\}$, then

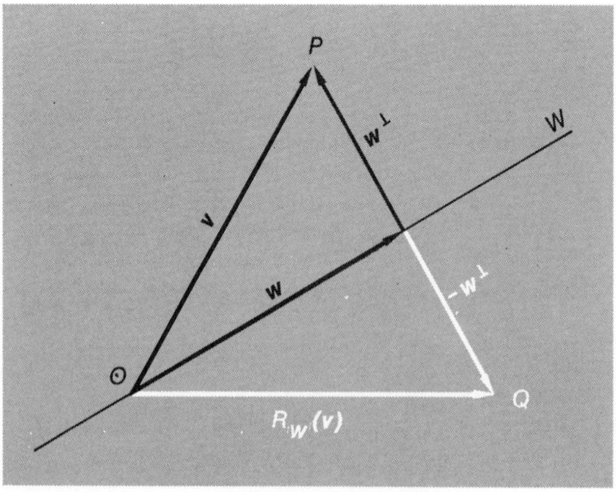

Figure 22-1

$R_W(v) = -v$. This latter reflection is called a reflection "about the origin" in coordinate geometry.

THEOREM 22-2

A reflection is a symmetric linear operator whose "square" is the identity operator.

Proof:

$$\begin{aligned} R_W(cv + u) &= R_W\big(c(w_1 + w_1^\perp) + (w_2 + w_2^\perp)\big) \\ &= R_W\big((cw_1 + w_2) + (cw_1^\perp + w_2^\perp)\big) \\ &= cw_1 + w_2 - cw_1^\perp - w_2^\perp \\ &= c(w_1 - w_1^\perp) + (w_2 - w_2^\perp) \\ &= cR_W(v) + R_W(u). \end{aligned}$$

Hence, R_W is linear.

To see that $R_W^2 = I$ we write

$$R_W^2(v) = R_W\big(R_W(w_1 + w_1^\perp)\big) = R_W(w_1 - w_1^\perp) = w_1 + w_1^\perp = v.$$

Finally, we show that R_W is symmetric.

$$\begin{aligned} \langle R_W(v), u\rangle &= \langle w_1 - w_1^\perp, w_2 + w_2^\perp\rangle \\ &= \langle w_1, w_2\rangle - \langle w_1^\perp, w_2^\perp\rangle \\ &= \langle w_1 + w_1^\perp, w_2 - w_2^\perp\rangle \\ &= \langle v, R_W(u)\rangle. \end{aligned}$$

∎

THEOREM 22-3

A reflection is an isometry.

Proof: Because $R_W^* = R_W$ and $R_W^2 = I$,

$$\begin{aligned} \langle R_W(v), R_W(u)\rangle &= \langle v, R_W^*(R_W(u))\rangle \\ &= \langle v, R_W^2(u)\rangle = \langle v, u\rangle. \end{aligned}$$

∎

The converse of Theorem 22-3 is true in a one-dimensional Euclidean space V. For if F is a linear operator in V, then $F(v) = cv$ for every vector v. If we require F to be an isometry, then $|F(v)| = |v|$, so $|c| = 1$. It follows that either $F = I$ (a reflection about V) or $F(v) = -v$ (a reflection about the origin). Thus, the only isometries in a one dimensional space are reflections. In two dimensions there are isometries that are not reflections. For example, a rotation T of $70°$ about the origin (see Fig. 22-2) in a coordinate plane is an isometry, but not a reflection. However, this rotation can be written as the composition of two reflections: first, a reflection R_1 about the X-axis, and then a reflection R_2 about the line making an angle of $35°$ with the X-axis (see Fig. 22-2).

We can show that every isometry in two dimensions can be written as the composition of two reflections.

Case I. Suppose that there is a non-zero vector $\boldsymbol{w}_0$ that is mapped onto itself by the operator F; that is, $F(\boldsymbol{w}_0) = \boldsymbol{w}_0$. (We say that $\boldsymbol{w}_0$ is a ***fixed vector*** of the operator F, or that F has a fixed vector $\boldsymbol{w}_0$.) In this case, for any $\boldsymbol{w}$ in $W = \text{Sp}\{\boldsymbol{w}_0\}$, $\boldsymbol{w} = k\boldsymbol{w}_0$ and

$$F(\boldsymbol{w}) = F(k\boldsymbol{w}_0) = kF(\boldsymbol{w}_0) = k\boldsymbol{w}_0 = \boldsymbol{w}.$$

Thus, every vector in W is fixed. Geometrically, W is a fixed "line" of the operator F.

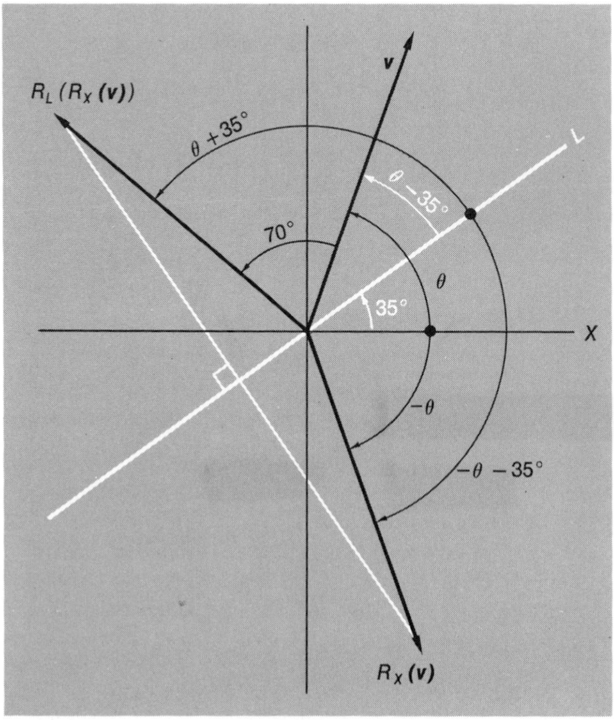

Figure 22-2

Now suppose that w is in W and $w^\perp$ is in $W^\perp$. Because w is fixed,

$$\langle w, F(w^\perp)\rangle = \langle F(w), F(w^\perp)\rangle. \tag{22-3}$$

But F is an isometry, so

$$\langle F(w), F(w^\perp)\rangle = \langle w, w^\perp\rangle = 0. \tag{22-4}$$

It follows from Equations 22-3 and 22-4 that $\langle w, F(w^\perp)\rangle = 0$. Thus, $F(w^\perp)$ is in $W^\perp$. In other words, $F(W^\perp) \subseteq W^\perp$. Hence, we can consider the operator F as an operator in $W^\perp$ by restricting the domain of F to $W^\perp$. Since the restriction of F to $W^\perp$ is an isometry in $W^\perp$ and $\dim W^\perp = 1$, it follows from our discussion of isometries in one-dimensional spaces that either

$$F(w^\perp) = w^\perp \quad \text{or} \quad F(w^\perp) = -w^\perp. \tag{22-5}$$

Now consider any vector v in $V = W \oplus W^\perp$. We have

$$F(v) = F(w + w^\perp) = F(w) + F(w^\perp) = w + F(w^\perp).$$

It follows from Equations 22-5 that either

$$F(v) = v \quad \text{or} \quad F(v) = w - w^\perp.$$

If the first equation is true, then F is the identity operator (a reflection about V), and if the second equation is true, then $F = R_W$ (a reflection about W).

Case II. Now we consider the possibility that F is an isometry in a two-dimensional space that does not have a fixed non-zero vector (such as the rotation T, above). To deal with this possibility we will prove a fact that is true not only for two dimensions, but for higher dimensions as well. Because we will use the fact to help us prove another theorem, we will call it a lemma.

LEMMA 22-1

Let F be an isometry in a Euclidean space V, $\dim V = n > 1$. If F does not have a non-zero fixed vector, then there is an $n - 1$ dimensional subspace W such that the isometry $R_W \circ F$ does have a non-zero fixed vector.

Proof: Let $z \neq \mathbf{0}$ and let $u = F(z) - z$. Because F does not have a non-zero fixed vector we know that $u \neq \mathbf{0}$, and so $U = \mathrm{Sp}\,\{u\}$ has dimension 1. Let us set $W = U^\perp$ so that $W^\perp = U$ and $\dim W = n - 1$. Consider the vector $w = F(z) + z$.

$$\begin{aligned}\langle \boldsymbol{w}, \boldsymbol{u} \rangle &= \langle F(z) + z, F(z) - z \rangle \\ &= \langle F(z), F(z) \rangle - \langle z, z \rangle.\end{aligned}$$

Because F is an isometry, the right side of the preceding equation is zero. Thus $\langle \boldsymbol{w}, \boldsymbol{u} \rangle = 0$; or in other words, $\boldsymbol{w} \perp \boldsymbol{u}$, which means that $\boldsymbol{w}$ is in $W = U^{\perp}$. But $\boldsymbol{u}$ is in $W^{\perp}$, so

$$R_W(\boldsymbol{w}) = \boldsymbol{w}$$

and

$$R_W(\boldsymbol{u}) = -\boldsymbol{u}.$$

Writing out these two equations gives us

$$R_W\big(F(z) + z\big) = F(z) + z$$

and

$$R_W\big(F(z) - z\big) = -F(z) + z.$$

Now R_W is a linear operator, so these equations can be written as

$$\begin{aligned}R_W\big(F(z)\big) + R_W(z) &= F(z) + z \\ R_W\big(F(z)\big) - R_W(z) &= -F(z) + z.\end{aligned}$$

From the addition of these two equations it follows that

$$R_W\big(F(z)\big) = z,$$

or

$$(R_W \circ F)(z) = z.$$

Hence z is a fixed vector of $R_W \circ F$, and because $z \neq \mathbf{0}$, we have found a non-zero fixed vector of $R_W \circ F$. ∎

Now to return to the two-dimensional case. If F is an isometry in a two-dimensional Euclidean space, and if F does not have a fixed vector, then there is a one-dimensional subspace W such that $R_W \circ F$ does have a fixed vector. Thus, from Case I, the isometry $R_W \circ F = R_1$ where R_1 is a reflection (perhaps the identity). Hence,

$$R_W \circ R_W \circ F = R_W \circ R_1.$$

Because $R_W^2 = I$, this equation tells us that

$$F = R_W \circ R_1.$$

We have shown that in a two-dimensional Euclidean space every isometry can be written as the product of two reflections.

We can use the above result for two dimensions to prove a similar result for three dimensions; namely, that every isometry in a three-dimensional Euclidean space can be written as the product of three reflections, each reflection being either the identity reflection or a reflection about a two-dimensional subspace (plane).

Using the three-dimensional result, we could prove a similar fact for the four-dimensional case, and so on. These extensions are not really very difficult, but the proofs do involve some detailed work. The details for the extension from two to three dimensions are presented in Appendix B, and they are representative of the induction argument that must be used to prove the following important theorem.

THEOREM 22-4

Let F be an isometry in an n-dimensional Euclidean space. Then F can be written as the product of n reflections,

$$F = R_n \circ R_{n-1} \circ \cdots \circ R_2 \circ R_1$$

where each reflection is either the identity reflection or a reflection about an $n - 1$ dimensional subspace.

PROBLEMS 22

1. Find $[P_W]$ if $\dim V = 2$ and $W = \mathrm{Sp}\,\{\boldsymbol{e}_1\}$.
2. Let V be R^2 with the standard inner product, and let $W = \mathrm{Sp}\,\{(1,2)\}$. Find $P_W(\boldsymbol{u})$ if:
   (a) $\boldsymbol{u} = (0,1)$ (b) $\boldsymbol{u} = (0,-1)$ (c) $\boldsymbol{u} = (-1,0)$ (d) $\boldsymbol{u} = (1,1)$
3. Find $[P_W]$ (in the natural basis) for the projection operator P_W defined in the preceding problem.
4. Let V be R^3 with the standard inner product, and let $W = \mathrm{Sp}\,\{(1,2,0), (0,1,2)\}$. Find $P_W(\boldsymbol{u})$ if:
   (a) $\boldsymbol{u} = (0,0,1)$ (b) $\boldsymbol{u} = (0,-1,0)$ (c) $\boldsymbol{u} = (4,-2,1)$ (d) $\boldsymbol{u} = (1,1,1)$

5. Find $[P_W]$ (in the natural basis) for the projection operator P_W defined in the preceding problem.
6. How is dim W related to rank P_W? Is P_W an invertible operator?
7. Find $[R_W]$ if dim $V = 2$ and $W = \text{Sp}\,\{e_1\}$. (Do not assume that E is an orthonormal basis, but discuss the case in which it is.)
8. Let V be R^2 with the standard inner product, and let $W = \text{Sp}\,\{(1,2)\}$. Find $R_W(\boldsymbol{u})$ if:
   (a) $\boldsymbol{u} = (0,1)$ (b) $\boldsymbol{u} = (0,-1)$ (c) $\boldsymbol{u} = (-1,0)$ (d) $\boldsymbol{u} = (1,1)$
9. Find $[R_W]$ (in the natural basis) for the reflection operator R_W defined in the preceding problem.
10. Let V be R^3 with the standard inner product, and let $W = \text{Sp}\,\{(1,2,0), (0,1,2)\}$. Find $R_W(\boldsymbol{u})$ if:
    (a) $\boldsymbol{u} = (0,0,1)$ (b) $\boldsymbol{u} = (0,-1,0)$ (c) $\boldsymbol{u} = (4,-2,1)$ (d) $\boldsymbol{u} = (1,1,1)$
11. Find $[R_W]$ (in the natural basis) for the reflection operator R_W defined in the preceding problem.
12. Show that $(1/2)(I + R_W) = P_W$. Solve for R_W and from your equation conclude that $R_W^2 = I$.
13. (a) Show that $|R_W| = \pm 1$.
    (b) Show that if dim $W =$ dim $V - 1$, then $|R_W| = -1$.
14. The matrix representing a rotation of the cartesian coordinate plane through an angle of $\pi/2$ radians is

$$[T] = \begin{bmatrix} 0 & -1 \\ 1 & 0 \end{bmatrix}.$$

    Find two matrices $[R_1]$ and $[R_2]$ that represent reflections such that $[T] = [R_2][R_1]$.
15. Work the preceding problem if the angle of $\pi/2$ is replaced by an angle ϕ whose measure is between 0 and 2π radians.

23 EIGENVALUES. THE SPECTRAL RESOLUTION IN EUCLIDEAN SPACES

A linear operator F in a Euclidean space V is a linear map whose domain and range is V. Suppose that we restrict the domain of F to be a subspace W of V. The set $F(W)$ is a subspace of V but may not be a subspace of W. The restricted map F is an operator in W only if $F(W) \subseteq W$. For example, suppose that $V = R^2$, and that F is the linear operator in R^2 defined by the equation $F(x^1,x^1) = (x^1,x^1)$. If $W = \text{Sp}\,\{(1,0)\}$ then F is not an operator in W because $F(1,0) = (1,1)$ is not in W. On the other hand, if P_W is the projection onto W, then for every vector $\boldsymbol{w}$ in W we know that $P_W(\boldsymbol{w}) = \boldsymbol{w}$. Thus $P_W(W) \subseteq W$ (in fact, $P(W) = W$ in this case), so that P_W is an operator in W. A subspace W of V such that an operator F in V is also an operator in W is called an invariant subspace of F according to the following definition.

DEFINITION 23-1

A subspace W of V is called an *invariant* subspace of the linear operator F in V if $F(W) \subseteq W$.

Example 23-1 Show that W and $W^{\perp}$ are invariant subspaces of the reflection operator R_W.

Solution: Let $V = W \oplus W^{\perp}$. If $\mathbf{w}$ is in W and $\mathbf{w}^{\perp}$ is in $W^{\perp}$, then $R_W(\mathbf{w}) = \mathbf{w}$ and $R_W(\mathbf{w}^{\perp}) = -\mathbf{w}^{\perp}$. Thus, $R_W(\mathbf{w})$ is in W and $R_W(\mathbf{w}^{\perp})$ is in $W^{\perp}$; that is, $R_W(W) \subseteq W$ and $R_W(W^{\perp}) \subseteq W^{\perp}$.

It is not always easy to find the invariant subspaces of a linear operator in a Euclidean space V. Of course, V and $\{\mathbf{0}\}$ are invariant subspaces of every linear operator. Let us see what is involved in finding a one-dimensional invariant subspace W of an operator F. Suppose that $\mathbf{w}$ is any non-zero vector in W. Then $\{\mathbf{w}\}$ is a basis for W and any vector in W can be written as $c\mathbf{w}$ for some number c. Now $F(W) \subseteq W$ means that $F(\mathbf{w}) = \lambda\mathbf{w}$ for some number λ. Conversely, if $F(\mathbf{w}) = \lambda\mathbf{w}$ for some number λ, then

$$F(c\mathbf{w}) = cF(\mathbf{w}) = c\lambda\mathbf{w} = \lambda(c\mathbf{w})$$

and $F(W) \subseteq W$. Thus, finding a one-dimensional invariant subspace W of a linear operator F is equivalent to finding a non-zero vector $\mathbf{w}$ such that $F(\mathbf{w}) = \lambda\mathbf{w}$ for some number λ.

DEFINITION 23-2

Let F be a linear operator in a vector space V. An ***eigenvector*** of F is a non-zero vector such that

$$F(\mathbf{w}) = \lambda\mathbf{w} \tag{23-1}$$

for some number λ. The number λ in Equation 21-1 is called an ***eigenvalue*** of F. We say that $(\lambda, \mathbf{w})$ is an ***eigenpair*** for F. The subset

$$W_{\lambda} = \{\mathbf{w} : F(\mathbf{w}) = \lambda\mathbf{w}\}$$

is the ***eigenspace*** of F corresponding to λ.

Remarks: Eigenvectors and eigenvalues are also called characteristic vectors and values, or principal vectors and values, by some authors. We have suggested in our definition that W_λ is a subspace, not just a subset. We ask you to prove in Problem 23-2 that *W_λ is an invariant subspace of $\boldsymbol{F}$*.

Let P_W be a projection in a Euclidean space V. Then any non-zero vector $\boldsymbol{w}$ in W is an eigenvector of P_W with corresponding eigenvalue 1. Thus, $(1,\boldsymbol{w})$ is an eigenpair for P_W for any $\boldsymbol{w}$ in W. The eigenspace W_1 is simply W. The pair $(1,\boldsymbol{w})$ is also an eigenpair for the reflection operator R_W. For any vector $\boldsymbol{w}^\perp$ in $W^\perp$ the pair $(0,\boldsymbol{w}^\perp)$ is an eigenpair for P_W, and $(-1,\boldsymbol{w}^\perp)$ is an eigenpair for R_W. The subspace $W^\perp$ is the eigenspace W_0 of P_W, and it is the eigenspace W_{-1} of R_W.

Example 23-2 Show that $(-1,s)$ is an eigenpair for the second derivative operator D^2 in the space $C^\infty(R)$, where s is the sine function.

Solution: Our result follows from differentiation:

$$D_x^2(\sin x) = D_x(\cos x) = -\sin x.$$

As the preceding example shows, it makes sense to talk about eigenpairs in infinite dimensional spaces. But we will restrict ourselves to the case in which V is a Euclidean space for the remainder of our discussion in this section.

To find an eigenvector of F we must find a number λ and a non-zero vector $\boldsymbol{w}$ such that $F(\boldsymbol{w}) = \lambda \boldsymbol{w}$. This equation may be written as

$$F(\boldsymbol{w}) - \lambda \boldsymbol{w} = \boldsymbol{0},$$

$$F(\boldsymbol{w}) - \lambda I(\boldsymbol{w}) = \boldsymbol{0},$$

$$(F - \lambda I)(\boldsymbol{w}) = \boldsymbol{0},$$

$$F_\lambda(\boldsymbol{w}) = \boldsymbol{0} \quad \text{where} \quad F_\lambda = F - \lambda I.$$

An eigenvector of F corresponding to λ is a non-zero vector in $K(F_\lambda)$. The operator F has an eigenvalue if, and only if, $K(F_\lambda) \neq \{\boldsymbol{0}\}$ for some number λ. But $K(F_\lambda) \neq \{\boldsymbol{0}\}$ precisely when F_λ is not invertible; that is (see Theorem 20-3), when

$$|F_\lambda| = |F - \lambda I| = 0. \tag{23-2}$$

This equation is called the ***characteristic equation*** of F. The number λ is an eigenvalue of F if, and only if, it is a solution to the characteristic equation of F. If λ is found by solving Equation 23-2, then the equation $(F - \lambda I)(\boldsymbol{w}) = \boldsymbol{0}$ can be solved to yield an eigenvector $\boldsymbol{w}$. If a basis is chosen in V, then this equation is represented by a homogeneous system of equations, written in matrix form as

$$[F - \lambda I][\boldsymbol{w}] = [\boldsymbol{0}].$$

Example 23-3 Let F be the linear operator in R^2 defined by the equation $F(x^1, x^2) = (3x^1 + 2x^2, 2x^1)$. Find eigenpairs of F.

Solution: Using the natural basis,

$$[F] = \begin{bmatrix} 3 & 2 \\ 2 & 0 \end{bmatrix}.$$

The characteristic equation of F is

$$|F - \lambda I| = \begin{vmatrix} 3 - \lambda & 2 \\ 2 & 0 - \lambda \end{vmatrix} = (\lambda - 4)(\lambda + 1) = 0.$$

The eigenvalues of F are $\lambda_1 = 4$ and $\lambda_2 = -1$. An eigenvector corresponding to $\lambda_1 = 4$ is found by solving the equation

$$\begin{bmatrix} 3 - 4 & 2 \\ 2 & -4 \end{bmatrix} \begin{bmatrix} w_1^1 \\ w_1^2 \end{bmatrix} = \begin{bmatrix} -1 & 2 \\ 2 & -4 \end{bmatrix} \begin{bmatrix} w_1^1 \\ w_1^2 \end{bmatrix} = \begin{bmatrix} 0 \\ 0 \end{bmatrix}. \tag{23-3}$$

One solution to this equation is (2,1), so $w_1 = (2,1)$ is an eigenvector corresponding to the eigenvalue 4. Thus, $(4,(2,1))$ is an eigenpair of F. The solution space of Equation 23-3 is the eigenspace $W_4 = \text{Sp}\{(2,1)\}$.

Similarly, an eigenvector corresponding to $\lambda_2 = -1$ is found by solving

$$\begin{bmatrix} 3 + 1 & 2 \\ 2 & 1 \end{bmatrix} \begin{bmatrix} w_2^1 \\ w_2^2 \end{bmatrix} = \begin{bmatrix} 4 & 2 \\ 2 & 1 \end{bmatrix} \begin{bmatrix} w_2^1 \\ w_2^2 \end{bmatrix} = \begin{bmatrix} 0 \\ 0 \end{bmatrix}.$$

One solution is $(1,-2)$. Thus, $(-1,(1,-2))$ is an eigenpair for F and $W_{-1} = \text{Sp}\{(1,-2)\}$.

In the preceding example we can easily verify that $W_4 \cap W_{-1} = \{\mathbf{0}\}$. This observation prompts us to ask, "Can we find a single eigenvector w that corresponds to both λ and μ if $\lambda \neq \mu$?" The answer to that question is contained in the next theorem.

THEOREM 23-1

If $\lambda \neq \mu$, then $W_\lambda \cap W_\mu = \{\mathbf{0}\}$.

Proof: If w is in $W_\lambda \cap W_\mu$, then

$$F(w) = \lambda w \quad \text{and} \quad F(w) = \mu w.$$

It follows that

$$F(w - w) = (\lambda - \mu)w,$$
$$\mathbf{0} = (\lambda - \mu)w.$$

But $\lambda \neq \mu$ so this last equation states that $w = \mathbf{0}$. ∎

The characteristic equation of the operator F in Example 23-3 is a polynomial equation of degree 2 so that the degree of the polynomial is the dimension of the space. Proceeding in the n-dimensional case as we did in Example 23-3 we can choose a basis and write the characteristic equation by finding the determinant of a square matrix. Thus, if $[A]$ is the matrix of F in some fixed basis, the characteristic equation is

$$|F - \lambda I| = \begin{vmatrix} a_1^1 - \lambda & a_2^1 & \dots & a_n^1 \\ a_1^2 & a_2^2 - \lambda & \dots & a_n^2 \\ \vdots & \vdots & & \\ a_1^n & a_2^n & \dots & a_n^n - \lambda \end{vmatrix} = 0.$$

From our knowledge of determinants (See Section 19) we know that $|F - \lambda I|$ is a sum of terms, and each term is a product of n factors. One term in this sum is the product of the diagonal elements, so the expansion of $|F - \lambda I|$ leads to a polynomial in λ of degree n. Thus, the characteristic equation is a polynomial equation of degree n and hence it has at most n (real) roots. We state this fact as a theorem.

THEOREM 23-2

If $\dim V = n$, then F has at most n distinct eigenvalues.

You might also have observed in Example 23-3 that $W_4 \perp W_{-1}$; and you might be tempted to conclude that $W_\lambda \perp W_\mu$ if $\lambda \neq \mu$. This conclusion is not correct for operators in general. But for symmetric operators our next theorem shows that such a conclusion is valid.

THEOREM 23-3

Eigenvectors of a symmetric operator corresponding to different eigenvalues are orthogonal. In other words, if $\lambda \neq \mu$, then $W_\lambda \perp W_\mu$.

Proof: Let (λ, w) and (μ, u) be eigenpairs of a symmetric operator S with $\lambda \neq \mu$. Then

$$\langle S(\boldsymbol{w}), \boldsymbol{u}\rangle = \lambda\langle \boldsymbol{w}, \boldsymbol{u}\rangle,$$

and

$$\langle \boldsymbol{w}, S(\boldsymbol{u})\rangle = \mu\langle \boldsymbol{w}, \boldsymbol{u}\rangle.$$

Now subtract the second of these equations from the first. Because S is a symmetric operator the left sides of these equations are equal, and so

$$0 = (\lambda - \mu)\langle \boldsymbol{w}, \boldsymbol{u}\rangle.$$

Since $\lambda \neq \mu$ we conclude that $\langle \boldsymbol{w}, \boldsymbol{u}\rangle = 0$. ∎

We are now ready to discuss a special case involving an important theorem (called the Spectral Theorem) that we will discuss in more detail in the next section. Suppose that S is a symmetric operator and that it has n distinct eigenvalues. Furthermore, let us choose unit eigenvectors $\boldsymbol{u}_1, \ldots, \boldsymbol{u}_n$ such that $\boldsymbol{u}_j$ is in W_{λ_j} for $j = 1, \ldots, n$. (See Problem 23-3.) In view of the preceding theorem we see that $\{\boldsymbol{u}_1, \ldots, \boldsymbol{u}_n\}$ is an orthonormal set of vectors, and hence forms a basis for V. It follows that if $\boldsymbol{v}$ is any vector in V, then

$$\begin{aligned} \boldsymbol{v} &= x^1\boldsymbol{u}_1 + \cdots + x^n\boldsymbol{u}_n \\ &= \boldsymbol{w}_1 + \cdots + \boldsymbol{w}_n, \quad \text{where } \boldsymbol{w}_j \text{ is in } W_{\lambda_j} \text{ for each } j. \end{aligned}$$

Let us denote by P_j the projection on W_{λ_j}. Then $\boldsymbol{w}_1 = P_1(\boldsymbol{v}), \ldots, \boldsymbol{w}_n = P_n(\boldsymbol{v})$. Thus, we may write

$$\begin{aligned} S(\boldsymbol{v}) &= S(\boldsymbol{w}_1) + \cdots + S(\boldsymbol{w}_n) \\ &= \lambda_1\boldsymbol{w}_1 + \cdots + \lambda_n\boldsymbol{w}_n \\ &= \lambda_1 P_1(\boldsymbol{v}) + \cdots + \lambda_n P_n(\boldsymbol{v}). \end{aligned}$$

In other words,

(23-4) $$S = \lambda_1 P_1 + \cdots + \lambda_n P_n.$$

The sum on the right of this equation is called the (orthogonal) ***spectral resolution*** of S. The set of eigenvalues is called the ***spectrum*** of S. We have proved the following theorem.

THEOREM 23-4

(Special Spectral Theorem.) If the spectrum of a symmetric operator in an n-dimensional Euclidean space contains n distinct eigenvalues, then it can be written as a linear combination of the n projections on the eigenspaces of the operator; that is, it has a spectral resolution as given by Equation 23-5.

Our work in the next section will be devoted to removing the phrase "with n distinct eigenvalues" from Theorem 23-4.

It is easy to show that the only operators that can have (orthogonal) spectral resolutions are symmetric operators. For even if we allow m to be less than n; that is, if we suppose that some of the eigenspaces may have dimension greater than 1, the equation

$$S = \lambda_1 P_1 + \cdots + \lambda_m P_m$$

tells us that S is symmetric because a linear combination of projections is a symmetric operator.

Example 23-4 What is the spectral resolution of the operator F in Example 23-3?

Solution: Because F has two distinct eigenvalues and $n = 2$ in Example 23-3, Equation 23-5 tells us that

$$F = 4P_1 - P_2,$$

where P_1 is the projection on W_4 and P_2 is the projection on W_{-1}.

If S is a symmetric operator with n distinct eigenvalues, there is an orthonormal basis $\hat{E}$ for V consisting of eigenvectors of S. If we choose this basis to represent S as a matrix, then

$$[S]_{\hat{E}}^{\hat{E}} = \begin{bmatrix} \lambda_1 & & & 0 \\ & \lambda_2 & & \\ & & \ddots & \\ 0 & & & \lambda_n \end{bmatrix} = [\Lambda]$$

where $[\Lambda]$ is a diagonal matrix. If E is *any* orthonormal basis, then $[S]_E^E$ is a symmetric matrix, and $[I]_E^{\hat{E}}$ is an orthogonal matrix. Furthermore (Theorem 9-4),

$$[S]_{\hat{E}}^{\hat{E}} = [M]^{-1}[S]_E^E[M] = [M]^*[S]_E^E[M]$$

where $[M] = [I]_E^{\hat{E}}$. We can now interpret our special spectral theorem in terms of matrices. Any symmetric matrix $[S]$ can be regarded as a symmetric operator S in R^n with the natural basis and the standard inner product. The spectrum of $[S]$ is the spectrum of the operator S. Our special spectral theorem states the following:

THEOREM 23-5

(A Diagonalization Theorem for Matrices.) If $[S]$ is a symmetric n by n matrix with n distinct eigenvalues, then there is an orthogonal matrix $[M]$ such that

$$[M]^{-1}[S][M] = [M]^*[S][M] = [\Lambda]$$

where $[\Lambda]$ is a diagonal matrix whose numbers along the main diagonal are the eigenvalues of $[S]$. The columns of the matrix $[M]$ are unit eigenvectors of $[S]$ (considered as vectors in R^n with the natural basis).

Example 23-5 Find $[M]$ and $[\Lambda]$ if $[S]$ is the matrix of Example 23-3.

Solution: We find that $|w_1| = |w_2| = \sqrt{5}$ from Example 23-3. Thus,

$$[M] = \frac{1}{\sqrt{5}}\begin{bmatrix} 2 & 1 \\ 1 & -2 \end{bmatrix},$$

$$[M]^*[S][M] = \begin{bmatrix} 4 & 0 \\ 0 & -1 \end{bmatrix} = [\Lambda].$$

If the columns of $[M]$ are interchanged, so are the columns of $[\Lambda]$, but that is not an important interchange.

PROBLEMS 23

1. The projection operator P_W in V also is an operator in W. Describe P_W considered as an operator in W. Is P_W an operator in $W^\perp$? If so, describe it when considered as an operator in $W^\perp$.
2. Suppose that λ is an eigenvalue of F. Show that $\{w : F(w) = \lambda w\}$ is an invariant subspace of F.
3. Show that you can always find a unit eigenvector corresponding to a given eigenvalue.
4. Let $\{e_1, e_2\}$ be an orthonormal basis for a Euclidean space V. Find eigenpairs and eigenspaces for the operator F in each of the following cases. Write the spectral resolution of F if it exists.
   (a) $F(e_1) = -e_2$ and $F(e_2) = -e_1$.

(b) $F(e_1) = 5e_1 - 3e_2$ and $F(e_2) = -3e_1 + 5e_2$.
(c) $F(e_1) = 5e_1$ and $F(e_2) = e_1 + 5e_2$.

5. Let $\{e_1, e_2\}$ be an orthonormal basis for V and suppose that $F(e_1) = -e_2$ and $F(e_2) = e_1$. Show that F has no invariant one-dimensional subspaces. Interpret F as a geometric transformation of a coordinate plane to verify that the preceding statement is not surprising.

6. Let $\{e_1, e_2, e_3\}$ be an orthonormal basis for V. Describe the spectral resolution of the operator F if

$$F(e_1) = e_1 + e_2 + e_3$$
$$F(e_2) = e_1 + 2e_2$$
$$F(e_3) = e_1 + 2e_3.$$

7. Find an orthogonal matrix $[M]$ such that $[M]^{-1}[A][M]$ is a diagonal matrix $[\Lambda]$ and find $[\Lambda]$ if $[A]$ is:

(a) $\begin{bmatrix} 7 & -4 \\ -4 & 1 \end{bmatrix}$ (b) $\begin{bmatrix} 2 & 3 \\ 3 & -2 \end{bmatrix}$

(c) $\begin{bmatrix} 5 & -1 & -1 \\ -1 & 3 & 1 \\ -1 & 1 & 3 \end{bmatrix}$ (d) $\begin{bmatrix} 1 & 0 & 2 \\ 0 & 1 & 2 \\ 2 & 2 & 0 \end{bmatrix}$

8. Prove that an operator in a Euclidean space is invertible if, and only if, it does not have a zero eigenvalue.

9. Let $\lambda_1, \ldots, \lambda_m$ be distinct eigenvalues of F, and let $w_j \in W_{\lambda_j}$. Let $F_{\lambda_j} = F - \lambda_j I$, and assume that $v = w_1 + \cdots + w_m = \mathbf{0}$.
(a) Show that $F_{\lambda_1}(w_2 + \cdots + w_m) = \mathbf{0}$.
(b) Conclude from part (a) that

$$(\lambda_2 - \lambda_1)w_2 + \cdots + (\lambda_m - \lambda_1)w_m = \mathbf{0}.$$

(c) Apply F_{λ_2} to both sides of the equation in part (b) to conclude that

$$(\lambda_3 - \lambda_2)(\lambda_3 - \lambda_1)w_3 + \cdots + (\lambda_m - \lambda_2)(\lambda_m - \lambda_1)w_m = \mathbf{0}.$$

(d) Continue the procedure used in the above parts to conclude that

$$(\lambda_m - \lambda_{m-1})\cdots(\lambda_m - \lambda_1)w_m = \mathbf{0},$$

and hence that $w_m = \mathbf{0}$.

24 THE SPECTRAL THEOREM

An operator S in a Euclidean space V is symmetric if, and only if, for every pair of vectors $\boldsymbol{u}$ and $\boldsymbol{v}$ in V

$$\langle S(\boldsymbol{u}), \boldsymbol{v} \rangle = \langle \boldsymbol{u}, S(\boldsymbol{v}) \rangle.$$

If S is a symmetric operator in V, then this equation certainly holds for each pair of vectors in a given subspace of V. Thus, to prove that S is a symmetric operator *in a subspace* (this phrase means the domain and range of S is a subspace) we need only show that the subspace is invariant under S. If $(\lambda,\boldsymbol{w})$ is an eigenpair of S, then the set of all vectors orthogonal to $\boldsymbol{w}$ is an $n - 1$ dimensional subspace. Our first step in the proof of the Spectral Theorem is to show that S is a symmetric operator in this subspace.

LEMMA 24-1

Let $(\lambda,\boldsymbol{w})$ be an eigenpair of a symmetric operator S in a Euclidean space V. Let $W^{\perp} = \{\boldsymbol{v} : \boldsymbol{v} \perp \boldsymbol{w}\}$. Then S is a symmetric operator in the $n - 1$ dimensional subspace $W^{\perp}$.

Proof: As we said, the only thing to prove is that $S(W^{\perp}) \subseteq W^{\perp}$. If $\boldsymbol{v}$ is any vector in $W^{\perp}$ and w is any vector in W, then

$$\langle S(\boldsymbol{v}), \boldsymbol{w} \rangle = \langle \boldsymbol{v}, S(\boldsymbol{w}) \rangle = \langle \boldsymbol{v}, \lambda \boldsymbol{w} \rangle = \lambda \langle \boldsymbol{v}, \boldsymbol{w} \rangle = 0.$$

Thus, for each $\boldsymbol{v}$ in V, $S(\boldsymbol{v}) \perp \boldsymbol{w}$. In other words $S(\boldsymbol{v})$ is in $W^{\perp}$. ∎

Suppose that $\dim V = n$. In the preceding section we saw that a symmetric operator could not have more than n distinct eigenvalues. We proved a special Spectral Theorem based on the assumption that a symmetric operator S had n distinct eigenvalues. The difficulty in removing the hypothesis of n distinct eigenvalues stems from the fact that we do not yet know whether a symmetric operator need have any eigenvalues. To explain this difficulty consider the two-dimensional case. The characteristic equation is a quadratic equation with real numbers for coefficients. But a quadratic equation may have *no* real roots (for example, $x^2 + 1 = 0$). However, we will prove that the characteristic equation of a symmetric operator does have a real root. If $\dim V = 1$, then $S(\boldsymbol{v})$ must be some multiple of $\boldsymbol{v}$. Thus, S always has an eigenvalue in the one-dimensional case, and we can confine our attention to the case in which $\dim V > 1$.

Throughout the remainder of this section we assume that V is a Euclidean space of dimension greater than 1, and S is a symmetric operator in V. The set of vectors

$$C = \{\boldsymbol{v} : |\boldsymbol{v}| = 1\}$$

is called *the unit sphere*. If dim $V = 2$ it is also called the unit circle (see Fig. 24-1). Consider the real valued function $F : C \to R$ defined by the formula

$$F(\boldsymbol{v}) = \langle S(\boldsymbol{v}), \boldsymbol{v} \rangle. \tag{24-1}$$

For example, suppose that dim $V = 2$ and $\{\boldsymbol{e}_1, \boldsymbol{e}_2\}$ is an orthonormal basis for V. For any $\boldsymbol{v}$ in C we can find a number t in $[-\pi, \pi]$ such that (see Fig. 24-1)

$$\boldsymbol{v} = g(t) = (\cos t)\boldsymbol{e}_1 + (\sin t)\boldsymbol{e}_2.$$

Thus,

$$S(\boldsymbol{v}) = (\cos t)S(\boldsymbol{e}_1) + (\sin t)S(\boldsymbol{e}_2)$$

and

$$\langle S(\boldsymbol{v}), \boldsymbol{v} \rangle = (\cos^2 t)\langle S(\boldsymbol{e}_1), \boldsymbol{e}_1 \rangle + (\sin^2 t)\langle S(\boldsymbol{e}_2, \boldsymbol{e}_2 \rangle$$
$$+ \sin t \cos t(\langle S(\boldsymbol{e}_2), \boldsymbol{e}_1 \rangle + \langle S(\boldsymbol{e}_1), \boldsymbol{e}_2 \rangle).$$

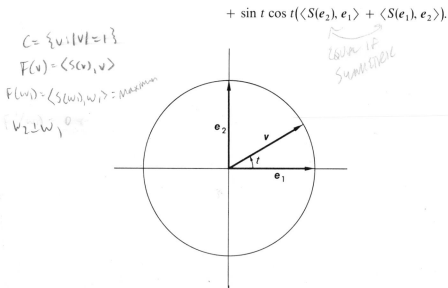

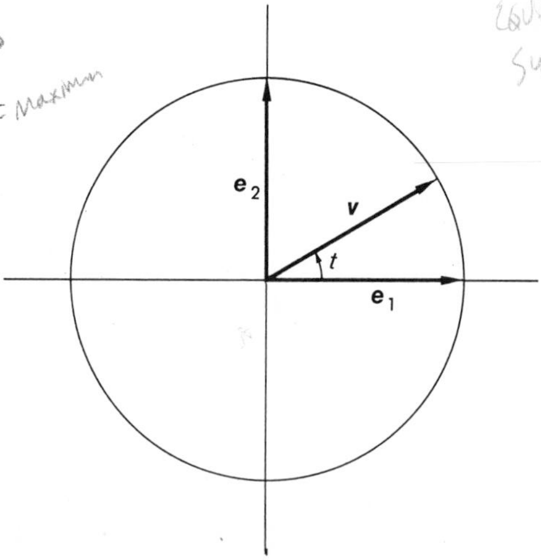

Figure 24-1

Because S is symmetric, the two inner products in the parenthesis in the preceding equation are equal. Thus, $F(\boldsymbol{v}) = \langle S(\boldsymbol{v}), \boldsymbol{v} \rangle$ is given by

$$(24\text{-}2) \qquad f(t) = \cos^2 t \langle S(\boldsymbol{e}_1), \boldsymbol{e}_1 \rangle + \sin^2 t \langle S(\boldsymbol{e}_2), \boldsymbol{e}_2 \rangle + 2 \sin t \cos t \langle S(\boldsymbol{e}_1), \boldsymbol{e}_2 \rangle$$

where $f = F \circ g$; that is, $f(t) = F(g(t))$. The function f defined by Equation 24-2 is a continuous function on the closed interval $[-\pi, \pi]$, and from calculus we know that f takes a maximum value for some t in $[-\pi, \pi]$. In other words, in two dimensions in which $\boldsymbol{w}_1 = g(t_1)$:

> There is a $\boldsymbol{w}_1$ in C at which F defined by Equation 24-1 takes its maximum value; that is, $F(\boldsymbol{w}_1) \geq F(\boldsymbol{v})$ for all $\boldsymbol{v}$ in C.

It seems reasonable to suppose that this fact is also true if $\dim V > 2$, and in advanced mathematics it is proved to be true. We will assume the truth of this basic fact in the proof of our next lemma.

LEMMA 24-2

A symmetric operator S in a Euclidean space has an eigenvalue.

Proof: Consider the function F defined on the unit sphere C by Equation 24-1 and let $\boldsymbol{w}_1$ be the vector in C at which F takes its maximum value. Let $\boldsymbol{w}_2$ be any unit vector such that $\boldsymbol{w}_2 \perp \boldsymbol{w}_1$. Consider the set of points $\Gamma = \{\gamma(t): -\pi \leq t \leq \pi\}$ where

$$\gamma(t) = (\cos t)\boldsymbol{w}_1 + (\sin t)\boldsymbol{w}_2.$$

Because $|\gamma(t)|^2 = \langle \gamma(t), \gamma(t) \rangle = 1$ (write it out!), every point of Γ is a point of C. Geometrically speaking, Γ is the circle of intersection of C and the plane $\operatorname{Sp}\{\boldsymbol{w}_1, \boldsymbol{w}_2\}$. Consider the function $f = F \circ \gamma$; that is, $f(t) = F(\gamma(t))$. If we replace $\boldsymbol{e}_1$ and $\boldsymbol{e}_2$ with $\boldsymbol{w}_1$ and $\boldsymbol{w}_2$ in the derivation of Equation 24-2, we find that

$$f(t) = \cos^2 t \langle S(\boldsymbol{w}_1), \boldsymbol{w}_1 \rangle + \sin^2 t \langle S(\boldsymbol{w}_2), \boldsymbol{w}_2 \rangle + 2 \sin t \cos t \langle S(\boldsymbol{w}_1), \boldsymbol{w}_2 \rangle.$$

Differentiating this equation, we get

$$(24\text{-}3) \qquad f'(t) = 2 \sin t \cos t (\langle S(\boldsymbol{w}_2), \boldsymbol{w}_2 \rangle - \langle S(\boldsymbol{w}_1), \boldsymbol{w}_1 \rangle) + 2(\cos^2 t - \sin^2 t) \langle S(\boldsymbol{w}_1), \boldsymbol{w}_2 \rangle.$$

Because f takes its maximum value at $t = 0$, we know from calculus that $f'(0) = 0$. From Equation 24-3 with t replaced by zero, we conclude that

$$0 = \langle S(\boldsymbol{w}_1), \boldsymbol{w}_2 \rangle.$$

Now let $W_1 = \text{Sp}\{\boldsymbol{w}_1\}$. Because $\boldsymbol{w}_2$ was *any* vector orthogonal to $\boldsymbol{w}_1$; that is, any vector in $W_1^\perp$, we have shown that $S(\boldsymbol{w}_1) \perp W_1^\perp$. In other words, $S(\boldsymbol{w}_1)$ is in $(W_1^\perp)^\perp = W_1$, from which it follows that $S(\boldsymbol{w}_1)$ is a multiple of $\boldsymbol{w}_1$. Thus, $S(\boldsymbol{w}_1) = \lambda \boldsymbol{w}_1$ for some number λ, and $(\lambda, \boldsymbol{w}_1)$ is an eigenpair of S. ∎

The preceding proof remains valid if the word "maximum" is replaced wherever it occurs with the word "minimum." Thus, the minimum value of the function F also occurs at an eigenvector of S, say $\boldsymbol{u}_1$. Let $S(\boldsymbol{u}_1) = \mu \boldsymbol{u}_1$. (In a special case μ and λ may be equal!) Because $|\boldsymbol{w}_1| = |\boldsymbol{u}_1| = 1$,

$$\langle S(\boldsymbol{w}_1), \boldsymbol{w}_1 \rangle = \lambda \langle \boldsymbol{w}_1, \boldsymbol{w}_1 \rangle = \lambda$$

$$\langle S(\boldsymbol{u}_1), \boldsymbol{u}_1 \rangle = \mu \langle \boldsymbol{u}_1, \boldsymbol{u}_1 \rangle = \mu.$$

Thus, there are two eigenvalues λ and μ of S such that for all $\boldsymbol{v}$ of length 1,

(24-4) $$\mu \leq \langle S(\boldsymbol{v}), \boldsymbol{v} \rangle \leq \lambda.$$

As we pointed out in the preceding section, one form of the Spectral Theorem is the following:

THEOREM 24-1

If S is a symmetric operator in a Euclidean space V, then there is an orthonormal basis E for V that consists of eigenvectors of S.

Proof: If $\dim V = 1$ and $\boldsymbol{w}$ is any non-zero vector in V, then $\{\boldsymbol{w}\}$ is a basis. Thus, there is a number λ such that $S(\boldsymbol{w}) = \lambda \boldsymbol{w}$, and so $\boldsymbol{w}$ is an eigenvector. The set $\{\boldsymbol{w}/|\boldsymbol{w}|\}$ is an "orthonormal basis."

Suppose that $\dim V = 2$. The operator S has a unit eigenvector $\boldsymbol{w}_1$ according to Lemma 24-2. Let $W_1 = \text{Sp}\{\boldsymbol{w}_1\}$. Then $\dim W_1^\perp = \dim V - 1 = 1$. The operator S is a symmetric operator in $W_1^\perp$ by Lemma 24-1. From the above argument for the one-dimensional case, we can find a unit eigenvector $\boldsymbol{w}_2$ of S such that $\{\boldsymbol{w}_2\}$ is a basis for $W_1^\perp$. Because $\{\boldsymbol{w}_1, \boldsymbol{w}_2\}$ is an orthonormal set, it is a basis for V.

Suppose that $\dim V = 3$. Again, according to Lemma 24-2 S has a unit eigenvector $\boldsymbol{w}_1$. Let $W_1 = \text{Sp}\{\boldsymbol{w}_1\}$. Then $\dim W_1^\perp = \dim V - 1 = 2$, and according to Lemma 24-1 S is a symmetric operator in $W_1^\perp$. From the two-dimensional case argument, we know that there is an orthonormal basis of eigenvectors $\{w_2, w_3\}$ for $W_1^{\perp}$. The set $\{w_1, w_2, w_3\}$ is an orthonormal set, and hence, a basis of eigenvectors for V.

And so it goes. A rigorous proof could now be supplied by carrying out an "induction step," but we will omit this detail. ∎

If S is a symmetric operator in V and E is an orthonormal basis of eigenvectors of S for V, then

$$\begin{aligned} S(v) &= S(x^1 e_1 + \cdots + x^n e_n) \\ &= x^1 S(e_1) + \cdots + x^n S(e_n) \\ &= x^1 \lambda_1 e_1 + \cdots + x^n \lambda_n e_n, \end{aligned}$$

where some of the λ's may be equal to other λ's. For example, suppose that $\lambda_1 = \lambda_2$. Then

$$\begin{aligned} x^1 \lambda_1 e_1 + x^2 \lambda_2 e_2 &= \lambda_1 (x^1 e_1 + x^2 e_2) \\ &= \lambda_1 P_1(v), \end{aligned}$$

where P_1 is the projection onto the two-dimensional space generated by e_1 and e_2. It follows from these observations and Theorem 24-1 that the following theorem is true.

THEOREM 24-2

(Spectral Theorem.) If S is a symmetric operator in a Euclidean space V, then there are orthogonal eigenspaces $W_{\lambda_1}, \ldots, W_{\lambda_m}$ of V and projections $P_1, \ldots, P_m$ onto these subspaces such that

$$S = \lambda_1 P_1 + \cdots + \lambda_m P_m.$$

Remark: The dimension of W_{λ_j} is called the "multiplicity of λ_j."

Example 24-1 Find an orthonormal basis of eigenvectors of F in R^2 with the standard inner product if $F(x) = 2x$.

Solution: Because $F(1,0) = 2(1,0)$ and $F(0,1) = 2(0,1)$, each vector in the natural basis is an eigenvector corresponding to 2, and so the natural basis is one solution to our problem. As a matter of fact, any orthonormal basis in R^2 will do!

Example 24-2 Suppose that the matrix of an operator S in R^3 in the natural basis is

$$\begin{bmatrix} 8 & 4 & 2 \\ 4 & 8 & -2 \\ 2 & -2 & 11 \end{bmatrix}.$$

Find an orthonormal basis of eigenvectors with respect to the standard inner product, and find the matrix of the operator in that eigenbasis.

Solution: The characteristic equation is

$$\begin{vmatrix} 8-\lambda & 4 & 2 \\ 4 & 8-\lambda & -2 \\ 2 & -2 & 11-\lambda \end{vmatrix} = -\lambda^3 + 27\lambda^2 - 216\lambda + 432$$

$$= (12-\lambda)^2(3-\lambda) = 0.$$

The eigenvalues of S are $\lambda_1 = 3$ and $\lambda_2 = 12$. To find an eigenvector corresponding to λ_1 we solve the homogeneous system

$$[S - 3I][\boldsymbol{w}_1] = [\mathbf{0}].$$

Written out, this system is

$$\begin{aligned} 5\,w_1^1 + 4\,w_1^2 + 2\,w_1^3 &= 0 \\ 4\,w_1^1 + 5\,w_1^2 - 2\,w_1^3 &= 0 \\ 2\,w_1^1 - 2\,w_1^2 + 8\,w_1^3 &= 0. \end{aligned}$$

Adding the first and second of these equations leads to the equation

$$w_1^2 = -w_1^1.$$

Substituting in the third equation tells us that

$$w_1^3 = -w_1^1/2.$$

Thus, $\boldsymbol{w}_1 = w_1^1(1, -1, -\frac{1}{2})$ is an eigenvector whose length is $3w_1^1/2$. If $w_1^1 = \frac{2}{3}$, then

$$\boldsymbol{u}_1 = (\tfrac{2}{3}, -\tfrac{2}{3}, -\tfrac{1}{3})$$

is a unit eigenvector corresponding to $\lambda_1 = 3$.

To find an eigenvector $\boldsymbol{w}_2$ corresponding to $\lambda_2 = 12$ we are led to solve the system

$$\begin{aligned} -4\,w_2^1 + 4\,w_2^2 + 2\,w_2^3 &= 0 \\ 4\,w_2^1 - 4\,w_2^2 - 2\,w_2^3 &= 0 \\ 2\,w_2^1 - 2\,w_2^2 - w_2^3 &= 0. \end{aligned}$$

All three of these equations are equivalent, and the solution space of this system is of dimension 2. The only condition that the coordinates of $\boldsymbol{w}_2$ must satisfy in order to be an eigenvector corresponding to λ_2 is that

$$w_2^3 = 2w_2^1 - 2w_2^2. \tag{24-5}$$

Thus, $\boldsymbol{w}_2 = (w_2^1, w_2^2, 2w_2^1 - 2w_2^2)$. Notice that $\boldsymbol{u}_1 \perp \boldsymbol{w}_2$ because

$$\boldsymbol{u}_1 \cdot \boldsymbol{w}_2 = (\tfrac{1}{3})(2w_2^1 - 2w_2^2 - 2w_2^1 + 2w_2^2) = 0.$$

If we set $w_2^1 = 2$ and $w_2^2 = 1$, then we get an eigenvector (2,1,2) of length 3, so that

$$\boldsymbol{u}_2 = (\tfrac{2}{3}, \tfrac{1}{3}, \tfrac{2}{3})$$

is a unit eigenvector corresponding to λ_2. Now let us find another eigenvector $\boldsymbol{w}_3$ corresponding to λ_2 such that $\boldsymbol{u}_2 \perp \boldsymbol{w}_3$. Using Equation 24-5,

$$\boldsymbol{u}_2 \cdot \boldsymbol{w}_3 = (\tfrac{1}{3})(2w_3^1 + w_3^2 + 4w_3^1 - 4w_3^2) = 0.$$

Thus,

$$2w_3^1 = w_3^2.$$

If we set $w_3^2 = \frac{2}{3}$, then we obtain the unit eigenvector

$$\boldsymbol{u}_3 = (\tfrac{1}{3}, \tfrac{2}{3}, -\tfrac{2}{3}).$$

The set $\{\boldsymbol{u}_1, \boldsymbol{u}_2, \boldsymbol{u}_3\}$ is an orthonormal basis of eigenvectors of S. If $[U]$ is the square matrix defined by $[U] = [\boldsymbol{u}_1\, \boldsymbol{u}_2\, \boldsymbol{u}_3]$, then $[U]$ is an orthogonal matrix, and the matrix of S in the eigenbasis that we have found is

$$[U]^*[S][U] = \begin{bmatrix} 3 & 0 & 0 \\ 0 & 12 & 0 \\ 0 & 0 & 12 \end{bmatrix}.$$

PROBLEMS 24

1. Find an orthonormal basis of eigenvectors in R^n if the standard inner product is used and the operator is represented in the natural basis by the matrix:

(a) $\begin{bmatrix} 1 & 1 & 1 \\ 1 & 1 & 1 \\ 1 & 1 & 1 \end{bmatrix}$ (b) $\begin{bmatrix} 2 & 0 & 1 \\ 0 & 1 & 0 \\ 1 & 0 & 2 \end{bmatrix}$.

2. Find an orthogonal matrix $[T]$ such that $[T]^*[S][T]$ is a diagonal matrix if $[S]$ is the matrix of
(a) Problem 1(a) (b) Problem 1(b).
3. What can you conclude about $[S]$ if all the eigenvalues of S are equal?
4. Let $[S]$ be a symmetric n by n matrix. Let S be the operator in R^n represented by this matrix in the natural basis. Define $\langle x, y\rangle = S(x) \cdot y$ for x and y in R^n. Show that if all the eigenvalues of S are positive, then this equation defines an inner product in R^n.
5. A symmetric operator S in a Euclidean space V is called a ***positive operator*** if $\langle S(v), v\rangle \geq 0$ for all v. Prove that S is a positive operator if, and only if, the eigenvalues of S are non-negative.
6. Prove that $F^* \circ F$ is a positive operator (see preceding problem for definition).
7. Let $S = \lambda_1 P_1 + \cdots + \lambda_m P_m$ be the spectral resolution of a symmetric operator in an n-dimensional Euclidean space. What is the spectral resolution of S^2?

25 THE GEOMETRIC DESCRIPTION OF A LINEAR OPERATOR IN A EUCLIDEAN SPACE

In this section F will denote an operator in an n-dimensional Euclidean space V. Algebraically speaking the operator F is "simply a square matrix." Of course the matrix representing F is different for different bases in V. In this section we will describe F geometrically. Let us begin by saying what we mean by a geometric description.

A reflection about a subspace is a linear operator that has an intuitive geometric description. A reflection maps every point onto its "mirror image" where the subspace is the "mirror." Thus, Theorem 22-4, which states that every isometry in V is the product of not more than n reflections about $n - 1$ dimensional subspaces, is a "geometric description" of an isometry in V.

A projection P_W has an intuitive geometric description. The vector $P_W(v)$ is the "shadow" of v on W (created by considering "rays" perpendicular to W). We might also say that $P_W(v)$ is the "part of v" that lies in W. Let $n = 2$ and consider the operator $S = 2P_W + (1/2)P_W^{\perp}$, where $\dim W = \dim W^{\perp} = 1$. This operator S stretches the part of v in W to twice its length and shrinks the part of v in $W^{\perp}$ to one-half its length (see Fig. 25-1). To simplify the terminology we say that S "magnifies" a vector in W and $W^{\perp}$, even though the magnification factor may be less than 1. Thus, a positive symmetric operator has a spectral resolution

$$\lambda_1 P_1 + \cdots + \lambda_m P_m$$

that can be interpreted as a magnification operation. The Spectral Theorem gives us a "geometric description" of a positive symmetric operator in V. The

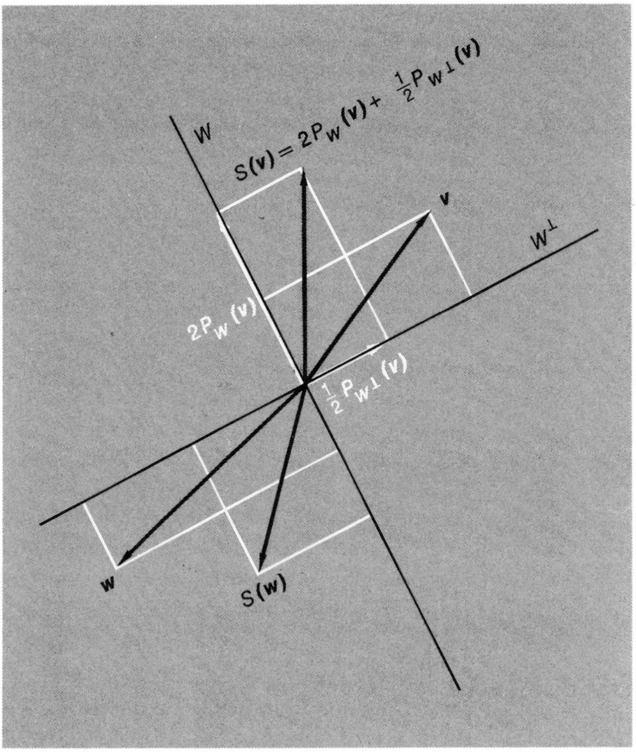

Figure 25-1

purpose of this section is to show that *every linear operator* can be described in terms of reflections and magnifications. That goal will be accomplished if we can show that every linear operator can be represented as a composition of a positive symmetric operator (a magnification operator) followed by an isometry (a product of reflections).

If F is any linear operator, the operator $F^* \circ F$ is a symmetric operator with non-negative eigenvalues (Problem 24-6). The Spectral Theorem states that $F^* \circ F$ has a spectral resolution

$$F^* \circ F = \lambda_1 P_1 + \cdots + \lambda_m P_m \quad (\lambda_j \geq 0,\ j = 1, \ldots, m).$$

Let S be the positive symmetric operator defined by the equation

(25-1) $$S = \sqrt{\lambda_1} P_1 + \cdots + \sqrt{\lambda_m} P_m.$$

You can verify that $S^2 = F^* \circ F$ (Problem 24-7). Some additional facts about S and F will be needed.

LEMMA 25-1

Let S be defined by Equation 25-1. Let $W = S(V)$ and $U = F(V)$. Then
(i) $K(S) = K(F)$
(ii) There is an isometry $Q: W^{\perp} \to U^{\perp}$.

Proof: From the equations

$$\text{(25-2)} \quad \langle S(\boldsymbol{v}), S(\boldsymbol{v})\rangle = \langle S^2(\boldsymbol{v}), \boldsymbol{v}\rangle = \langle (F^* \circ F)(\boldsymbol{v}), \boldsymbol{v}\rangle = \langle F(\boldsymbol{v}), F(\boldsymbol{v})\rangle$$

we conclude that $|S(\boldsymbol{v})| = |F(\boldsymbol{v})|$. Thus, $S(\boldsymbol{v}) = \mathbf{0}$ if, and only if, $F(\boldsymbol{v}) = \mathbf{0}$. Hence, $K(S) = K(F)$.

We also know that

$$\dim W^{\perp} = n - \dim S(V) = \dim K(S)$$
$$= \dim K(F) = n - \dim F(V) = \dim V^{\perp}.$$

But two Euclidean spaces of the same dimension are isometric (see Section 12), and so there is an isometry Q that maps $W^{\perp}$ onto $U^{\perp}$. ∎

Again, let S be defined by Equation 25-1. Our next task is to define an isometry T in V such that

$$\text{(25-3)} \qquad F(\boldsymbol{v}) = (T \circ S)(\boldsymbol{v}).$$

Whether or not this equation is true depends only on the values that T takes for vectors in $W = S(V)$. This fact suggests that we define T on W and $W^{\perp}$ separately. First, suppose that $\boldsymbol{w}$ is in W and let us denote by T_1 the map defined on W that is to be used in the definition of the operator T in V. Equation 25-3 is equivalent to

$$\text{(25-4)} \qquad F(\boldsymbol{v}) = T_1(\boldsymbol{w}) \quad \text{where} \quad \boldsymbol{w} = S(\boldsymbol{v}).$$

Because S is not necessarily injective, at first glance it would seem that Equation 25-4 could not be used to define a map T_1 on W, but it turns out that it can. To define $T_1(\boldsymbol{w})$ by Equation 25-4 means that we make the following definition:

DEFINITION 25-1

Let $W = S(V)$ and $U = F(V)$. Define $T_1 : W \to U$ by the statement

$$T_1(\boldsymbol{w}) = F(\boldsymbol{v}) \text{ where } \boldsymbol{v} \text{ is any vector such that } S(\boldsymbol{v}) = \boldsymbol{w}.$$

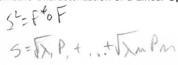

Given $\boldsymbol{w}$, there may be two different vectors $\boldsymbol{v}_1$ and $\boldsymbol{v}_2$ such that $S(\boldsymbol{v}_1) = \boldsymbol{w}$ and $S(\boldsymbol{v}_2) = \boldsymbol{w}$. This apparent objection to Definition 25-1 can be removed by using Lemma 25-1. For if $S(\boldsymbol{v}_1) = S(\boldsymbol{v}_2) = \boldsymbol{w}$, then $S(\boldsymbol{v}_1 - \boldsymbol{v}_2) = \mathbf{0}$. Using Lemma 25-1, we conclude that

$$\boldsymbol{v}_1 - \boldsymbol{v}_2 \in K(S) = K(F).$$

Hence,

$$F(\boldsymbol{v}_1 - \boldsymbol{v}_2) = \mathbf{0},$$

or

$$F(\boldsymbol{v}_1) = F(\boldsymbol{v}_2).$$

Thus, it makes no difference whether $\boldsymbol{v}_1$ or $\boldsymbol{v}_2$ is chosen such that $\boldsymbol{w} = S(\boldsymbol{v}_1) = S(\boldsymbol{v}_2)$. In either case, $T_1(\boldsymbol{w})$ is the same. In short, we say that T_1 is "well defined" on W by Definition 25-1.

Our next step is to show that the mapping T_1 defined by Definition 25-1 is an isometry. With the aid of Equation 25-2 we can write

$$\langle T_1(\boldsymbol{w}), T_1(\boldsymbol{w})\rangle = \langle F(\boldsymbol{v}), F(\boldsymbol{v})\rangle = \langle S(\boldsymbol{v}), S(\boldsymbol{v})\rangle = \langle \boldsymbol{w}, \boldsymbol{w}\rangle.$$

Thus, $|T_1(\boldsymbol{w})| = |\boldsymbol{w}|$. It follows from this equation that T_1 is an isometry (Problem 25-1).

An isometric mapping on W has now been defined such that Equation 25-3 holds. To complete the task we set out to accomplish, we must "extend" the definition of T_1 so as to obtain an isometry in V for which Equation 25-3 is true. Every $\boldsymbol{v}$ in V can be written as a unique sum $\boldsymbol{w} + \boldsymbol{w}^{\perp}$ with $\boldsymbol{w}$ in W and $\boldsymbol{w}^{\perp}$ in $W^{\perp}$. From Lemma 25-1 we know that there is an isometry $Q: W^{\perp} \to U^{\perp}$. We define $T: V \to V$ by the equation

$$T(\boldsymbol{v}) = T(\boldsymbol{w} + \boldsymbol{w}^{\perp}) = T_1(\boldsymbol{w}) + Q(\boldsymbol{w}^{\perp}). \tag{25-5}$$

A schematic diagram of the situation using three copies of V is shown in Fig. 25-2. Gathering together the above results, we can prove the theorem that we set out to prove.

THEOREM 25-1

Let F be a linear operator in a Euclidean space V. Then there is a positive symmetric operator S and an isometry T such that $F = T \circ S$.

Proof: If S is defined by Equation 25-1 and T is defined by Equation 25-5,

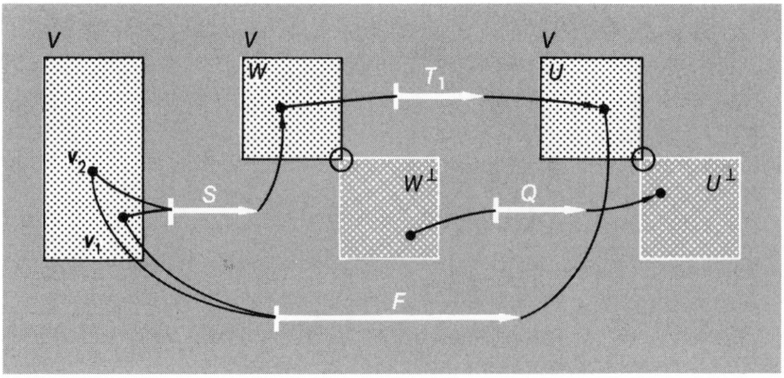

Figure 25-2

then Equation 25-3 does hold, so $F = T \circ S$. The operator S is clearly a positive symmetric operator. To show that T is an isometry in V we compute

$$\langle T(\boldsymbol{v}), T(\boldsymbol{v})\rangle = \langle T(\boldsymbol{w} + \boldsymbol{w}^\perp), T(\boldsymbol{w} + \boldsymbol{w}^\perp)\rangle. \tag{25-6}$$

Utilizing the fact that $T(\boldsymbol{w}) = T_1(\boldsymbol{w}) \varepsilon U$ and $T(\boldsymbol{w}^\perp) = Q(\boldsymbol{w}^\perp) \varepsilon U^\perp$, we deduce from Equation 23-6 that

$$\langle T(\boldsymbol{v}), T(\boldsymbol{v})\rangle = \langle T_1(\boldsymbol{w}), T_1(\boldsymbol{w})\rangle + \langle Q(\boldsymbol{w}^\perp), Q(\boldsymbol{w}^\perp)\rangle.$$

Because both T_1 and Q are isometries, it follows from this equation that

$$\langle T(\boldsymbol{v}), T(\boldsymbol{v})\rangle = \langle \boldsymbol{w}, \boldsymbol{w}\rangle + \langle \boldsymbol{w}^\perp, \boldsymbol{w}^\perp\rangle = \langle \boldsymbol{v}, \boldsymbol{v}\rangle.$$

Thus, $|T(\boldsymbol{v})| = |\boldsymbol{v}|$ and T is an isometry in V (see Problem 25-1). ∎

If $\dim W^\perp > 0$, the isometry Q of Lemma 25-1 is not uniquely determined, so T is not uniquely defined. Because $\dim U^\perp = \dim W^\perp = \dim K(F) = \dim K(S)$, we see that $\dim W^\perp = 0$ precisely when $K(F) = K(S) = \{\boldsymbol{0}\}$. Thus, S is an invertible operator if, and only if, F is an invertible operator, and in that case T is uniquely defined by the equation

$$T = F \circ S^{-1}.$$

Given an operator F, we may apply Theorem 25-1 to the operator F^* to write

$$F^* = T \circ S$$

Then

SINCE $(T \circ S)^* = S^* \circ T^* = S \circ T^*$

$$F = (T \circ S)^* = S \circ T^*.$$

It can be shown that if T is an isometry, then so is T^* (see Problem 25-2). Thus, F can be described as a composition of an isometry and a positive symmetric operator, and this composition can be taken in either order. Geometrically speaking, it means that we can interpret F as a magnification operation followed by reflections, or as a product of reflections followed by a magnification.

Our task of describing linear operators in Euclidean spaces is now complete. Algebraically speaking, linear operators "are" matrices. Geometrically speaking, they "are" magnifications and reflections. One could hardly hope for a better ending to our story.

PROBLEMS 25

1. Using the definition of an isometry given in Section 12, F is an isometric operator if, and only if, $\langle F(\boldsymbol{u}), F(\boldsymbol{v})\rangle = \langle \boldsymbol{u}, \boldsymbol{v}\rangle$ for all $\boldsymbol{u}$ and $\boldsymbol{v}$. Prove that the following identity holds, and use it to show that F is an isometry if, and only if, $|F(\boldsymbol{v})| = |\boldsymbol{v}|$ for every $\boldsymbol{v}$.

$$2\langle \boldsymbol{u}, \boldsymbol{v}\rangle = |\boldsymbol{u} + \boldsymbol{v}|^2 - |\boldsymbol{u}|^2 - |\boldsymbol{v}|^2$$

2. Use Problem 21-3 to prove that if T is an isometry, then T^* is an isometry.
3. Let F be the operator in R^2 (with the standard inner product) whose matrix (in the natural basis) is

$$\frac{1}{5}\begin{bmatrix} 10 & 11 \\ 5 & -2 \end{bmatrix}.$$

(a) Find the matrix of $F^* \circ F$.
(b) Show that the eigenvalues of $F^* \circ F$ are 9 and 1.
(c) Find an orthogonal matrix $[B]$ such that

$$[B]^*[F^* \circ F][B] = \begin{bmatrix} 9 & 0 \\ 0 & 1 \end{bmatrix}.$$

(d) Let S be a symmetric positive matrix such that $S^2 = F^* \circ F$. Show that

$$[S] = [B]\begin{bmatrix} 3 & 0 \\ 0 & 1 \end{bmatrix}[B]^*.$$

(e) Compute $[S]^{-1}$.
(f) Find an orthogonal matrix $[T]$ such that $[F] = [T][S]$.

(g) Draw a cartesian coordinate system and describe the geometric stretching due to S. Interpret T as a rotation, or a rotation followed by a reflection, in the plane.

4. Write the given matrix as a product of an orthogonal matrix times a positive symmetric matrix.

(a) $\begin{bmatrix} 0 & -1 \\ 2 & 0 \end{bmatrix}$ (b) $\begin{bmatrix} 0 & 3 & 0 \\ -3 & 0 & 4 \\ 0 & 4 & 0 \end{bmatrix}$.

Appendix A

In this appendix there are some flow charts that describe the computation of the solution of a system of equations and the $[LU]$ decomposition of a matrix $[A]$. In the flow charts an arrow $\leftarrow$ is used to indicate a replacement. Sometimes an equality sign means the same thing as a replacement arrow. For example, the statement "$j \leftarrow 1$" is read "replace j with 1" and could have been written "set $j = 1$." Similarly, $y = 2x$ could be written "$y \leftarrow 2x$." On the other hand, the arrow may be used in a statement in which the use of an equality sign would require a special interpretation. For instance, to use an equality sign for the replacement arrow in the statement "$x \leftarrow x/2$" would change the meaning of the statement from "replace x with $x/2$" to "x is equal to $x/2$ (and hence $x = 0$)", unless some special use of the equality sign is understood. Some programing languages use the equality sign for the replacement arrow, but we will use the arrow when there is any chance for misinterpretation.

As we pointed out in Section 16, the solution of a triangular system of equations is obtained by using a substitution procedure. In particular, the system

$$\begin{aligned} y^1 \qquad\qquad\qquad &= b^1 \\ l^2_1 y^1 + y^2 \qquad\quad &= b^2 \\ \vdots \qquad\qquad\qquad & \ \ \vdots \\ l^n_1 y^1 + \cdots + y^n &= b^n \end{aligned}$$

has for its solution

$$\begin{aligned} y^1 &= b^1 \\ y^2 &= b^2 - l^2_1 y^1 \\ &\vdots \\ y^n &= b^n - l^n_1 y^1 - \cdots - l^n_{n-1} y^{n-1} \end{aligned}$$

In short, for each $j = 1, \ldots, n$;

$$y^j = b^j - l^j_\alpha y^\alpha, \alpha = 1, \ldots, j - 1.$$

A flow chart for the solution described by this equation is given in Fig. A-1.

The solution for the system

$$\begin{aligned} u^1_1 x^1 + u^1_2 x^2 + \cdots + u^1_n x^n &= y^1 \\ u^2_2 x^2 + \cdots + u^2_n x^n &= y^2 \\ &\vdots \\ u^n_n x^n &= y^n \end{aligned}$$

is obtained by a substitution procedure that is similar to the one given above, except that a division step is required. Thus

$$\begin{aligned} x^n &= y^n / u^n_n \\ x^{n-1} &= (y^{n-1} - u^{n-1}_n x^n)/u^{n-1}_{n-1} \\ &\vdots \\ x^1 &= (y^1 - u^1_2 x^2 - \cdots - u^1_n x^n)/u^1_1. \end{aligned}$$

Using summation notation, for each $j = 0, \ldots, n - 1$

$$x^{n-j} = (y^{n-j} - u^{n-j}_{n-\alpha+1} x^{n-\alpha+1})/u^{n-j}_{n-j}, \ (\alpha = 1, \ldots, j).$$

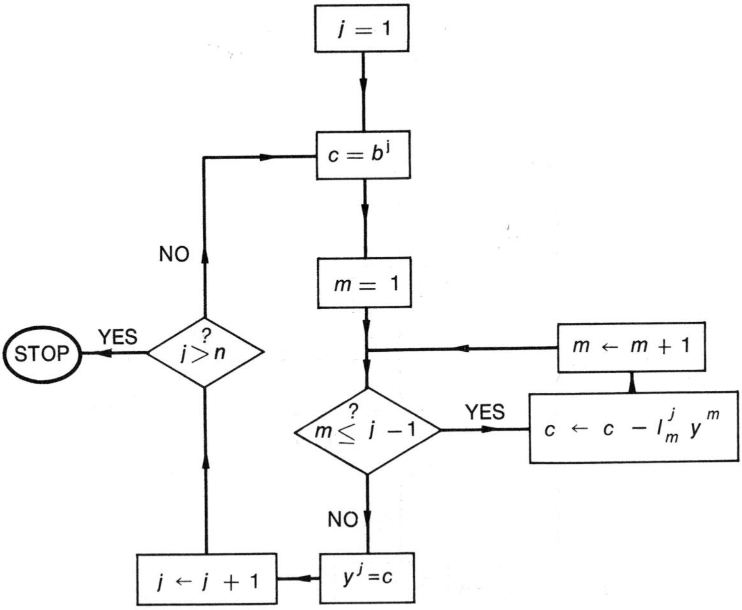

Figure A-1

A flow chart for this computation is pictured in Fig. A-2.

Using the notation of Equations 16-9 we can use Equations 16-4 to compute $[LU]$ as follows:

$$a^i_j = lu^i_\alpha lu^\alpha_j + lu^i_j, \qquad (\alpha = 1, \ldots, i - 1) \text{ if } i \leqq j;$$
$$a^i_j = lu^i_\beta lu^\beta_j + lu^i_j lu^j_j, \qquad (\beta = 1, \ldots, j - 1) \text{ if } i > j.$$

Assuming that $lu^j_j \neq 0$ and solving these equations yields

$$\text{(A-1)} \qquad lu^i_j = \begin{cases} a^i_j - lu^i_\alpha lu^\alpha_j, & (\alpha = 1, \ldots, i - 1) \text{ if } i \leqq j, \\ (a^i_j - lu^i_\beta lu^\beta_j)/lu^j_j, & (\beta = 1, \ldots, j - 1) \text{ if } i > j. \end{cases}$$

Let

$$m = \min(i, j) \text{ (that is, the smaller of } i \text{ and } j)$$

and let

$$\text{(A-2)} \qquad v^i_j = a^i_j - lu^i_\alpha lu^\alpha_j, \qquad (\alpha = 1, \ldots, m - 1).$$

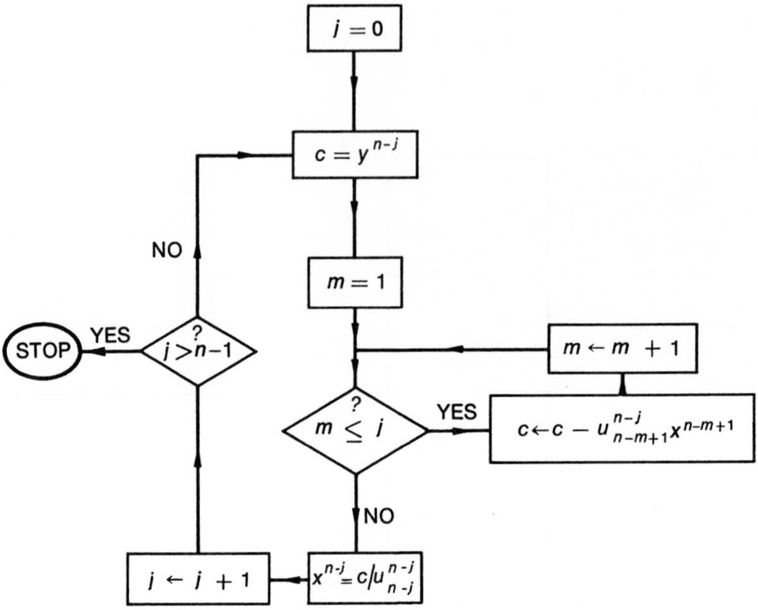

Figure A-2

To compute lu^i_j we first compute v^i_j, and then if $j < i$, we divide by lu^j_j.

There are a number of different sequences by which the numbers in the $[LU]$ matrix can be computed. For example, the numbers in $[LU]$ can be computed "row by row" or "column by column" or by a "column-row, column-row" scheme. Because our modification in the computation that is required if some $lu^j_j = 0$ is to search down a column for a non-zero number, we will compute $[LU]$ in a column by column manner. Thus we set $j = 1$ in Equation A-1 and compute:

$$lu^1_1 = a^1_1,$$
$$lu^i_1 = a^i_1/lu^1_1 \text{ if } i > 1.$$

Next we set $j = 2$ in Equations A-1 and compute

$$lu^1_2 = a^1_2$$
$$lu^2_2 = a^2_2 - lu^2_1 lu^1_2$$
$$lu^i_2 = (a^i_2 - lu^i_1 lu^1_2)/lu^2_2 \text{ if } i > 2.$$

And so it goes. Our machine procedure will be the following. We start with the matrix $[A]$ and modify its first column so as to obtain the first column of $[LU]$. Next we modify the second column, and so on. In non-technical language our machine instructions can be listed as follows:

1. Set $lu_j^i = a_j^i$ for each i,j.
2. Set $j = 1$.
3. Set $i = 1$.
4. Compute lu_j^i.
5. Increase i by 1. If $i \leqq n$ return to step 4, otherwise go to the next step.
6. Increase j by 1. If $j \leqq n$ return to step 3, otherwise stop.

The computational scheme is represented diagrammatically by the flow chart of Fig. A-3.

The box in which the statement "compute lu_j^i" is found can be replaced by a flow chart representing this computation. The key calculation here is given in Equation A-2. Since we began by setting $[LU] = [A]$, that calculation can be described as

(A-3) $$lu_j^i \leftarrow lu_j^i - lu_1^i lu_j^1 - \cdots - lu_{m-1}^i lu_j^{m-1}.$$

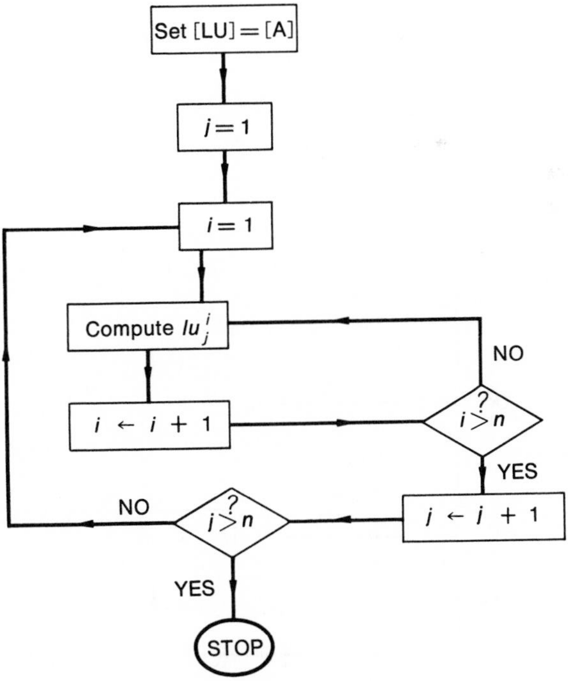

Figure A-3

Since a computing machine does only one operation at a time, this subtraction is carried out by an iteration process shown as a "loop" in Fig. A-4.

Following this calculation, which gives us the number v_j^i in Equation A-2, the computation of lu_j^i is completed by dividing by lu_j^j if $i > j$. The flow chart in Fig. A-4 describes the complete calculation of lu_j^i. If the flow chart is inserted for the "compute box" in Fig. A-3 a complete flow chart for the computation of $[LU]$ is obtained.

The computation described by the flow charts in Figs. A-3 and A-4 cannot be completed if $lu_j^j = 0$ for some number j since the division lu_j^i/lu_j^j for $i > j$ cannot be carried out. In that case our procedure can be modified as described in Section 16. If the number v_j^i defined by Equation A-2 is not zero for some $i = j + 1, \ldots, n$, then interchange row i and row j and proceed as before. If $v_j^i = 0$ for $i = j, \ldots, n$, then $lu_j^i = v_j^i = 0$ for $i = j, \ldots, n$. Thus, the modified computation consists of the following steps.

MC1: Carry out the calculation described by Equation A-3 for $i = 1, \ldots, n$.

MC2: If $j = n$, or if $lu_j^i = 0$ for $i = j, \ldots, n$, then the computation for column j is finished.

MC3: If $lu_j^i = 0$ for $i = j, \ldots, k - 1$, but $lu_j^k \neq 0$ for $k \leqq n$, interchange row k and row j.

MC4: Divide lu_j^i by lu_j^j for $i = j + 1$ to n.

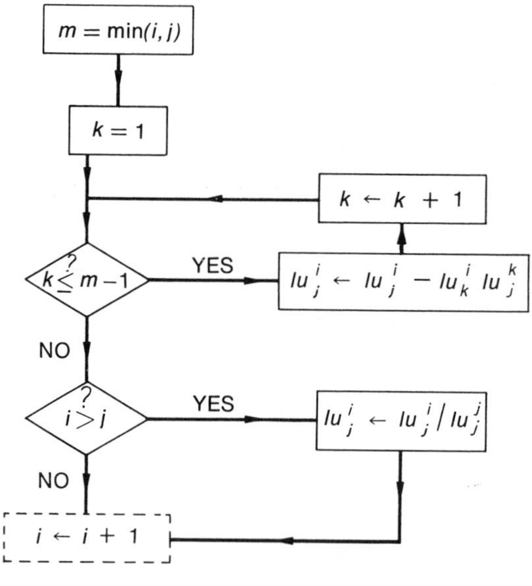

Figure A-4

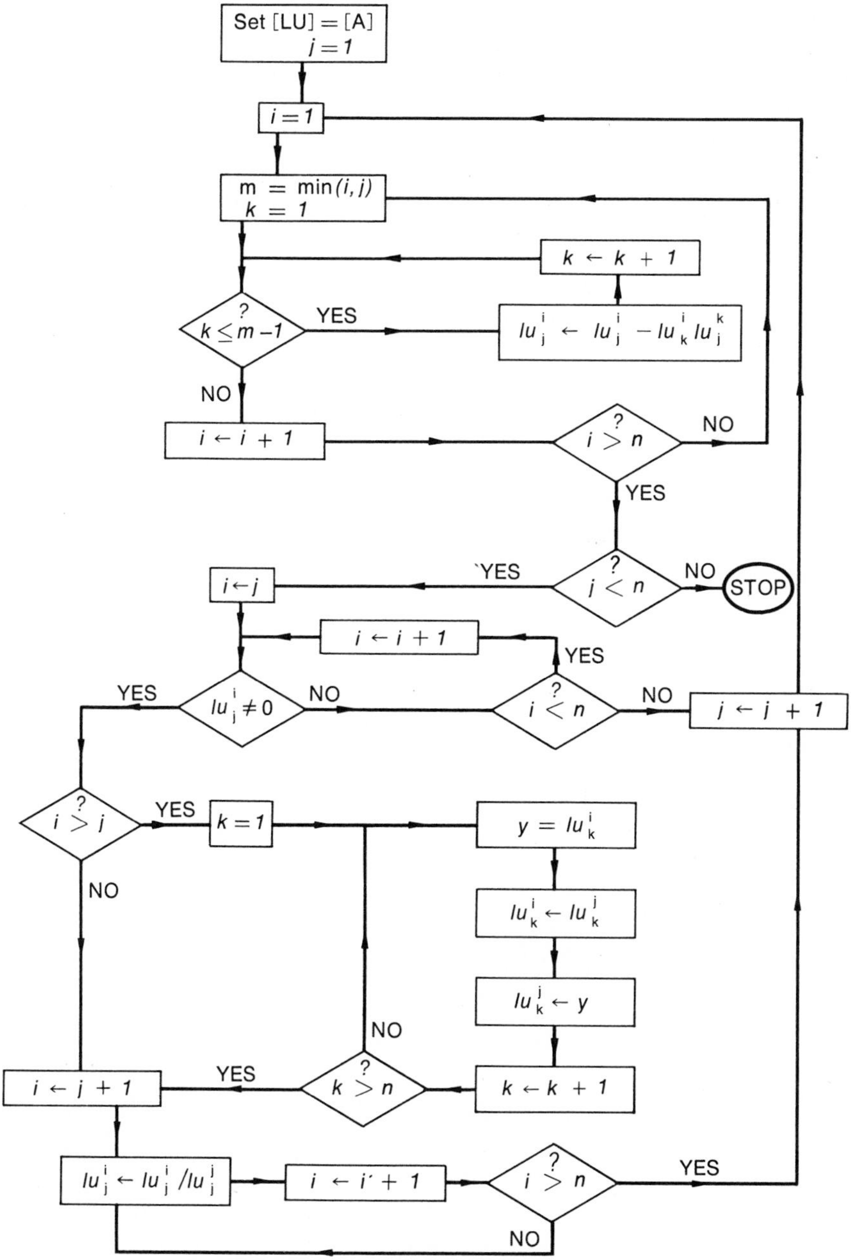
Set [LU] = [A]
j = 1
i = 1
m = min(i, j)
k = 1
k ← k + 1
?
k ≤ m − 1
YES
lu ← lu − lu lu
NO
i ← i + 1
?
i > n
NO
YES
'YES
?
j < n
NO
STOP
i ← j
i ← i + 1
YES
YES
lu ≠ 0
NO
?
i < n
NO
j ← j + 1
?
i > j
YES
k = 1
y = lu
NO
lu ← lu
lu ← y
NO
i ← j + 1
YES
?
k > n
k ← k + 1
lu ← lu /lu
i ← i′ + 1
?
i > n
YES
NO

Figure A-5

The interchange of a row k and row j described in Step MC3 above can be effected by the following procedure: For each j set $y = lu_j^k$, then replace lu_j^k by lu_j^j, and then replace lu_j^i by y. Thus the complete flow chart for the triangular decomposition is shown in Fig. A-5.

In actual computing work it is important to consider the errors that may be involved in a calculation by a machine. Such considerations lead to other modifications of the $[LU]$ decomposition procedure we have given in Fig. A-5. But the flow chart we have depicted there is the basis for many useful programs that are used to solve systems of equations.

Appendix B

In this appendix the proof of the following theorem is presented.

THEOREM B-1

Every isometry in a three-dimensional Euclidean space can be written as the product of three reflections, each reflection being either a reflection about a two-dimensional subspace (plane), or the identity reflection.

Proof: We consider two possibilities. Either the isometry F has a fixed vector, or it does not.

Case I. The isometry F has a fixed non-zero vector $\boldsymbol{w}_0$.

As in the two-dimensional case (see Section 22), let $W = \text{Sp}\,\{\boldsymbol{w}_0\}$. If $\boldsymbol{w}^\perp$ is in $W^\perp$, then from Equations 22-3 and 22-4 (which are true for any dimension) we know that

$$F(W^\perp) \subseteq W^\perp.$$

Thus, F is an isometry in the two-dimensional subspace $W^{\perp}$. From our discussion of the two-dimensional case in Section 22 we know that if we consider F restricted to $W^{\perp}$, then F is the product of two reflections $\hat{R}_2 \circ \hat{R}_1$ where each reflection is either the identity operator or a reflection about a one-dimensional subspace of $W^{\perp}$. Suppose that $\hat{R}_1$ is the reflection in $W^{\perp}$ about W_1. Then

$$W^{\perp} = W_1 \oplus W_1^{\perp}$$

and

$$V = W \oplus W_1 \oplus W_1^{\perp}.$$

Let R_1 be the reflection in V about $W \oplus W_1$ (see Fig. B-1). If $\boldsymbol{v} = \boldsymbol{w} + \boldsymbol{w}^{\perp}$, then $\boldsymbol{w}^{\perp} = \boldsymbol{w}_1 + \boldsymbol{w}_1^{\perp}$, and

$$R_1(\boldsymbol{v}) = R_1(\boldsymbol{w} + \boldsymbol{w}^{\perp}) = R_1(\boldsymbol{w} + \boldsymbol{w}_1 + \boldsymbol{w}_1^{\perp}) = \boldsymbol{w} + \boldsymbol{w}_1 - \boldsymbol{w}_1^{\perp}.$$

Thus,

(B-1) $$R_1(\boldsymbol{v}) = \boldsymbol{w} + \hat{R}_1(\boldsymbol{w}^{\perp}).$$

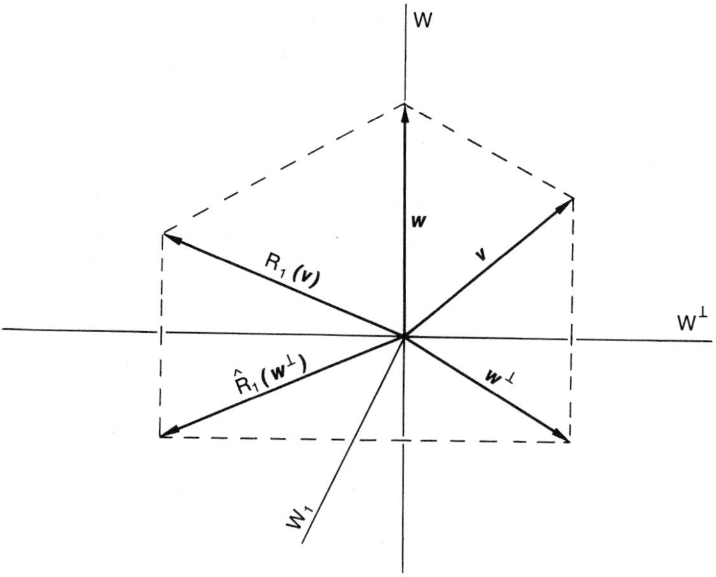

Figure B-1

In exactly the same way, if $\hat{R}_2$ is the reflection in $W^\perp$ about W_2, and R_2 is the reflection in V about $W \oplus W_2$, then

(B-2) $$R_2(\boldsymbol{v}) = R_2(\boldsymbol{w} + \boldsymbol{w}^\perp) = \boldsymbol{w} + \hat{R}_2(\boldsymbol{w}^\perp).$$

Using Equation B-1, we have

(B-3) $$(R_2 \circ R_1)(\boldsymbol{v}) = R_2(\boldsymbol{w} + \hat{R}_1(\boldsymbol{w}^\perp)).$$

Using Equation B-2 with $\boldsymbol{w}^\perp$ replaced by $\hat{R}_1(\boldsymbol{w}^\perp)$, we have

$$R_2(\boldsymbol{w} + \hat{R}_1(\boldsymbol{w}^\perp)) = \boldsymbol{w} + (\hat{R}_2 \circ \hat{R}_1)(\boldsymbol{w}^\perp).$$

Since $\hat{R}_2 \circ \hat{R}_1 = F$ in $W^\perp$, this last equation and Equation B-3 tell us that

$$(R_2 \circ R_1)(\boldsymbol{v}) = \boldsymbol{w} + F(\boldsymbol{w}^\perp).$$

But $\boldsymbol{w}$ is a fixed vector of F, so we have

$$(R_2 \circ R_1)(\boldsymbol{v}) = F(\boldsymbol{w}) + F(\boldsymbol{w}^\perp) = F(\boldsymbol{w} + \boldsymbol{w}^\perp) = F(\boldsymbol{v}).$$

In short, $F = R_2 \circ R_1$. If $\dim W_1 = 1$, then $\dim W \oplus W_1 = 2$; and R_1 is a reflection about this two-dimensional subspace. If $\dim W_1 = 2$, then $\dim W \oplus W_1 = 3$; and R_1 is the reflection about V; that is, the identity reflection. Similarly, R_2 is either the identity reflection or a reflection about a two-dimensional subspace of V.

Case II. If F is an isometry in a three-dimensional Euclidean space that does not have a non-zero fixed vector, then according to Lemma 22-1 $R_W \circ F$ does have a fixed vector, where R_W is a reflection about a two-dimensional subspace. Thus, in this case $R_W \circ F = R_2 \circ R_1$, from which $F = R_W \circ R_2 \circ R_1$.

Answers to Selected Problems

PROBLEMS 1

1. (a) (4,4); (b) $\sqrt{5} + \sqrt{2}$ and $\sqrt{5}$; (c) $\frac{1}{2}\boldsymbol{PQ} + \frac{1}{2}\boldsymbol{PR}$; (d) $(2t + 1, t + 1)$. **5.** $\boldsymbol{v} - \boldsymbol{w}$. **10.** Yes; No.

PROBLEMS 2

1. (a) and (f). **3.** (a) Yes; (b) No, not always. **4.** (a) Yes; (b) No. **5.** $\boldsymbol{v}_1 = (2, 1, -4)$, $\boldsymbol{v}_2 = (-1, -3, 1)$. $\boldsymbol{v}_3$ any linear combination of $\boldsymbol{v}_1$ and $\boldsymbol{v}_2$. No. **7.** Any multiple of $(-6, -63, -12)$.

PROBLEMS 3

3. Yes. No. For any I and non-negative integers n and k $C^{n+k}(I)$ is a subspace of $C^n(I)$, but not conversely. **4.** (a) and (b). **5.** No. **7.** (a) dependent; (b) independent. **12.** Yes. **14.** The homogeneous system has a non-trivial solution if, and only if, the set $\{(a,c), (b,d)\}$ is a dependent set in R^2.

PROBLEMS 4

1. (a) $\begin{bmatrix} 2 \\ 1 \end{bmatrix}$ (c) $\begin{bmatrix} \frac{3}{5} \\ -\frac{4}{5} \end{bmatrix}$ **2.** None. **4.** (b) $\begin{bmatrix} \frac{8}{3} \\ \frac{11}{3} \\ \frac{8}{3} \end{bmatrix}$ (c) $\begin{bmatrix} \frac{10}{27} \\ -\frac{2}{27} \\ \frac{1}{27} \end{bmatrix}$ **5.** (b) $\begin{bmatrix} 1 \\ -1 \\ 0 \end{bmatrix}$

6. (1,1,1) is a basis for W. The set $\{(1,1,1), (1,0,0), (0, 1, 0)\}$ is a basis for R^3. **9.** (a) $\begin{bmatrix} \cos a \\ \sin a \end{bmatrix}$

PROBLEMS 5

3. $F(x) = cx$. A line containing the origin. $F(R^1)$ is either R^1 or $\{0\}$. Injective if slope is not zero. **4.** (b) No. (c) No. (d) No. **5.** Yes. **7.** (a) Yes. (b) No. (c) Yes. (d) No. **10.** (a) 2 and 0. (b) Yes. (c) R^1 (d) No. Yes. **11.** (a) Yes. (b) Yes. (c) No. Notice that $g \varepsilon C^1(R)$.

PROBLEMS 6

1. (a) Yes. $\{0\}$. (c) Yes. $\{(0,0)\}$. (e) Yes. $\{f : f(0) = 0\}$ **2.** (a) $(x^1 - x^2 - x^3, x^1 + x^2 - x^3)$. (c) $\{(1,0,1)\}$. **3.** (a) $(1, -1, 0)$. (c) $\{(1, -1, 0), (1, 0, -1)\}$. **5.** $\dim K(F) = \dim F(V) = 1$. **6.** (1, 2). $\dim K(F) = 1$. $\dim F(R^3) = 2$. No. Yes. Projection of 3-space onto a coordinate plane. **9.** $K(D) = \{\mathbf{0}\}$. **11.** (a) Reflection about line $x^2 = x^1$. $F^{-1} = F$. (c) Rotation about origin of 180°, $F^{-1} = F$. **13.** $D(e_2) = 2e_1$; $D(e_1) = e_0$; $D(e_0) = \mathbf{0}$.

PROBLEMS 7

1. $\begin{bmatrix} 1 \\ 2 \end{bmatrix}$ **2.** A matrix of zeros. **3.** (a) $\begin{bmatrix} 1 & -1 & -1 \\ 1 & 1 & -1 \end{bmatrix}$ (b) $\begin{bmatrix} 1 & 1 & 1 \\ 0 & 0 & 0 \end{bmatrix}$

4. (a) $\begin{bmatrix} 1 & -1 & 0 \\ 1 & 0 & -1 \end{bmatrix}$ (b) $\begin{bmatrix} 0 & -1 & 0 \\ 1 & 0 & -1 \end{bmatrix}$ (c) $\begin{bmatrix} 1 & -\frac{1}{2} & -\frac{1}{2} \\ 0 & -\frac{1}{2} & \frac{1}{2} \end{bmatrix}$

(d) $\begin{bmatrix} \frac{1}{2} & -\frac{1}{2} & -\frac{1}{2} \\ -\frac{1}{2} & -\frac{1}{2} & \frac{1}{2} \end{bmatrix}$ **5.** (a) $\begin{bmatrix} 4 \\ -6 \end{bmatrix}$ (b) $\begin{bmatrix} 1 \\ 1 \\ 1 \end{bmatrix}$ **6.** (a) $n = 2$, (7,8); (b) $n = 1$, (32);

(c) $n = 3, (4,5,3)$; (d) $n = 4, (3, -4, 8, 10)$. **7.** $\begin{bmatrix} -1 & 1 \\ \frac{1}{2} & 0 \end{bmatrix}$ and $\begin{bmatrix} 0 & 2 \\ 1 & 2 \end{bmatrix}$ **11.** $\begin{bmatrix} 6 \\ 2 \end{bmatrix}$

PROBLEMS 8

1. (a) $\begin{bmatrix} 2 \\ -2 \end{bmatrix}$ (c) $\begin{bmatrix} 2 & 7 \\ -2 & 8 \end{bmatrix}$ **2.** (a) $\begin{bmatrix} -5 \\ 10 \\ 6 \end{bmatrix}$ (c) $\begin{bmatrix} 2 & 3 & 1 \\ 4 & 5 & 2 \\ 5 & 6 & 3 \end{bmatrix}$ **3.** (a) $[A]^3 = [I]$; (b) $[A]^3 = [\mathbf{0}]$. **4.** (a) $(2x^1, 2x^2 + 2x^3, 2x^1 + 2x^2, 2x^3)$; (b) $\begin{bmatrix} 2 & 0 & 0 \\ 0 & 2 & 2 \\ 2 & 2 & 2 \end{bmatrix}$ (c) $(4x^1, 2x^2 - 2x^1)$; (d) $\begin{bmatrix} 4 & 0 \\ -2 & 2 \end{bmatrix}$. **7.** $[F \circ G] = \begin{bmatrix} 2 & 0 & 0 \\ 0 & -1 & 1 \\ 2 & -1 & 1 \end{bmatrix}$; $[G \circ F] = \begin{bmatrix} 1 & -1 & 2 \\ 2 & 1 & 1 \\ 1 & 1 & 0 \end{bmatrix}$; $\dim F(R^3) = 2$; $\dim G(R^3) = 3$; $\dim F \circ G(R^3) = 2$. **9.** $[I]^{\hat{E}}_{E} = \begin{bmatrix} 0 & 2 \\ 1 & 2 \end{bmatrix}$;

$$[I]^{E}_{\hat{E}} = \begin{bmatrix} -1 & 1 \\ \frac{1}{2} & 0 \end{bmatrix}.$$

PROBLEMS 9

4. (a) $\begin{bmatrix} 1 & -1 \\ 1 & 1 \end{bmatrix}$ (b) $\begin{bmatrix} 1 & 1 \\ -1 & 1 \end{bmatrix}$ (c) $\frac{1}{2}\begin{bmatrix} 1 & 1 \\ 1 & -1 \end{bmatrix}$ and $\begin{bmatrix} 1 & 1 \\ 1 & -1 \end{bmatrix}$. **5.** There is an operator such that it is represented in one basis by $[A]$, and in another basis by $[C]$. **6.** (a) $\begin{bmatrix} 1 & 0 \\ 0 & 1 \end{bmatrix}$ (b) $\begin{bmatrix} 1 & 0 \\ 0 & 0 \end{bmatrix}$ (c) $\begin{bmatrix} -1 & 0 \\ 0 & -2 \end{bmatrix}$ **8.** $\begin{bmatrix} 7 & 12 \\ 4 & 7 \end{bmatrix}$. The zero operator. **9.** Assume that e_2 is obtained from e_1 by a 90° rotation. Then $\hat{E}$ is obtained from E by a rotation of $-45°$ and a stretching by a factor of $1/\sqrt{2}$. F projects a vector onto $\hat{e}_2$ and multiplies it by 2. **10.** $\begin{bmatrix} 0 & 0 & \cdots & 0 & 1 \\ 1 & 0 & \cdots & 0 & 0 \\ 0 & 1 & \cdots & 0 & 0 \\ \vdots & \vdots & & \ddots & \vdots \\ 0 & 0 & \cdots & 1 & 0 \end{bmatrix}$; Yes; $[I]$; The zero subspace.

PROBLEMS 10

2. (a) $\sqrt{2}$; (b) 1. **3.** Yes. 1. **5.** (a) 0; (c) $\sqrt{\pi}$; (e) $4\pi^4$; (g) -2π. **7.** $\boldsymbol{OP}$ where (a) $P = (0,1)$; (c) $P = (\frac{28}{13}, \frac{42}{13})$.

PROBLEMS 11

1. (a) $(\frac{1}{3}, \frac{1}{3}, \frac{1}{3})$; (c) $(\frac{1}{3}, \frac{1}{3}, \frac{1}{3})$. **4.** $\boldsymbol{u} . \boldsymbol{v} = k\boldsymbol{u}$.

PROBLEMS 12

1. $t(\langle \boldsymbol{e}_2, \boldsymbol{e}_1 \rangle + 2\langle \boldsymbol{e}_2, \boldsymbol{e}_2 \rangle) = -\langle \boldsymbol{e}_1, \boldsymbol{e}_1 \rangle - 2\langle \boldsymbol{e}_1, \boldsymbol{e}_2 \rangle$. $t = -\frac{1}{2}$. **3.** $\{\pi^{-1/2}\boldsymbol{s}, \pi^{-1/2}\boldsymbol{c}\}$. **4.** (a) $\{5^{-1/2}(1,2), 5^{-1/2}(-2,1)\}$. **5.** $1/\sqrt{2}$, $\sqrt{\frac{3}{2}}x$, $(\sqrt{\frac{10}{4}})(3x^2 - 1)$. **15.** Yes. **16.** (a) 1. **17.** (a) $[I]_E^{\hat{E}}$.

PROBLEMS 13

1. (a) $(\frac{1}{2}, \frac{1}{2}) + (-\frac{1}{2}, \frac{1}{2})$; (c) $(0,1) + (0,0)$. **2.** (a) $(-\frac{1}{3}, \frac{2}{3}, -\frac{1}{3}) + (\frac{1}{3}, \frac{1}{3}, \frac{1}{3})$; (c) $(0,1,0) + (0,0,0)$. **3.** $U_1 = \text{Sp}\,\{(0,1)\}$ and $U_2 = \text{Sp}\,\{(1,1)\}$. **4.** No; check the dimensions. **5.** (a) $(1,0,0) + (0,0,0)$; (c) $(1,2,0) + (0,0,3)$.

PROBLEMS 14

1. (a) $S_0 = \{\boldsymbol{0}\}$; $S_1 = \{(1,0)\}$. Three lines containing point $(1,0)$; (c) $S_0 = \text{Sp}\,\{(7,3,-5)\}$; $S = (-\frac{28}{5}, -\frac{7}{5}, 3) + S_0$. **4.** $\{(1,0,1,0,-2,0), (0,1,0,1,0,-2), (1,1,-1,-1,0,0), (1,-1,-1,1,0,0)\}$. **5.** $S = (1,1,0,0,0,0) + S_0$ where S_0 is generated by basis in preceding problem. **6.** (a) 2; (c) 3. **7.** Yes; $(0,0,0,1)$ is a solution. **8.** $x - 3y + 2z = 0$. **9.** The line $\{t(1,-1,-2)\}$. **10.** (a) The point $(0,0,0)$.

PROBLEMS 15

1. (a) 2; (c) 4. **2.** $[A]^{-1} = \frac{1}{3}\begin{bmatrix} -1 & 2 & 0 \\ 5 & -7 & 3 \\ 17 & -22 & 9 \end{bmatrix}$ **3.** (a) (1, −1,1); (c) (2,0, −1,1); (e) no solution. **4.** (a) $[A]^{-1} = [A]$; (c) $\begin{bmatrix} 3 & -1 \\ -5 & 2 \end{bmatrix}$ (e) $\begin{bmatrix} -5 & -1 & 6 \\ 1 & 0 & -1 \\ -9 & -2 & 10 \end{bmatrix}$.

5. $[A]^{-1}$ exists if, and only if, $ad - bc \neq 0$, and then $[A]^{-1} = \frac{1}{ad - bc}\begin{bmatrix} d & -b \\ -c & a \end{bmatrix}$.

6. (a) $(\frac{1}{2}, -\frac{1}{2}, \frac{1}{2}), (\frac{1}{2}, \frac{1}{2}, -\frac{1}{2}), (-\frac{1}{2}, \frac{1}{2}, \frac{1}{2})$.

PROBLEMS 16

1. (a) (3,21). **2.** (a) (0,0,1). **3.** (a) $\begin{bmatrix} 1 & 0 \\ 2 & 1 \end{bmatrix}\begin{bmatrix} 1 & 1 \\ 0 & 0 \end{bmatrix}$; (c) $\begin{bmatrix} 1 & 0 & 0 \\ 1 & 1 & 0 \\ 1 & 1 & 1 \end{bmatrix}\begin{bmatrix} 1 & 1 & 0 \\ 0 & 1 & 1 \\ 0 & 0 & 0 \end{bmatrix}$

4. (a) $\begin{bmatrix} 1 & 1 \\ 2 & 0 \end{bmatrix}$; (c) $\begin{bmatrix} 1 & 1 & 0 \\ 1 & 1 & 1 \\ 1 & 1 & 0 \end{bmatrix}$ **5.** (a) $[L][U] = [P][A]$ where $[LU] = [U] =$ $\begin{bmatrix} 1 & 0 & 0 & 0 \\ 0 & 1 & 1 & 1 \\ 0 & 0 & 1 & 1 \\ 0 & 0 & 0 & 1 \end{bmatrix}$ and $[P] = \begin{bmatrix} 0 & 0 & 0 & 1 \\ 0 & 0 & 1 & 0 \\ 0 & 1 & 0 & 0 \\ 1 & 0 & 0 & 0 \end{bmatrix}$.

PROBLEMS 17

1. (a) $\begin{bmatrix} 1 & 0 & 1 \\ 0 & 1 & 0 \\ 0 & 0 & 1 \end{bmatrix}$ (c) $\begin{bmatrix} 1 & 0 & 1 \\ 0 & 1 & 3 \\ 0 & 0 & 1 \end{bmatrix}$ (e) $\begin{bmatrix} 1 & 0 & 0 \\ 0 & \frac{1}{2} & 0 \\ 0 & 0 & 1 \end{bmatrix}$ **3.** $\begin{bmatrix} 1 & -1 \\ 0 & 1 \end{bmatrix}$ and

$\begin{bmatrix} 1 & 0 \\ -1 & 1 \end{bmatrix}$ **5.** (a) $\begin{bmatrix} 1 & 0 \\ -2 & 1 \end{bmatrix}$ (c) $\begin{bmatrix} 1 & 0 & 0 \\ -1 & 1 & 0 \\ 0 & -1 & 1 \end{bmatrix}$ **6.** (a) $\begin{bmatrix} 0 & 0 & 0 & 1 \\ 0 & -1 & 1 & 0 \\ -1 & 1 & 0 & 0 \\ 1 & 0 & 0 & 0 \end{bmatrix}$

PROBLEMS 18

5. (a) -7; (c) 1; (e) 0. 0. **6.** $x^2 D(U)$. **7.** (a) Yes; (c) No.

PROBLEMS 19

1. (a) -2; (c) 1. **2.** (a) $\begin{bmatrix} 5 & 0 & -3 \\ 0 & -2 & 0 \\ -4 & 0 & 2 \end{bmatrix}$ (c) $\begin{bmatrix} -1 & 0 & 1 & 0 \\ 0 & -1 & 0 & 1 \\ 2 & 0 & -1 & 0 \\ 0 & 2 & 0 & -1 \end{bmatrix}$

3. (a) $-\frac{1}{2}$ times the matrix in Problem 2(a); (c) The matrix in Problem 2(c).
7.

$$x = \frac{\begin{vmatrix} c & b \\ f & e \end{vmatrix}}{D}, \quad y = \frac{\begin{vmatrix} a & c \\ d & f \end{vmatrix}}{D} \quad \text{where } D = \begin{vmatrix} a & b \\ d & e \end{vmatrix}.$$

PROBLEMS 20

1. (a) 2; (c) $F^{-1}(e_1) = 3e_1 - 3e_2 + e_3$; $F^{-1}(e_2) = -3e_1 + 5e_2 - 2e_1$; $F^{-1}(e_3) = e_1 - 2e_2 + e_3$; (e) F^{-1} does not exist. **3.** (a) $D(U) = 1$; $D(F(U)) = 2$; (c) $D(U) = -18$, $D(F(U)) = -36$.

PROBLEMS 21

1. (a) $\begin{bmatrix} 1 & 3 \\ 2 & 4 \end{bmatrix}, \begin{bmatrix} -2 & -4 \\ 3 & 7 \end{bmatrix}, \begin{bmatrix} -1 & -2 \\ 2 & 6 \end{bmatrix}$; (c) $\begin{bmatrix} 1 & 2 \\ 2 & 3 \end{bmatrix}, \begin{bmatrix} -1 & -2 \\ 2 & 5 \end{bmatrix}, \begin{bmatrix} -1 & -2 \\ 2 & 5 \end{bmatrix}$. **6.** $\begin{bmatrix} \langle e_1, e_1 \rangle & \langle e_2, e_1 \rangle & \langle e_3, e_1 \rangle \\ 0 & 0 & 0 \\ 0 & 0 & 0 \end{bmatrix}$ has rank one. **8.** (b) No; (c) Yes.

PROBLEMS 22

1. $\begin{bmatrix} 1 & 0 \\ 0 & 0 \end{bmatrix}$ **2.** (a) $(\frac{2}{5}, \frac{4}{5})$; (c) $(-\frac{1}{5}, -\frac{2}{5})$. **3.** $\begin{bmatrix} \frac{1}{5} & \frac{2}{5} \\ \frac{2}{5} & \frac{4}{5} \end{bmatrix}$ **4.** (a) $(0, \frac{2}{5}, \frac{4}{5})$; (c) $(0,0,0)$.

5. $\begin{bmatrix} \frac{1}{5} & \frac{2}{5} & 0 \\ \frac{2}{5} & 1 & \frac{2}{5} \\ 0 & \frac{2}{5} & \frac{4}{5} \end{bmatrix}$ **7.** $\begin{bmatrix} 1 & 2\langle e_1, e_2\rangle/\langle e_1, e_1\rangle \\ 0 & -1 \end{bmatrix}$ **8.** (a) $(\frac{4}{5}, \frac{3}{5})$; (c) $(\frac{3}{5}, -\frac{4}{5})$. **9.** $\begin{bmatrix} -\frac{3}{5} & \frac{4}{5} \\ \frac{4}{5} & \frac{3}{5} \end{bmatrix}$

10. (a) $(-\frac{8}{21}, \frac{4}{21}, \frac{19}{21})$; (c) $(-4,2,-1)$. **11.** $\frac{1}{21}\begin{bmatrix} -11 & 16 & -8 \\ 16 & 13 & 4 \\ -8 & 4 & 19 \end{bmatrix}$ **14.** $\begin{bmatrix} 0 & 1 \\ 1 & 0 \end{bmatrix}\begin{bmatrix} 1 & 0 \\ 0 & -1 \end{bmatrix}$

15. $\begin{bmatrix} \cos\phi & \sin\phi \\ \sin\phi & -\cos\phi \end{bmatrix}\begin{bmatrix} 1 & 0 \\ 0 & -1 \end{bmatrix}$.

PROBLEMS 23

1. P_W restricted to W is the identity operator in W. **4.** (a) Let $w_1 = e_1 - e_2$ and $w_2 = e_1 + e_2$. Eigenpairs are $(1, w_1)$ and $(-1, w_2)$. Eigenspaces are Sp $\{w_1\}$ and Sp $\{w_2\}$. Spectral resolution is $P_1 - P_2$. (c) $(5, e_1)$ is an eigenpair; Sp $\{e_1\}$ is an eigenspace. **6.** $F = 2P_2 + 3P_3$ where P_2 is projection on Sp $\{(0,1,-1)\}$, and P_3 is projection on Sp $\{(1,1,1)\}$. **7.** (a) $\frac{1}{\sqrt{5}}\begin{bmatrix} 2 & 1 \\ -1 & 2 \end{bmatrix}$; (c) $\frac{1}{\sqrt{6}}\begin{bmatrix} 0 & \sqrt{2} & -2 \\ \sqrt{3} & \sqrt{2} & 1 \\ -\sqrt{3} & \sqrt{2} & 1 \end{bmatrix}$.

PROBLEMS 24

1. (a) $\{(1/\sqrt{2})(1,-1,0), (1/\sqrt{3})(1,1,-2), (1/\sqrt{3})(1,1,1)\}$.

2. (a) $\frac{1}{\sqrt{3}}\begin{bmatrix} \sqrt{3}/\sqrt{2} & 1 & 1 \\ -\sqrt{3}/\sqrt{2} & 1 & 1 \\ 0 & -2 & 1 \end{bmatrix}$ **3.** $[S] = \lambda[I]$. **7.** $S^2 = \lambda_1^2 P_1 + \cdots + \lambda_m^2 P_m$.

PROBLEMS 25

3. (a) $\begin{bmatrix} 5 & 4 \\ 4 & 5 \end{bmatrix}$; (c) $\dfrac{1}{\sqrt{2}}\begin{bmatrix} 1 & 1 \\ 1 & -1 \end{bmatrix}$; (e) $\dfrac{1}{3}\begin{bmatrix} 2 & -1 \\ -1 & 2 \end{bmatrix}$; (f) $\dfrac{1}{5}\begin{bmatrix} 3 & 4 \\ 4 & -3 \end{bmatrix}$.

4. (a) $\begin{bmatrix} 0 & -1 \\ 1 & 0 \end{bmatrix}\begin{bmatrix} 2 & 0 \\ 0 & 1 \end{bmatrix}$; (b) $\dfrac{1}{25}\begin{bmatrix} -16 & 15 & -12 \\ -15 & 0 & 20 \\ 12 & 20 & 9 \end{bmatrix} \cdot \dfrac{1}{5}\begin{bmatrix} 9 & 0 & -12 \\ 0 & 25 & 0 \\ -12 & 0 & 16 \end{bmatrix}$.

Index